# Open Court Reading

## Book 4

**Risks and Consequences**

•

**Dreams to Jobs**

•

**From Mystery to Medicine**

•

**Surviving**

•

**Communication**

•

**Trail of Freedom**

# SRA Open Court Reading

## Book 4

### Program Authors

Carl Bereiter

Marilyn Jager Adams

Michael Pressley

Marsha Roit

Robbie Case

Anne McKeough

Jan Hirshberg

Marlene Scardamalia

Ann Brown

Joe Campione

Iva Carruthers

Gerald H. Treadway, Jr.

SRA

A Division of The McGraw-Hill Companies

*Columbus, Ohio*

# Acknowledgments

Grateful acknowledgment is given to the following publishers and copyright owners for permissions granted to reprint selections from their publications. All possible care has been taken to trace ownership and secure permission for each selection included.

Abingdon Press: "Sewed Up His Heart" adapted from SURE HANDS, STRONG HEART: THE LIFE OF DANIEL HALE WILLIAMS by Lillie Patterson. Copyright © 1981 by Abingdon Press. Reprinted with permisssion of Abingdon Press.

Atheneum Books for Young Readers, an imprint of Simon & Schuster Children's Publishing Division: Reprinted with the permission of Atheneum Books for Young Readers, an imprint of Simon & Schuster Children's Publishing Division from EDDIE, INCORPORATED by Phyllis Reynolds Naylor. Text copyright © 1980 Phyllis Reynolds Naylor. "Many Thousand Gone" by Ashley Bryan. Reprinted with the permission of Atheneum Books for Young Readers, an imprint of Simon & Schuster Children's Publishing Division from I'M GOING TO SING: BLACK AMERICAN SPIRITUALS Selected and illustrated by Ashley Bryan. Copyright © 1982 Ashley Bryan. "Mrs. Frisby and the Crow" by Robert C. O'Brien. Reprinted with the permission of Atheneum Books for Young Readers, an imprint of Simon & Schuster Children's Publishing Division from MRS. FRISBY AND THE RATS OF NIMH by Robert C. O'Brien. Copyright © 1971 Robert C. O'Brien. "Nachito's Teachings" by Ardath Mayhar. Reprinted with the permission of Atheneum Books

for Young Readers, an imprint of Simon & Schuster Children's Publishing Division from MEDICINE WALK by Ardath Mayhar. Copyright © 1985 Ardath Mayhar. Reprinted with the permission of Atheneum Books for Young Readers, an imprint of Simon & Schuster Children's Publishing Division from SHADOW OF A BULL by Maia Wojciechowska. Copyright © 1964 by Maia Wojciechowska. "Walk Together Children" by Ashley Bryan. Reprinted with the permission of Atheneum Books for Young Readers, an imprint of Simon & Schuster Children's Publishing Division from WALK TOGETHER CHILDREN: BLACK AMERICAN SPIRITUALS Selected and illustrated by Ashley Bryan. Copyright © 1974 Ashley Bryan.

Peter Bedrick Books Inc.: From Two Tickets to Freedom. Text © 1971 Florence B. Freedman, illustrations © 1971 Ezra Jack Keats. Reprinted by permission of Peter Bedrick Books Inc., 156 Fifth Avenue, New York, NY 10010.

Carolrhoda Books, Inc., An excerpt from ARCTIC EXPLORER: THE STORY OF MATTHEW HENSON by Jeri Ferris. Copyright © 1989 by Jeri Ferris. Reprinted with permission of Carolrhoda Books, Inc., "Birth of a Baby Food" from THE PROBLEM SOLVERS: PEOPLE WHO TURNED PROBLEMS INTO PRODUCTS by Nathan Aaseng. Copyright © 1989 by Lerner Productions Company of Carolrhoda Books, Inc. Reprinted by permission. THE BRIDGE DANCERS by Carol Saller. Text copyright © 1991 by Carol Saller. Reprinted with permission of Carolrhoda Books, Inc.

The Child's World, Inc.: from MARTHA HELPS THE REBEL by Carole Charles. Copyright © 1975 by The Child's World, Inc. Reprinted with permission of The Child's World, Inc.

Children's Press, Inc.: MAE JEMISON: SPACE SCIENTIST by Gail Sakurai. Copyright © 1995 by Children's Press, Inc. Reprinted with permission of Children's Press, Inc. "Phyllis Wheatley: Poet" from EXTRAORDINARY BLACK AMERICANS FROM COLONIAL TO CONTEMPORARY TIMES by Susan Altman. Copyright © 1989 by Children's Press, Inc. Reprinted with permission of Children's Press, Inc. "Pocahontas" from THE VIRGINIA COLONY by Dennis Fradin. Copyright © 1986 by Children's Press, Inc. Reprinted with permission of Children's Press, Inc.

Cobblestone Publishing Company: **"Judith: The Life of a Slave" from COBBLESTONE'S February 1990 issue: The People of Williamsburg, © 1990, Cobblestone Publishing Company, 30 Grove Street, Suite C, Peterborough, NH 03458. Reprinted by permission of the publisher. "The Voyage of the Mayflower" from COBBLESTONE'S November 1989 issue: Pilgrims to a New World, © 1989, Cobblestone Publishing Company, 30 Grove Street, Suite C, Peterborough, NH 03458. Reprinted by permission of the publisher.**

Coward-McCann, Inc., a division of Penguin Putnam Inc.: From TOTO by Marietta Moskin, Rocco Negri, illustrator. Copyright © 1971 by Rocco Negri, illustrations. Used by permission of Coward-McCann, Inc., a division of Penguin Putnam Inc.

Doubleday, a division of Bantam Doubleday Dell Publishing Group, Inc.: From ANNE FRANK: THE DIARY OF A YOUNG GIRL by Anne Frank. Copyright 1952 by Otto H. Frank. Used by permission of Doubleday, a division of Bantam Doubleday Dell Publishing Group, Inc.

Dutton Children's Books, a division of Penguin Putnam Inc.: THE KING'S FOUNTAIN by

Lloyd Alexander, illustrations by Ezra Jack Keats. Copyright © 1971 by Lloyd Alexander, text. Copyright © 1971 by Ezra Jack Keats, illustrations. Used by permission of Dutton Children's Books, a division of Penguin Putnam Inc. "Solitude," from NOW WE ARE SIX by A. A. Milne, illustrations by E. H. Shepard. Copyright 1927 by E. P. Dutton, renewed © 1955 by A. A. Milne. Used by permission of Dutton Children's Books, a division of Penguin Putnam Inc.

Faber and Faber Limited: "Whalesong" from DRAGONSFIRE by Judith Nicholls. Reprinted with permission of Faber and Faber Limited.

Farrar, Straus, & Giroux, Inc.: SALT by Harve Zemach, pictures by Margot Zemach. Copyright © 1965 by Margot Zemach. Reprinted by permission of Farrar, Straus, & Giroux, Inc., on behalf of the Estate of Margot Zemach.

Field Mouse Productions: "The Story of Susan La Flesche Picotte" from HOMEWARD THE ARROW'S FLIGHT by Marion Marsh Brown. Copyright © 1980 by Marion Marsh Brown. Revised edition © 1995 (Grand Island, Nebraska: Field Mouse Productions) by Marion Marsh Brown. Reprinted with permission of Field Mouse Productions.

The Gorilla Foundation: KOKO'S KITTEN by Dr. Francine Patterson. Copyright © 1985 by The Gorilla Foundation. Reprinted with permission of The Gorilla Foundation (www.gorilla.org).

Greenhaven Press, Inc.: "Whales: Song from the Deep" from ANIMAL COMMUNICATION: OPPOSING VIEWPOINTS by Jacci Cole. Copyright © 1989 by Greenhaven Press, Inc. Reprinted with permission of Greenhaven Press, Inc.

Greenwillow Books, a division of William Morrow & Company, Inc.: MCBROOM AND THE BIG WIND by Sid Fleischman. Text copyright © 1967 by Sid Fleischman. By permission of Greenwillow Books, a division of William Morrow & Company, Inc.

*(continued on page 631)*

## SRA/McGraw-Hill

*A Division of The McGraw·Hill Companies*

Send all inquiries to:
SRA/McGraw-Hill
8787 Orion Place
Columbus, OH  43240

Printed in the United States of America.

ISBN 0-02-830956-1

3 4 5 6 7 8 9 VHP 04 03 02 01 00

# Program Authors

**Carl Bereiter, Ph.D.**
University of Toronto

**Marilyn Jager Adams, Ph.D.**
BBN Technologies

**Michael Pressley, Ph.D.**
University of Notre Dame

**Marsha Roit, Ph.D.**
National Reading Consultant

**Robbie Case, Ph.D.**
University of Toronto

**Anne McKeough, Ph.D.**
University of Toronto

**Jan Hirshberg, Ed.D.**
Reading Consultant

**Marlene Scardamalia, Ph.D.**
University of Toronto

**Ann Brown, Ph.D.**
University of California at Berkeley

**Joe Campione, Ph.D.**
University of California at Berkeley

**Iva Carruthers, Ph.D.**
Northeastern Illinois University

**Gerald H. Treadway, Jr., Ed.D.**
San Diego State University

# Table *of* Contents

**Mrs. Frisby and the Crow** . . . . . . . . . . . . . . . . . . . . . . 20

*from* Mrs. Frisby and the Rats of NIMH

*a fantasy by* Robert C. O'Brien

*illustrated by* Barbara Lanza

Newbery Medal

Meet the Author, Robert C. O'Brien

Meet the Illustrator, Barbara Lanza . . . . . . . . . . . . . . . . . . . . 30

**Theme Connections** . . . . . . . . . . . . . . . . . . . . . . . . . . . . . . 31

**Toto** . . . . . . . . . . . . . . . . . . . . . . . . . . . . . . . . . . . . . . . 32

*realistic fiction by* Marietta D. Moskin

*illustrated by* Rocco Negri

Meet the Author, Marietta D. Moskin

Meet the Illustrator, Rocco Negri . . . . . . . . . . . . . . . . . . . . . . 46

**Theme Connections** . . . . . . . . . . . . . . . . . . . . . . . . . . . . . . 47

**Sarah, Plain and Tall** . . . . . . . . . . . . . . . 48

*from* Sarah, Plain and Tall

*historical fiction by* Patricia MacLachlan

*illustrated by* Meg Kelleher Aubrey

Newbery Medal

Meet the Author, Patricia MacLachlan

Meet the Illustrator, Meg Kelleher Aubrey . . 64

**Theme Connections** . . . . . . . . . . . . . . . . . 65

**The King's Fountain** . . . . . . . . . . . . . . . . . . . . . . . . . . . . 66

*a folktale by* Lloyd Alexander

*illustrated by* Ezra Jack Keats

Meet the Author, Lloyd Alexander

Meet the Illustrator, Ezra Jack Keats . . . . . . 72

**Theme Connections** . . . . . . . . . . . . . . . . 73

# Fine Art . . . . . . . . . . . . . . . . . . . . . . . 74

## Mae Jemison: Space Scientist . . . . . . . . . . . . . . . 76
*a biography by* Gail Sakurai

Meet the Author, Gail Sakurai . . . . . . . . . . . . . . . . . . . . . . . . 90

**Theme Connections** . . . . . . . . . . . . . . . . . . . . . . . . . . . . . . 91

## The Acrobats . . . . . . . . . . . . . . . . . . . . . . . . . . . . . 92
*a poem by* Dorothy Aldis
*illustrated by* Laura Huliska-Beith

## People Who Must . . . . . . . . . . . . . . . . . . . 93
*a poem by* Carl Sandburg
*illustrated by* Laura Huliska-Beith

## Two Tickets to Freedom . . . . . . . . . . . . . . . . . . . 94
*from* Two Tickets to Freedom: The True Story
of Ellen and William Craft, Fugitive Slaves
*a biography by* Florence B. Freedman
*illustrated by* Doris Ettlinger

Meet the Author, Florence B. Freedman

Meet the Illustrator, Doris Ettlinger . . . . . . . . . . . . . . . . . . . 106

**Theme Connections** . . . . . . . . . . . . . . . . . . . . . . . . . . . . . . 107

## The Girl Who Loved the Wind . . . . . . . . . . . . . . . . . 108
*a folktale by* Jane Yolen
*illustrated by* Ed Young

*Children's Book Showcase*

Meet the Author, Jane Yolen

Meet the Illustrator, Ed Young . . . . . . . . . . . . . . . . . . . . . 118

**Theme Connections** . . . . . . . . . . . . . . . . . . . . . . . . . . . . . . 119

# Bibliography . . . . . . . . . . . . . . . . . . . . . . . . . . . 120

# Table *of* Contents

**Eddie, Incorporated** . . . . . . . . . . . . . . . . . . . . . . . . . . .124
*from* Eddie, Incorporated
*realistic fiction by* Phyllis Reynolds Naylor
*illustrated by* Charmie Curran
Meet the Author, Phyllis Reynolds Naylor
Meet the Illustrator, Charmie Curran . . . . . . . . . . . . . . . . . .136
**Theme Connections** . . . . . . . . . . . . . . . . . . . . . . . . . . . . .137

**Lemonade Stand** . . . . . . . . . . . . . . . . . . . . . . . . . . . .138
*a poem by* Myra Cohn Livingston
*illustrated by* Bob Barner

**Elias Sifuentes, Restaurateur** . . . . . . . . . . . . .140
*from* All in a Day's Work: Twelve Americans
Talk About Their Jobs
*nonfiction by* Neil Johnson
Meet the Author and Photographer, Neil Johnson . .146
**Theme Connections** . . . . . . . . . . . . . . . . . . . . . . . . . .147

**Ice Cream Cones: A New Scoop** . . . . . . . .148
*from* What If?
*an informational article by* Dian Dincin Buchman
and Seli Groves
*illustrated by* Barbara Bruno
Meet the Author, Dian Dincin Buchman
Meet the Author, Seli Groves
Meet the Illustrator, Barbara Bruno . . . . . . . . . . . . . .150
**Theme Connections** . . . . . . . . . . . . . . . . . . . . . . . . . .151

**Fine Art** . . . . . . . . . . . . . . . . . . . . . . . . . . . . . . . . . . . . . . .152

**Food from the 'Hood: A Garden of Hope** ......154

*an informational article* by Marlene Targ Brill

Meet the Author, Marlene Targ Brill .....................166

**Theme Connections** ...........................167

**Business Is Looking Up** ...........................168

*realistic fiction by* Barbara Aiello and Jeffrey Shulman

*illustrated by* Diane Paterson

Meet the Author, Barbara Aiello

Meet the Author, Jeffrey Shulman

Meet the Illustrator, Diane Paterson ....................182

**Theme Connections** .............................183

**Birth of a Baby Food** ........................184

*from* The Problem Solvers

*an informational article by* Nathan Aaseng

*Notable Children's Trade Book, Social Studies*

Meet the Author, Nathan Aaseng ...................190

**Theme Connections** ...........................191

**Salt** ...................................192

*a folktale retold by* Harve Zemach

*illustrated by* Margot Zemach

*NY Herald Tribune Spring Book Festival Picture Book Award, First Prize*

Meet the Author, Harve Zemach

Meet the Illustrator, Margot Zemach ...................204

**Theme Connections** .............................205

**Bibliography** ...................................206

# Table *of* Contents

**Medicine: Past and Present** . . . . . . . . . . . . . . . . . . . . . 210
   *an informational article by* André W. Carus
   *illustrated by* Jim Roldan
   Meet the Author, André W. Carus
   Meet the Illustrator, Jim Roldan . . . . . . . . . . . . . . . . . . . . 224
   **Theme Connections** . . . . . . . . . . . . . . . . . . . . . . . . . . . . . 225

**The Microscope** . . . . . . . . . . . . . . . . . . . . . . . . . . . 226
   *a poem by* Maxine Kumin
   *illustrated by* Robert Byrd

**Sewed Up His Heart** . . . . . . . . . . . . . . 228
   *from* Sure Hands, Strong Heart:
   The Life of Daniel Hale Williams
   *a biography by* Lillie Patterson
   *illustrated by* Leslie Bowman
       *Notable Children's Trade Book,*
       *Social Studies*
   Meet the Author, Lillie Patterson
   Meet the Illustrator, Leslie Bowman . . . . . . . . . . . . . . . . . . . . 240
   **Theme Connections** . . . . . . . . . . . . . . . . . . . . . . . . . . . . . 241

**Surgeons Must Be Very Careful** . . . . . . . . . . . . . . . 242
   *a poem by* Emily Dickinson
   *illustrated by* Robert Byrd

**The Germ** . . . . . . . . . . . . . . . . . . . . . . . . . . . . . . . . . . . . 243
   *a poem by* Ogden Nash
   *illustrated by* Robert Byrd

## The Bridge Dancers .................. 244

*realistic fiction by* Carol Saller

*illustrated by* Gerald Talifero

*Carl Sandburg Literary Arts Award*

Meet the Author, Carol Saller

Meet the Illustrator, Gerald Talifero .............. 256

**Theme Connections** ...................... 257

## The New Doctor ...................... 258

*from* You Can Hear a Magpie Smile

*realistic fiction by* Paula G. Paul

*illustrated by* Roberta Collier-Morales

Meet the Author, Paula G. Paul

Meet the Illustrator, Roberta Collier-Morales .......... 278

**Theme Connections** ...................... 279

## Fine Art ...................... 280

## The Story of Susan La Flesche Picotte ....... 282

*from* Homeward the Arrow's Flight

*a biography by* Marion Marsh Brown

*illustrated by* Diane Magnuson

*Notable Children's Trade Book, Social Studies*

Meet the Author, Marion Marsh Brown

Meet the Illustrator, Diane Magnuson .............. 300

**Theme Connections** ...................... 301

## Shadow of a Bull ...................... 302

*from* Shadow of a Bull

*historical fiction by* Maia Wojciechowska

*illustrated by* Ramon Gonzalez Vicente

*Newbery Medal*

Meet the Author, Maia Wojciechowska

Meet the Illustrator, Ramon Gonzalez Vicente .......... 312

**Theme Connections** ...................... 313

## Bibliography ...................... 314

# Table *of* Contents

**Island of the Blue Dolphins** . . . . . . . . . . . . . . . . . . . . 318
> *from* Island of the Blue Dolphins
> *realistic fiction by* Scott O'Dell
> *illustrated by* Russ Walks
>
> *Newbery Medal*
>
> Meet the Author, Scott O'Dell . . . . . . . . . . . . . . . . . . . . . . . 328
> **Theme Connections** . . . . . . . . . . . . . . . . . . . . . . . . . . . 329

**Arctic Explorer:**
**The Story of Matthew Henson** . . . . . . . . . . . 330
> *from* Arctic Explorer: The Story of Matthew Henson
> *a biography by* Jeri Ferris
>
> *Notable Children's Trade Book,*
> *Social Studies*
>
> Meet the Author, Jeri Ferris . . . . . . . . . . . . . . . . . . . . 348
> **Theme Connections** . . . . . . . . . . . . . . . . . . . . . . . 349

**Nachito's Teachings** . . . . . . . . . . . . . . . . . . . . . . . . . . . 350
> *from* Medicine Walk
> *realistic fiction by* Ardath Mayhar
> *illustrated by* Sandy Rabinowitz
>
> Meet the Author, Ardath Mayhar
> Meet the Illustrator, Sandy Rabinowitz . . . . . . . . . . . . . . . . . 360
> **Theme Connections** . . . . . . . . . . . . . . . . . . . . . . . . . . . 361

**McBroom and the Big Wind** . . . . . . . . . . . . . . . . . . . 362
> *a tall tale by* Sid Fleischman
> *illustrated by* Walter Lorraine
>
> Meet the Author, Sid Fleischman
> Meet the Illustrator, Walter Lorraine . . . . . . . . . . . . . . 376
> **Theme Connections** . . . . . . . . . . . . . . . . . . . . . . . . . 377

**The Grasshopper** . . . . . . . . . . . . . . . . . . . . . . . 378
  *a poem by* David McCord
  *illustrated by* Nelle Davis

**The Big Wave** . . . . . . . . . . . . . . . . . . . . . . . . . 380
  *from* The Big Wave
  *realistic fiction by* Pearl S. Buck
  *illustrated by* Yoriko Ito
  *Children's Book Award*
  Meet the Author, Pearl S. Buck
  Meet the Illustrator, Yoriko Ito . . . . . . . . . . . . . . . . . . . 390
  **Theme Connections** . . . . . . . . . . . . . . . . . . . . . . . . 391

**Solitude** . . . . . . . . . . . . . . . . . . . . . . . . . . . . . . 392
  *a poem by* A. A. Milne
  *illustrated by* Ernest H. Shepard

**Anne Frank: The Diary of a Young Girl** . . . . . . . . 394
  *from* Anne Frank: The Diary of a Young Girl
  *a diary by* Anne Frank
  *translated by* B. M. Mooyaart-Doubleday
  *illustrated by* Susan Keeter
  Meet the Author, Anne Frank
  Meet the Illustrator, Susan Keeter . . . . . . . . . . . . . . . . . 404
  **Theme Connections** . . . . . . . . . . . . . . . . . . . . . . . . 405

**Fine Art** . . . . . . . . . . . . . . . . . . . . . . . . . . . . . . 406

**Music and Slavery** . . . . . . . . . . . . . . . . . . . . 408
  *an informational article by* Wiley Blevins
  *illustrated by* Ashley Bryan

**Many Thousand Gone** . . . . . . . . . . . . . . . . . 411
  *from* I'm Going to Sing
  *a spiritual illustrated by* Ashley Bryan

**Walk Together Children** . . . . . . . . . . . . . . . 412
  *from* Walk Together Children
  *a spiritual illustrated by* Ashley Bryan
  *American Library Association Notable Book*
  Meet the Author, Wiley Blevins
  Meet the Illustrator, Ashley Bryan . . . . . . . . . . . . . . . . 414
  **Theme Connections** . . . . . . . . . . . . . . . . . . . . . . . . 415

**Bibliography** . . . . . . . . . . . . . . . . . . . . . . . . . 416

# Table *of* Contents

**Whales: Songs from the Deep** .................. 420
> *from* Animal Communication
> *an informational article by* Jacci Cole

Meet the Ocean Explorer, Jacques Yves Cousteau ........ 432
**Theme Connections** ............................... 433

**Whalesong** ....................................... 434
> *a poem by* Judith Nicholls

**Wordless Speech** .......................... 436
> *from* My Friends the Wild Chimpanzees
> *excerpt printed in* The Importance of
> Jane Goodall *by Paula Bryant Pratt*
> *by* Jane Goodall

Meet the Author, Jane Goodall ................. 438
**Theme Connections** ........................ 439

**Koko's Kitten** ..................................... 440
> *from* Koko's Kitten
> *by* Dr. Francine Patterson
> *photographs by* Ronald H. Cohn

*School Library Journal Best Book of the Year*
Meet the Author, Dr. Francine Patterson
Meet the Photographer, Ronald H. Cohn ................. 452
**Theme Connections** ............................... 453

**Breaking into Print: Before and After the Invention of the Printing Press** . . . . . . . . . . . . . . . . 454

*expository text by* Stephen Krensky

*illustrated by* Bonnie Christensen

Notable Children's Trade Book, Social Studies

Meet the Author, Stephen Krensky

Meet the Illustrator, Bonnie Christensen . . . . . . . . . . . . . . . 462

**Theme Connections** . . . . . . . . . . . . . . . . . . . . . . . . . . . . . . 463

**Fine Art** . . . . . . . . . . . . . . . . . . . . . . . . . . . . . . . . . . . . . . . . 464

**Louis Braille: The Boy Who Invented Books for the Blind** . . . . . . . . . . . . . . . . . . . 466

*from* Louis Braille: The Boy Who Invented Books for the Blind

*a biography by* Margaret Davidson

*illustrated by* Bob Dorsey

Meet the Author, Margaret Davidson

Meet the Illustrator, Bob Dorsey . . . . . . . . . . . . . . . . . . . . . 478

**Theme Connections** . . . . . . . . . . . . . . . . . . . . . . . . . . . . . . 479

**Connections** . . . . . . . . . . . . . . . . . . . . . . . . . . . . . . . . . . . . 480

*a poem by* Diane Siebert

*illustrated by* Aaron Meshon

**One TV Blasting and a Pig Outdoors** . . . . . . . . . 482

*from* One TV Blasting and a Pig Outdoors

*realistic fiction by* Deborah Abbott and Henry Kisor

*illustrated by* Daniel Powers

Meet the Author, Deborah Abbott

Meet the Author, Henry Kisor

Meet the Illustrator, Daniel Powers . . . . . . . . . . . . . . . . . . 496

**Theme Connections** . . . . . . . . . . . . . . . . . . . . . . . . . . . . . . 497

**Bibliography** . . . . . . . . . . . . . . . . . . . . . . . . . . . . . . . . . . . 498

# Table *of* Contents

**Early America** . . . . . . . . . . . . . . . . . . . . . . . . . . . . . . . 502
   *an informational article by* Trevor Matheney
   Meet the Author, Trevor Matheney . . . . . . . . . . . . . . . . . . . . . 508
   Theme Connections . . . . . . . . . . . . . . . . . . . . . . . . . . . . 509

**The Voyage of the *Mayflower*** . . . . . 510
   *nonfiction by* Patricia M. Whalen
   *illustrated by* James Watling
   Meet the Illustrator, James Watling . . . . . . . . . . . . . . . . . . . 516
   Theme Connections . . . . . . . . . . . . . . . . . . . . . . . . . . . . 517

**The Early Houses** . . . . . . . . . . . . . . . . . . . . . . . . . . . . 518
   *from* The Pilgrims of Plymouth
   *an informational article by* Barbara Beck
   Meet the Author, Barbara Beck . . . . . . . . . . . . . . . . . . . . . . 522
   Theme Connections . . . . . . . . . . . . . . . . . . . . . . . . . . . . 523

**Pocahontas** . . . . . . . . . . . . . . . . . . . . . . . . . . . . . . . . 524
   *from* The Virginia Colony
   *a biography by* Dennis B. Fradin
   *illustrated by* Robert Roth
   Meet the Author, Dennis B. Fradin
   Meet the Illustrator, Robert Roth . . . . . . . . 528
   Theme Connections . . . . . . . . . . . . . . 529

**Fine Art** . . . . . . . . . . . . . . . . . . . . . . . . . . . 530

## Judith: The Life of a Slave . . . . . . . . . . . . . . . . . . . . . 532

*historical fiction by* Cathleene Hellier and Brandon Miller
*illustrated by* Alexander Farquharson

Meet the Author, Cathleene Hellier

Meet the Author, Brandon Miller

Meet the Illustrator, Alexander Farquharson . . . . . . . . . . . . 538

**Theme Connections** . . . . . . . . . . . . . . . . . . . . . . . . . . 539

## Freedom . . . . . . . . . . . . . . . . . . . . . . . . . . . . . . . . . . . . 540

*a poem by* Langston Hughes
*illustrated by* Tyrone Geter

## Phillis Wheatley: Poet . . . . . . . . . . . . . 542

*a biography by* Susan Altman
*illustrated by* George Crespo

Meet the Author, Susan Altman

Meet the Illustrator, George Crespo . . . . . . . . . . . . . . . . . 546

**Theme Connections** . . . . . . . . . . . . . . . . . . . . . . . . . . 547

## Martha Helps the Rebel . . . . . . . . . . . . . . . . . . . . 548

*a play by* Carole Charles
*illustrated by* Charles Shaw *and* Dennis Hockerman

Meet the Illustrator, Charles Shaw

Meet the Illustrator, Dennis Hockerman . . . . . . . . . . . . . . 558

**Theme Connections** . . . . . . . . . . . . . . . . . . . . . . . . . . 559

## Bibliography . . . . . . . . . . . . . . . . . . . . . . . . . . . . . . . 560

## Writer's Handbook . . . . . . . . . . . . . . . . . . . . . . . 562

## Glossary . . . . . . . . . . . . . . . . . . . . . . . . . . . . . . . . . 615

## Acknowledgments . . . . . . . . . . . . . . . . . . . . . . . . 631

# Risks and Consequences

**H**ave you ever taken a risk? What happened? We take risks every day—every time we decide to do something or not to do it. How do you decide which risks are worth taking?

# Mrs. Frisby and the Crow

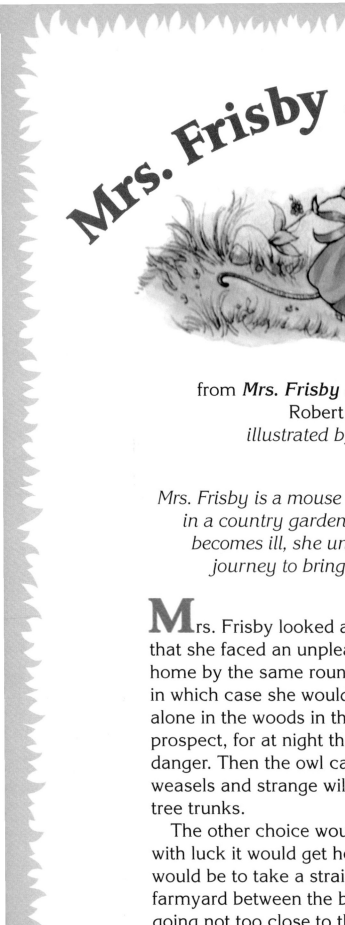

from *Mrs. Frisby and the Rats of NIMH*
Robert C. O'Brien
*illustrated by Barbara Lanza*

*Mrs. Frisby is a mouse that lives with her children in a country garden. When her son Timothy becomes ill, she undertakes a treacherous journey to bring him some medicine.*

**M**rs. Frisby looked again at the sun and saw that she faced an unpleasant choice. She could go home by the same roundabout way she had come, in which case she would surely end up walking alone in the woods in the dark——a frightening prospect, for at night the forest was alive with danger. Then the owl came out to hunt, and foxes, weasels and strange wild cats stalked among the tree trunks.

The other choice would be dangerous, too, but with luck it would get her home before dark. That would be to take a straighter route, across the farmyard between the barn and the chicken house, going not too close to the house but cutting the distance home by half. The cat would be there somewhere, but by daylight—and by staying in the open, away from the shrubs—she could probably spot him before he saw her.

The cat: He was called Dragon. Farmer Fitzgibbon's wife had given him the name as a joke when he was a small kitten pretending to be fierce. But when he grew up, the name turned out to be an apt one. He was enormous, with a huge, broad head and a large mouth full of curving fangs, needle sharp. He had seven claws on each foot and a thick, furry tail, which lashed angrily from side to side. In color he was orange and white, with glaring yellow eyes; and when he leaped to kill, he gave a high, strangled scream that froze his victims where they stood.

But Mrs. Frisby preferred not to think about that. Instead, as she came out of the woods from Mr. Ages' house and reached the farmyard fence she thought about Timothy. She thought of how his eyes shone with merriment when he made up small jokes, which he did frequently, and how invariably kind he was to his small, scatterbrained sister Cynthia. The other children sometimes laughed at her when she made mistakes, or grew impatient with her because she was forever losing things; but Timothy never did. Instead, he would help her find them. And when Cynthia herself had been sick in bed with a cold, he had sat by her side for hours and entertained her with stories. He made these up out of his head, and he seemed to have a bottomless supply of them.

Taking a firm grip on her packets of medicine, Mrs. Frisby went under the fence and set out toward the farmyard. The first stretch was a long pasture; the barn itself, square and red and big, rose in the distance to her right; to her left, farther off, were the chicken houses.

When at length she came abreast of the barn, she saw the cattle wire fence that marked the other end of the pasture; and as she approached it, she was startled by a sudden outburst of noise. She thought at first it was a hen, strayed from the chicken yard—caught by a fox? She looked down the fence and saw that it was no hen at all, but a young crow, flapping in the grass, acting most odd. As she watched, he fluttered to the top wire of the fence, where he perched nervously for a moment. Then he spread his wings, flapped hard, and took off—but after flying four feet he stopped with a snap and crashed to the ground again, shedding a flurry of black feathers and squawking loudly.

He was tied to the fence. A piece of something silvery—it looked like wire—was tangled around one of his legs; the other end of it was caught in the fence. Mrs. Frisby walked closer, and then she could see it was not wire after all, but a length of silver-colored string, probably left over from a Christmas package.

The crow was sitting on the fence, pecking ineffectively at the string with his bill, cawing softly to himself, a miserable sound. After a moment he spread his wings, and she could see he was going to try to fly again.

"Wait," said Mrs. Frisby.

The crow looked down and saw her in the grass.

"Why should I wait? Can't you see I'm caught? I've got to get loose."

"But if you make so much noise again the cat is sure to hear. If he hasn't heard already."

"You'd make noise, too, if you were tied to a fence with a piece of string, and with night coming on."

"I would not," said Mrs. Frisby, "if I had any sense and knew there was a cat nearby. Who tied you?" She was trying to calm the crow, who was obviously terrified.

He looked embarrassed and stared at his feet. "I picked up the string. It got tangled with my foot. I sat on the fence to try to get it off, and it caught on the fence."

"*Why* did you pick up the string?"

The crow, who was very young indeed—in fact, only a year old—said wearily, "Because it was shiny."

"You knew better."

"I had been told."

Birdbrain, thought Mrs. Frisby, and then recalled what her husband used to say: The size of the brain is no measure of its capacity. And well she might recall it, for the crow's head was double the size of her own.

"Sit quietly," she said. "Look toward the house and see if you see the cat."

"I don't see him. But I can't see behind the bushes. Oh, if I could just fly higher . . . "

"Don't," said Mrs. Frisby. She looked at the sun; it was setting behind the trees. She thought of Timothy, and of the medicine she was carrying. Yet she knew she could not leave the foolish crow there to be killed——and killed he surely would be before sunrise——just for want of a few minutes' work. She might still make it by dusk if she hurried.

"Come down here," she said. "I'll get the string off."

"How?" said the crow dubiously.

"Don't argue. I have only a few minutes." She said this in a voice so authoritative that the crow fluttered down immediately.

"But if the cat comes . . ." he said.

"If the cat comes, he'll knock you off the fence with one jump and catch you with the next. Be still." She was already at work with her sharp teeth, gnawing at the string. It was twined and twisted and twined again around his right ankle, and she saw she would have to cut through it three times to get it off.

As she finished the second strand, the crow, who was staring toward the house, suddenly cried out:

"I see the cat!"

"*Quiet!*" whispered Mrs. Frisby. "Does he see us?"

"I don't know. Yes. He's looking at me. I don't think he can see you."

"Stand perfectly still. Don't get in a panic." She did not look up, but started on the third strand.

"He's moving this way."

"Fast or slow?"

"Medium. I think he's trying to figure out what I'm doing."

She cut through the last strand, gave a tug, and the string fell off.

"There, you're free. Fly off, and be quick."

"But what about you?"

"Maybe he hasn't seen me."

"But he will. He's coming closer."

Mrs. Frisby looked around. There was not a bit of cover anywhere near, not a rock nor a hole nor a log; nothing at all closer than the chicken yard—and that was in the direction the cat was coming from, and a long way off.

"Look," said the crow. "Climb on my back. Quick. And hang on."

Mrs. Frisby did what she was told, first grasping the precious packages of medicine tightly between her teeth.

"Are you on?"

"Yes."

She gripped the feathers on his back, felt the beat of his powerful black wings, felt a dizzying upward surge, and shut her eyes tight.

"Just in time," said the crow, and she heard the angry scream of the cat as he leaped at where they had just been. "It's lucky you're so light. I can scarcely tell you're there." Lucky indeed, thought

Mrs. Frisby; if it had not been for your foolishness, I'd never have gotten into such a scrape. However, she thought it wise not to say so, under the circumstances.

"Where do you live?" asked the crow.

"In the garden patch. Near the big stone."

"I'll drop you off there." He banked alarmingly, and for a moment Mrs. Frisby thought he meant it literally. But a few seconds later—so fast does the crow fly—they were gliding to earth a yard from her front door.

"Thank you very much," said Mrs. Frisby, hopping to the ground.

"It's I who should be thanking you," said the crow. "You saved my life."

"And you mine."

"Ah, but that's not quite even. Yours wouldn't have been risked if it had not been for me—me and my piece of string." And since this was just what she had been thinking, Mrs. Frisby did not argue.

"We all help one another against the cat," she said.

"True. Just the same, I am in debt to you. If the time ever comes when I can help you, I hope you will ask me. My name is Jeremy. Mention it to any crow you see in these woods, and he will find me."

"Thank you," said Mrs. Frisby. "I will remember."

Jeremy flew away to the woods, and she entered her house, taking the three doses of medicine with her.

# Mrs. Frisby and the Crow

## Meet the Author

**Robert C. O'Brien** could sing before he could talk. His favorite "toy" was the family's wind-up Victrola (music player), and he spent hours listening to music. He learned to play piano when he was very young, and he stayed with it all his life.

His other favorite thing to do was create splendid imaginary worlds, with himself in dazzling, heroic roles. In his forties he decided to share those worlds with others so he started writing books.

*"When I get a story idea,"* he said, *"I write it down before I forget it. It isn't always for children, but those are the stories I most like to write."*

## Meet the Illustrator

**Barbara Lanza** says that fantasy books are her favorite genre. *"I love doing fantasy. I've always loved little secret worlds, whether they are in the backyard or in outer space."*

Her parents and her high school art teacher encouraged Ms. Lanza to pursue a career in art. She says of her work, *"You really need to understand yourself and be very committed to bringing your feelings into your work. When you are an illustrator, you're illuminating something for someone else. By having a clear focus yourself, you can better describe things for others."*

# Theme Connections

## Think About It

Why did Mrs. Frisby risk her life even when she knew of the danger involved? Here are some things to think about:

- Why did Mrs. Frisby risk her life to get medicine for her son?
- Why did she risk her life to remove the string from the crow's leg?
- Did she feel the same way about the two risks she took? Why or why not?
- Did she put her son in danger too by helping the crow?
- Would you like to have somebody like her for a friend?

## Record Ideas

What have you learned about the different types of risks from this story? Record your thoughts in your Writing Journal.

## Share a Story

Think of a time you took a risk for someone else and share it with your classmates. Listen to their stories as well.

# Toto

Marietta D. Moskin
*illustrated by Rocco Negri*

Deep in Africa, on the outer slopes of a gently rolling ring of hills, lived a timid young boy named Suku. His round thatched hut stood in a busy village where his tribe had always lived. Just a short distance away, on the other side of the blue and purple hills, was a quiet valley set aside for animals to live without fear of being hunted by men. Suku had often climbed to the top of the tallest hill and had watched the herds of animals moving through the grasslands far below. But that was as far as he ever went. His own world was outside the protected game reserve—with his family, in the safe, familiar village.

On a saucer-shaped plain sheltered by the ring of blue and purple hills lived a curious little elephant. His name was Toto—the little one—because he was the youngest and smallest elephant in the herd. With his large family he roamed across the silvery plains of his valley, feeding on the juicy grasses and bathing in the broad green river that twisted through the land. It was a good life for elephants and for the many other animals with whom they shared their peaceful valley.

Day by day the little elephant in the valley and the boy in the village grew stronger and bigger and learned the things they had to know.

Toto learned which berries and roots were good to eat and which ones would make him sick. He learned to recognize danger by smells in the air and sounds in the distance. He stood patiently while his mother doused him with water from her trunk, and he paid attention when she showed him how to powder himself with red dust to keep the insects away.

When his mother warned him never to stray outside their peaceful valley because there were dangers beyond the hills, Toto listened. Most of the time he was happy to play with his cousins among the thorn trees and with his friends, the antelope and the baby baboons. But sometimes Toto looked toward the blue and purple hills in the distance and wondered what lay behind their rounded crests.

Suku too learned a great many things a boy growing up in an African village had to learn. He carried water for his mother from the river and he collected dung to burn in the fire on which she cooked their midday meal. In the evening he helped his father and the other men to pen the tribe's cattle and goats within the village compound. But in the morning, when the boys and young men of the village went out to herd their cattle on the rich grazing lands in the valley, Suku did not go with them. He watched when the herd boys walked jauntily out of the village, brandishing their wooden staffs and shouting to their charges. At seven he was old enough to go, but Suku was frightened when he thought of the herd boys walking through the bush with nothing but a stick or crude iron spear to protect them from lions.

"Our ancestors were famous lion hunters," his mother scolded. "The men of our tribe have always walked fearlessly through the bush."

"Give Suku time," his father counseled. "Courage sometimes comes with need."

So Suku went on doing women's chores around the village and avoiding the boys who teased him.

And inside the ring of gently rolling purple hills, Toto, the little elephant, roamed with the herd across the grasslands. But whenever he saw the young weaverbirds flying from their hanging straw nests, he watched enviously as they sailed off into the sky far, far beyond the circle of hills.

One night Toto followed the elephant herd to the edge of their valley where the river flowed onto the plain through a gap in the hills. There, in a clearing between the trees, the young males of the herd fought mock battles with each other in the moonlight.

Sheltered by his mother's bulk, Toto watched for a while. Then, looking up at the velvety sky, he saw that the moon had traveled across the valley and was about to dip down below the highest hill.

I wonder where she goes, Toto thought. Perhaps I'll just follow the river a little ways and see. Not very far—just to where the river curves.

Slowly Toto moved away from the group of elephants. Nobody noticed. Not even his mother. But once he was in the shadows of trees, the moon was no longer there to guide him.

"Elephants have no enemies—Mother said so,"
he told himself bravely. Only the lion might stalk an
unprotected elephant child—but the lions had had
their kill earlier that night. Toto had seen them at
their meal.

Toto walked on through the darkness. Sometimes
he could see the moon reflected on the river, and he
hurried to catch up with it. But he didn't look back, and
so he didn't realize that the hills lay behind him now. He
didn't notice either that he could no longer hear the loud
trumpeting of the other elephants at play. He didn't know
that he was already in that mysterious world beyond
the hills he had longed to discover.

Suddenly Toto felt a sharp pain in his right front leg. Something hard and sharp had fastened around his foot. Toto pulled and pulled, but he couldn't free his foot. Each time he pulled, the pain got sharper.

Nothing his mother had told him about danger had prepared Toto for this. In fear and pain he trumpeted loudly. But he had walked too far to be heard. There was no answering call from his mother or from any of the other elephants. For the first time in his life, Toto was alone.

In the round thatched hut in the village, Suku slept on a woven mat next to his parents. Suku was a sound sleeper, but something—some noise—awoke him before dawn. It sounded like an elephant trumpeting, Suku thought sleepily. But elephants rarely strayed this far out of the game reserve in the valley. He must have been dreaming, Suku told himself. He couldn't have heard an elephant this close.

But Suku could not go back to sleep. When the first sunshine crept through the chinks under the door, he got up and slipped into his clothes. He had promised his mother he would cut some papyrus reeds at the river today so that she could mend their torn sleeping mats. Now that he was awake he would do it before the day grew hot.

Quietly, so as not to waken the rest of his family, Suku tiptoed out of the hut. Outside, no one stirred. Even the cattle were still asleep.

Clutching his sharp reed knife, Suku followed the winding path down the hill to the riverbank, searching for a good stand of feathery papyrus.

Suddenly the silence at the river was broken by a loud rustling sound. The sound came again—not just a rustling this time, but a snapping of twigs and a swishing of the tall grasses. Carefully, and a little fearfully, Suku moved around the next curve in the path. And then he stopped again.

Before him, in the trampled grass, lay a very young elephant. Around one of the elephant's legs the cruelly stiffened rope of a poacher's trap had been pulled so tight that the snare had bitten deeply into the flesh. The elephant had put up a fierce struggle, but now he was exhausted. He lay quietly on his side, squealing softly from time to time.

Anger exploded inside Suku—anger at the cruel poachers who had set their cunning trap so close to the game reserve. He approached the trapped elephant carefully. His father had taught him to be aware of wounded animals who could be far more dangerous in fear and pain. But the little elephant seemed to sense that Suku wanted to help him, and he held very still. Grasping his knife, Suku slashed at the thick, twisted rope. It took time to free the elephant's leg, but finally the last strand of the rope gave way. The boy jumped out of the way quickly, and the small elephant slowly got to his feet. Then he just stood there on the path, staring at Suku.

"Shoo, shoo, little elephant—quickly, run back into the valley," Suku urged. The poachers who had set the trap could be back at any time. But Toto, who had spent the night by himself, would not leave that strange two-legged creature with the oddly dangerous smell but the warm, comforting sounds. When Suku turned to walk back to the village, Toto started after him.

"Please, little one, please, hurry home," Suku pleaded. But the little elephant didn't budge.

"What are we going to do?" Suku asked in despair. "Will I have to lead you back to your family, you foolish little one?"

Suku didn't want to go into the bush. But he looked at the elephant baby and knew that there was no choice.

Suku began to walk, and the small elephant followed. He walked slowly and painfully, limping on the leg that had been cut so badly by the poacher's snare.

It was easy for Suku to find the way Toto had left the reserve. Trampled grass and elephant droppings formed a perfect track. After a while the boy and the elephant came to the clearing where the herd had watched the fight between the young bulls the night before. The clearing was empty, but a trail of droppings showed that the herd had moved on across the open bush.

Suku was so busy following the trail that he hadn't thought much about what he was doing. Suddenly he realized he was walking all by himself across the open grasslands. Just like the herd boys. And he didn't even have an iron spear for protection—nothing but a small reed cutting knife!

He walked on, trying not to think about the dangers. By now the sun was high in the sky, and at home they were surely wondering what had happened to him.

They walked and walked. Suku, who hadn't had any breakfast that morning, began to feel hungry and thirsty. Toto hadn't had breakfast either, but there was no time to stop and eat.

Suddenly Toto stopped. He raised his head and listened, trembling a little. Young as he was, Toto recognized the smells and sounds of danger.

Suku looked around to see what had frightened Toto. And then he saw the danger too. A few paces away, half-hidden in the silvery-tan grass, stood an enormous brown-maned lion.

The lion looked from the elephant to the boy, almost as if he were measuring which one would make the easier victim. He looked haughty and strong and very big. Suku's fist tightened around the handle of his knife. He wasn't sure at all whether the knife would do him any good, but he was prepared to defend himself if the lion attacked. Behind him he could sense the little elephant stiffen. Even though the lion looked awfully big to him too, Toto had raised his trunk and spread his ears the way the big elephants did when they were ready to attack.

"Oh, please, make him go away, make him go away," Suku prayed silently. His hand around the knife handle felt clammy and stiff. It seemed to him that he and the elephant and the lion had stood there facing one another, forever.

It was Toto who broke the silence. He took a step toward the lion, and he trumpeted a warning.

The next moment—almost like an echo—another elephant call sounded across the bush. Then another and another. Turning his head, Suku saw a large herd of elephants advancing from behind a nearby stand of thorn trees. Toto's family had come to rescue their littlest one!

Then Suku heard another, more familiar sound. It was the rattling and roaring sound of a car traveling fast across rough ground. A second later the game warden's battered white Landrover appeared over the next small hill. Suku recognized the warden at the wheel, and next to the warden Suku saw his father standing up in the car with a gun in his hand.

"Stand still, Suku—just don't move," his father shouted. He aimed his gun at the lion, waiting to see what the lion would do.

The lion looked at his two young victims. Then he looked at the menacing group of elephants on his right and at the men in the car to his left. Mustering what dignity he could, he stalked slowly and deliberately away. Within moments he had disappeared into the tall dry grass.

Another loud, single call sounded from the elephant herd. Toto was being summoned. His mother was coming to take him back to the herd.

Slowly Toto raised his trunk to the boy who had brought him home. Then, still limping badly, he turned and followed his mother.

The warden had waited for the elephants to withdraw. Now he drove the Landrover over to where Suku stood.

"Get in, Suku—let's go," the warden said.

"You came just in time," Suku said.

"We found the cut snare and the elephant tracks— and someone in the village had seen you going down to the river early this morning," his father explained.

"The poachers would have killed him for his hide," Suku said.

"You did right, Suku," the warden said. "I get so angry too when I catch these poachers. You would make a good game ranger some day, Suku. You love animals, and you are brave."

The warden's words made Suku feel good. He knew that he hadn't felt brave, but he had walked in the footsteps of his ancestors: he had gone into the bush, and he had faced a lion!

Now he would never feel shy of the village boys again. He knew he had earned his place in the tribe.

Under the leafy canopy of the forest, Toto nuzzled up close to his mother's flank. He had eaten his fill of crisp greens at the riverbank, and his mother had bathed his cut foot and smeared it with healing red mud. Now the herd was resting quietly in the shade near the river.

It was good to be back home, Toto thought contentedly. Let the moon and the sun and the birds travel beyond the hills if they wished. His place was here.

# Toto

## Meet the Author

**Marietta D. Moskin** said, *"I can't remember a time when I didn't want to write poems or stories."* As soon as she could write, Ms. Moskin began to create fantasy worlds. During World War II, Ms. Moskin and her family spent several years in concentration camps. Even then, she hoarded scraps of paper so she could write her stories and poems.

*"In my books,"* she once said, *"I have tried to draw as often as possible on my own experiences and remembered feelings."* "Toto" grew out of a family trip to East Africa (Kenya, Tanzania, and Uganda).

## Meet the Illustrator

**Rocco Negri** for a time thought he wanted to become a writer. He once said, *"As far as I can remember, I was always very quiet. I communicated more in writing."* But then he got interested in art and decided it was something he would enjoy enormously. Art allowed him to live in two worlds at the same time—the real world and the world of make-believe.

*"One of my greatest satisfactions in life is illustrating children's books, because children are so pure in appreciation and perception. They have no inhibition or discrimination to cloud their minds or hearts."*

# Theme Connections

## Think About It

Why did Suku and Toto take the risks they did? Here are some questions to help you decide:

- What risks did Suku take?
- What were the consequences of taking them?
- What might be the consequences of not taking them?
- Were Suku's risks worthwhile?
- What risks did Toto take?
- What were the consequences of taking them?
- What might be the consequences of not taking them?
- Were Toto's risks worthwhile?

## Record Ideas

Answer these questions in your Writing Journal:

- What does the selection teach us about risks?
- What lessons did the two main characters learn from the risks they took?

## Write or Tell a Story Sequel

Imagine that Suku became a park warden when he grew up and that he met Toto. Write or tell a story about their meeting.

# Sarah, Plain and Tall

from **Sarah, Plain and Tall** by Patricia MacLachlan
*illustrated by Meg Kelleher Aubrey*

"Did Mama sing every day?" asked Caleb. "Every-single-day?" He sat close to the fire, his chin in his hand. It was dusk, and the dogs lay beside him on the warm hearthstones.

"Every-single-day," I told him for the second time this week. For the twentieth time this month. The hundredth time this year? And the past few years?

"And did Papa sing, too?"

"Yes. Papa sang, too. Don't get so close, Caleb. You'll heat up."

He pushed his chair back. It made a hollow scraping sound on the hearthstones, and the dogs stirred. Lottie, small and black, wagged her tail and lifted her head. Nick slept on.

I turned the bread dough over and over on the marble slab on the kitchen table.

"Well, Papa doesn't sing anymore," said Caleb very softly. A log broke apart and crackled in the fireplace. He looked up at me. "What did I look like when I was born?"

"You didn't have any clothes on," I told him.

"I know that," he said.

"You looked like this." I held the bread dough up in a round pale ball.

"I had hair," said Caleb seriously.

"Not enough to talk about," I said.

"And she named me Caleb," he went on, filling in the old familiar story.

"*I* would have named you Troublesome," I said, making Caleb smile.

"And Mama handed me to you in the yellow blanket and said . . ." He waited for me to finish the story. "And said . . . ?"

I sighed. "And Mama said, 'Isn't he beautiful, Anna?'"

"And I was," Caleb finished.

Caleb thought the story was over, and I didn't tell him what I had really thought. He was homely and plain, and he had a terrible holler and a horrid smell. But these were not the worst of him. Mama died the next morning. That was the worst thing about Caleb.

"Isn't he beautiful, Anna?" Her last words to me. I had gone to bed thinking how wretched he looked. And I forgot to say good night.

I wiped my hands on my apron and went to the window. Outside, the prairie reached out and touched the places where the sky came down. Though winter was nearly over, there were patches of snow and ice everywhere. I looked at the long dirt road that crawled across the plains, remembering the morning that Mama had died, cruel and sunny. They had come for her in a wagon and taken her away to be buried. And then the cousins and aunts and uncles had come and tried to fill up the house. But they couldn't.

Slowly, one by one, they left. And then the days seemed long and dark like winter days, even though it wasn't winter. And Papa didn't sing.

*Isn't he beautiful, Anna?*

*No, Mama.*

It was hard to think of Caleb as beautiful. It took three whole days for me to love him, sitting in the chair by the fire, Papa washing up the supper dishes, Caleb's tiny hand brushing my cheek. And a smile. It was the smile, I know.

"Can you remember her songs?" asked Caleb. "Mama's songs?"

I turned from the window. "No. Only that she sang about flowers and birds. Sometimes about the moon at nighttime."

Caleb reached down and touched Lottie's head.

"Maybe," he said, his voice low, "if you remember the songs, then I might remember her, too."

My eyes widened and tears came. Then the door opened and wind blew in with Papa, and I went to stir the stew. Papa put his arms around me and put his nose in my hair.

"Nice soapy smell, that stew," he said.

I laughed. "That's my hair."

Caleb came over and threw his arms around Papa's neck and hung down as Papa swung him back and forth, and the dogs sat up.

"Cold in town," said Papa. "And Jack was feisty." Jack was Papa's horse that he'd raised from a colt. "Rascal," murmured Papa, smiling, because no matter what Jack did Papa loved him.

I spooned up the stew and lighted the oil lamp and we ate with the dogs crowding under the table, hoping for spills or handouts.

Papa might not have told us about Sarah that night if Caleb hadn't asked him the question. After the dishes were cleared and washed and Papa was filling the tin pail with ashes, Caleb spoke up. It wasn't a question, really.

"You don't sing anymore," he said. He said it harshly. Not because he meant to, but because he had been thinking of it for so long. "Why?" he asked more gently.

Slowly Papa straightened up. There was a long silence, and the dogs looked up, wondering at it.

"I've forgotten the old songs," said Papa quietly. He sat down. "But maybe there's a way to remember them." He looked up at us.

"How?" asked Caleb eagerly.

Papa leaned back in the chair. "I've placed an advertisement in the newspapers. For help."

"You mean a housekeeper?" I asked, surprised.

Caleb and I looked at each other and burst out laughing, remembering Hilly, our old housekeeper. She was round and slow and shuffling. She snored in a high whistle at night, like a teakettle, and let the fire go out.

"No," said Papa slowly. "Not a housekeeper." He paused. "A wife."

Caleb stared at Papa. "A wife? You mean a mother?"

Nick slid his face onto Papa's lap and Papa stroked his ears.

"That, too," said Papa. "Like Maggie."

Matthew, our neighbor to the south, had written to ask for a wife and mother for his children. And Maggie had come from Tennessee. Her hair was the color of turnips and she laughed.

Papa reached into his pocket and unfolded a letter written on white paper. "And I have received an answer." Papa read to us:

*"Dear Mr. Jacob Witting,*

*"I am Sarah Wheaton from Maine as you will see from my letter. I am answering your advertisement. I have never been married, though I have been asked. I have lived with an older brother, William, who is about to be married. His wife-to-be is young and energetic.*

*"I have always loved to live by the sea, but at this time I feel a move is necessary. And the truth is, the sea is as far east as I can go. My choice, as you can see, is limited. This should not be taken as an insult. I am strong and I work hard and I am willing to travel. But I am not mild mannered. If you should still care to write, I would be interested in your children and about where you live. And you.*

*"Very truly yours,*
*"Sarah Elisabeth Wheaton*
*"P.S. Do you have opinions on cats? I have one."*

No one spoke when Papa finished the letter. He kept looking at it in his hands, reading it over to himself. Finally I turned my head a bit to sneak a look at Caleb. He was smiling. I smiled, too.

"One thing," I said in the quiet of the room.

"What's that?" asked Papa, looking up.

I put my arm around Caleb.

"Ask her if she sings," I said.

Caleb and Papa and I wrote letters to Sarah, and before the ice and snow had melted from the fields, we all received answers. Mine came first.

*Dear Anna,*

*Yes, I can braid hair and I can make stew and bake bread, though I prefer to build bookshelves and paint.*

*My favorite colors are the colors of the sea, blue and gray and green, depending on the weather. My brother William is a fisherman, and he tells me that when he is in the middle of a fogbound sea the water is a color for which there is no name. He catches flounder and sea bass and bluefish. Sometimes he sees whales. And birds, too, of course. I am enclosing a book of sea birds so you will see what William and I see every day.*

*Very truly yours,*
*Sarah Elisabeth Wheaton*

Caleb read and read the letter so many times that the ink began to run and the folds tore. He read the book about sea birds over and over.

"Do you think she'll come?" asked Caleb. "And will she stay? What if she thinks we are loud and pesky?"

"You *are* loud and pesky," I told him. But I was worried, too. Sarah loved the sea, I could tell. Maybe she wouldn't leave there after all to come where there were fields and grass and sky and not much else.

"What if she comes and doesn't like our house?" Caleb asked. "I told her it was small. Maybe I shouldn't have told her it was small."

"Hush, Caleb. Hush."

Caleb's letter came soon after, with a picture of a cat drawn on the envelope.

*Dear Caleb,*

*My cat's name is Seal because she is gray like the seals that swim offshore in Maine. She is glad that Lottie and Nick send their greetings. She likes dogs most of the time. She says their footprints are much larger than hers (which she is enclosing in return).*

*Your house sounds lovely, even though it is far out in the country with no close neighbors. My house is tall and the shingles are gray because of the salt from the sea. There are roses nearby.*

*Yes, I do like small rooms sometimes. Yes, I can keep a fire going at night. I do not know if I snore. Seal has never told me.*

*Very truly yours,*
*Sarah Elisabeth*

"Did you really ask her about fires and snoring?" I asked, amazed.
"I wished to know," Caleb said.

He kept the letter with him, reading it in the barn and in the fields and by the cow pond. And always in bed at night.

One morning, early, Papa and Caleb and I were cleaning out the horse stalls and putting down new bedding. Papa stopped suddenly and leaned on his pitchfork.

"Sarah has said she will come for a month's time if we wish her to," he said, his voice loud in the dark barn. "To see how it is. Just to see."

Caleb stood by the stall door and folded his arms across his chest.

"I think," he began. Then, "I think," he said slowly, "that it would be good——to say yes," he finished in a rush.

Papa looked at me.

"I say yes," I told him, grinning.

"Yes," said Papa. "Then yes it is."

And the three of us, all smiling, went to work again.

The next day Papa went to town to mail his letter to Sarah. It was rainy for days, and the clouds followed. The house was cool and damp and quiet. Once I set four places at the table, then caught myself and put the extra plate away. Three lambs were born, one with a black face. And then Papa's letter came. It was very short.

*Dear Jacob,*
*I will come by train. I will wear a yellow bonnet. I am plain and tall.*
*Sarah*

"What's that?" asked Caleb excitedly, peering over Papa's shoulder. He pointed. "There, written at the bottom of the letter."

Papa read it to himself. Then he smiled, holding up the letter for us to see.

*Tell them I sing* was all it said.

Sarah came in the spring. She came through green grass fields that bloomed with Indian paintbrush, red and orange, and blue-eyed grass.

Papa got up early for the long day's trip to the train and back. He brushed his hair so slick and shiny that Caleb laughed. He wore a clean blue shirt, and a belt instead of suspenders.

He fed and watered the horses, talking to them as he hitched them up to the wagon. Old Bess, calm and kind; Jack, wild-eyed, reaching over to nip Bess on the neck.

"Clear day, Bess," said Papa, rubbing her nose.

"Settle down, Jack." He leaned his head on Jack.

And then Papa drove off along the dirt road to fetch Sarah. Papa's new wife. Maybe. Maybe our new mother.

Gophers ran back and forth across the road, stopping to stand up and watch the wagon. Far off in the field a woodchuck ate and listened. Ate and listened.

Caleb and I did our chores without talking. We shoveled out the stalls and laid down new hay. We fed the sheep. We swept and straightened and carried wood and water. And then our chores were done.

Caleb pulled on my shirt.

"Is my face clean?" he asked. "Can my face be *too* clean?" He looked alarmed.

"No, your face is clean but not too clean," I said.

Caleb slipped his hand into mine as we stood on the porch, watching the road. He was afraid.

"Will she be nice?" he asked. "Like Maggie?"

"Sarah will be nice," I told him.

"How far away is Maine?" he asked.

"You know how far. Far away, by the sea."

"Will Sarah bring some sea?" he asked.

"No, you cannot bring the sea."

The sheep ran in the field, and far off the cows moved slowly to the pond, like turtles.

"Will she like us?" asked Caleb very softly.

I watched a marsh hawk wheel down behind the barn.

He looked up at me.

"Of course she will like us." He answered his own question. "We are nice," he added, making me smile.

We waited and watched. I rocked on the porch and Caleb rolled a marble on the wood floor. Back and forth. Back and forth. The marble was blue.

We saw the dust from the wagon first, rising above the road, above the heads of Jack and Old Bess. Caleb climbed up onto the porch roof and shaded his eyes.

"A bonnet!" he cried. "I see a yellow bonnet!"

The dogs came out from under the porch, ears up, their eyes on the cloud of dust bringing Sarah. The wagon passed the fenced field, and the cows and sheep looked up, too. It rounded the windmill and the barn and the windbreak of Russian olive that Mama had planted long ago. Nick began to bark, then Lottie, and the wagon clattered into the yard and stopped by the steps.

"Hush," said Papa to the dogs.

And it was quiet.

Sarah stepped down from the wagon, a cloth bag in her hand. She reached up and took off her yellow bonnet, smoothing back her brown hair into a bun. She was plain and tall.

"Did you bring some sea?" cried Caleb beside me.

"Something from the sea," said Sarah, smiling. "And me." She turned and lifted a black case from the wagon. "And Seal, too."

Carefully she opened the case, and Seal, gray with white feet, stepped out. Lottie lay down, her head on her paws, staring. Nick leaned down to sniff. Then he lay down, too.

"The cat will be good in the barn," said Papa. "For mice."

Sarah smiled. "She will be good in the house, too."

Sarah took Caleb's hand, then mine. Her hands were large and rough. She gave Caleb a shell—a moon snail, she called it—that was curled and smelled of salt.

"The gulls fly high and drop the shells on the rocks below," she told Caleb. "When the shell is broken, they eat what is inside."

"That is very smart," said Caleb.

"For you, Anna," said Sarah, "a sea stone."

And she gave me the smoothest and whitest stone I had ever seen.

"The sea washes over and over and around the stone, rolling it until it is round and perfect."

"That is very smart, too," said Caleb. He looked up at Sarah. "We do not have the sea here."

Sarah turned and looked out over the plains.

"No," she said. "There is no sea here. But the land rolls a little like the sea."

My father did not see her look, but I did. And I knew that Caleb had seen it, too. Sarah was not smiling. Sarah was already lonely. In a month's time the preacher might come to marry Sarah and Papa. And a month was a long time. Time enough for her to change her mind and leave us.

Papa took Sarah's bags inside, where her room was ready with a quilt on the bed and blue flax dried in a vase on the night table.

Seal stretched and made a small cat sound. I watched her circle the dogs and sniff the air. Caleb came out and stood beside me.

"When will we sing?" he whispered.

I shook my head, turning the white stone over and over in my hand. I wished everything was as perfect as the stone. I wished that Papa and Caleb and I were perfect for Sarah. I wished we had a sea of our own.

# Sarah, Plain and Tall

## Meet the Author

**Patricia MacLachlan** grew up in Cheyenne, Wyoming, with parents who loved books and stories. *"We read them, discussed them, reread them, and acted out the parts."*

Ms. MacLachlan spent time writing about foster and adopted families for a family agency. When she decided to start writing books, she studied other writers first. She read 30 to 40 children's books each week.

Most of her books are about families, and her concern for families and for children has shaped her career. *"I write books about brothers and sisters, about what makes up a family, what works and what is nurturing."* Many of the characters she writes about are based on people in her own family.

## Meet the Illustrator

**Meg Kelleher Aubrey** creates her work from photos she has taken. She loves to use her friends and family as models because, she says, *"Using familiar faces make[s] the project more personal and fun."* She received her degree in illustration from the Rhode Island School of Design and has won several awards for her art.

# Theme Connections

## Think About It

How will the story end? Here are some questions to think about:

- Will Sarah stay with the family?
- What might her reasons be for staying or going?
- Will Anna and Caleb be glad about what happened?
- How will the father feel?

## Record Ideas

In your Writing Journal, write what you have learned about risks and consequences from the readings and class discussions. Also record any questions you have that arose from the discussions.

## Write a Letter

Pretend you are a friend of one of the story characters. Write a letter to him or her, telling what you think he or she should do.

# The King's Fountain

Lloyd Alexander
*illustrated by Ezra Jack Keats*

A king once planned to build a magnificent fountain in his palace gardens, for the splendor of his kingdom and the glory of his name.

This fountain, however, would stop all water from flowing to the city below.

A poor man heard of it, and said to his wife:

"Soon our children will cry for water, our animals will sicken, and all of us will die of thirst."

His wife answered:

"A man of highest learning must go to the King, speak to him out of wisdom, and show him the folly of his plan."

So the poor man went throughout the city, to the most learned of scholars, and begged him to plead the cause.

But the scholar, deep in his own grand thoughts, barely listened. He pondered lofty matters and had no interest in humbler ones.

And the scholar lectured him with so many cloudy words that the poor man could make no sense of them at all, and went away downcast, saying to himself:

"Alas, the grandest thought quenches no thirst. Besides, what good is all the learning in the world if there is no one who can understand it?"

He realized that someone must present the cause clearly and winningly, with a golden tongue, so the King would listen and agree.

So he went to the marketplace, to the merchants whose words were smooth as pearls and who could string them together endlessly.

But when these merchants heard what he wanted, they choked with fear and their glib words failed them. While they gladly offered clever advice, not one dared face the King.

The poor man left them and went away dismayed, saying to himself:

"Alas, the finest words are empty air without the deeds to fill them. Besides, what good is a golden tongue without a brave heart?"

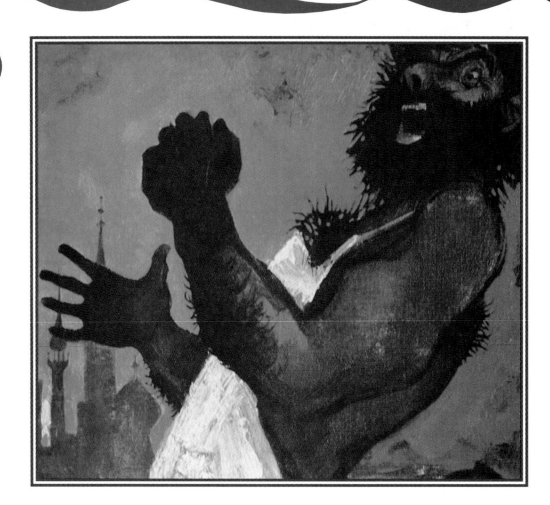

Then he realized that a man of strength and courage must go and force the King to change his plan.

Again he went throughout the city, to the strongest of all brave men: a fearless metalsmith who could knot an iron bar as easily as a shoestring.

The metalsmith, eager to stand against the King, swore that once inside the palace he would smash every window, crack every wall, and break the King's throne into firewood.

The poor man sadly shook his head, knowing the palace guards would strike down the rash metalsmith before he did even one of those deeds. And the King in his wrath would be all the more determined to build his fountain. So, leaving the metalsmith still pounding his fists, he went away in despair, saying to himself:

"Alas, the strongest hand is useless without a wise head to guide it. Besides, what good is all the bravery in the world if it serves no purpose?"

He trudged home, hopeless and heavy-hearted, and told his neighbors and his family that he could find no one to stop the building of the fountain.

His daughter spoke then, and said:

"But, Father——why not go yourself?"

Confused, unable to answer, the poor man looked at the faces of his wife and family. At last, he bowed his head and murmured:

"I hear my own flesh and blood. Indeed, there is no one else, and I myself must go to the King."

The poor man left his home. Alone, he slowly climbed the steep and seemingly endless hill.

Finally, he reached the King's high palace and for a long while stood outside, fearful and hesitant.

When the palace guards roughly seized him and threatened his life for intruding, the poor man trembled in such terror he could scarcely speak. Desperately he blurted out that he had an important message for the King alone.

The guards marched him to the throne room, where the King angrily demanded why he had come.

Knees knocking, teeth chattering, the poor man began to tell as well as he could of the suffering that the fountain would cause.

"Enough!" roared the King. "How dare you question what I do? I am the King!"

The poor man wished for the smallest crumb of the scholar's learning, but he could only stammer:

"Majesty——thirst is thirst, a poor man's no less than a king's."

Then his tongue dried in his mouth and he wished for even one of the merchants' golden words.

The King looked scornfully at him. "You come to trouble me for that? I need only snap my fingers and my swordsmen will cut you to pieces and be done with you."

The poor man wished for one drop of the metalsmith's bravery. With his own last ounce of courage, he answered:

"You have the power to kill me. But that changes nothing. Your people will still die of thirst. Remember them each time you see your splendid fountain."

The King started up, ready to call his guards. But he stopped and fell silent for a time, his frowns deep as his thoughts. Then he replied:

"You are too simple for clever debate with me; but you have a wiser head than a scholar. Your speech is halting; but there is more true eloquence in your words than in the golden tongue of a cunning counselor. You are too weak to crack a flea; but you have a braver heart than anyone in my kingdom. I will do as you ask."

The poor man returned to the city and told the news to all.
The scholar wrote a long account of the matter in one of his
books, and misplaced it. The merchants never stopped
ornamenting tales of the poor man's deed. The metalsmith
was so excited he tossed his anvil into the air and broke one of
his own windows.

The poor man, glad simply to be home with his rejoicing
family, was hardly able to believe what he had done.

"A wise head? A golden tongue? A brave heart?" he said to
himself. "Well, no matter. At least none of us will go thirsty."

# The King's Fountain

## Meet the Author

**Lloyd Alexander** spent so many hours reading books on mythology, poetry, and classic tales that he decided to become a poet and writer. He first started writing books for adults, but most of them were never published. So he worked as an editor and illustrator at a small magazine to make a living. Later he decided to write books for children.

Mr. Alexander invents his stories, but his characters are based on people he knows, including himself.

## Meet the Illustrator

**Ezra Jack Keats** taught himself how to paint. His parents were poor and couldn't buy paper for him very often. He painted on wooden boards he found and on top of the metal table in their kitchen. His mother would call in the neighbors to admire his work before wiping the table clean.

After high school, Keats painted murals, illustrated training manuals for the army, and drew Captain Marvel comic books.

Mr. Keats illustrated 33 books; 22 of those he also wrote. He considered his readers his friends, and he loved getting letters from them. He once said, *"Best of all are the letters and the pictures themselves that children send to me. I can now look up at my studio walls and see my friends—children of every color."*

# Theme Connections

## Think About It

- What did the story tell you about "taking risks?"
- Why was it so difficult for the poor man to face the king?
- Would you be able to overcome fear and risk danger to speak up for a just cause? Why or why not?

## Record Ideas

Use your Writing Journal to write down the ideas your group discussed. Tell how you can use the ideas in this selection in your unit activity.

## Create a Modern-day Story

Imagine that the story "The King's Fountain" was being written today.

- Work with a group of your classmates to make up a "modern-day" version of the story.
- Think about the parts of the story you would and wouldn't change.
- Join another group and share your stories.

# FINE Art

***Saint George Killing the Dragon.*** 1430–35. **Bernardo Martorell.**
Tempera on panel. 115.3 cm × 98 cm. The Art Institute of Chicago,
Gift of Mrs. Richard E. Danielson and Mrs. Chauncey McCormick.
Photograph ©1998, The Art Institute of Chicago, All Rights Reserved.

*Kajikazawa in Kai Province.* From the series Thirty-Six Views of Mount Fuji. 1823–29. **Katsushika Hokusai.** Woodblock print. $10 \times 15\frac{1}{8}$ in. The Metropolitan Museum of Art, Rogers Fund, 1936 (JP 2581). Photograph ©1991 The Metropolitan Museum of Art.

*Margaret Bourke-White Atop the Chrysler Building.* 1931–1933. Silver gelatin print. Photograph: Margaret Bourke-White Estate, courtesy Life Magazine ©Time Inc.

# Mae Jemison
## Space Scientist

by Gail Sakurai

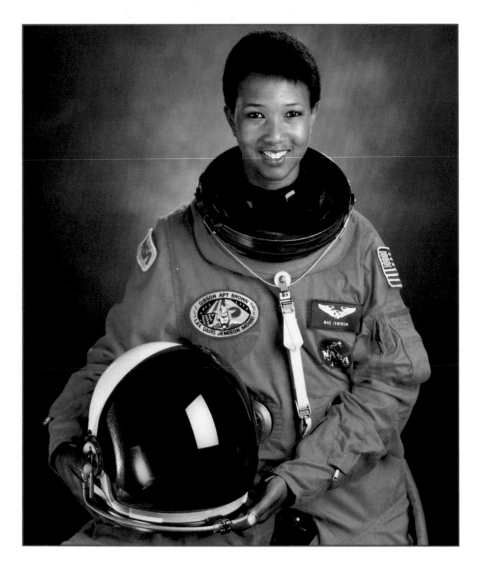

THREE . . .

Two . . .

One . . .

Liftoff!

The space shuttle
*Endeavour* thundered into the
morning sky above Kennedy
Space Center. Higher
and higher it soared over the
Atlantic Ocean. A few minutes
later, *Endeavour* was in orbit
around Earth.

Aboard the spacecraft,
astronaut Mae Jemison
could feel her heart pounding
with excitement. A wide,
happy grin split her face. She
had just made history. She
was the first African-American
woman in space. The date
was September 12, 1992.

But Mae wasn't thinking
about dates in history books.
Her thoughts were of the
wonder and adventure of
space travel. "I'm closer to
the stars——somewhere I've
always dreamed to be," Mae
said during a live television
broadcast from space.

Mae's dream didn't come
true overnight. It happened
only after many long years of
hard work, training, and
preparation. Her success

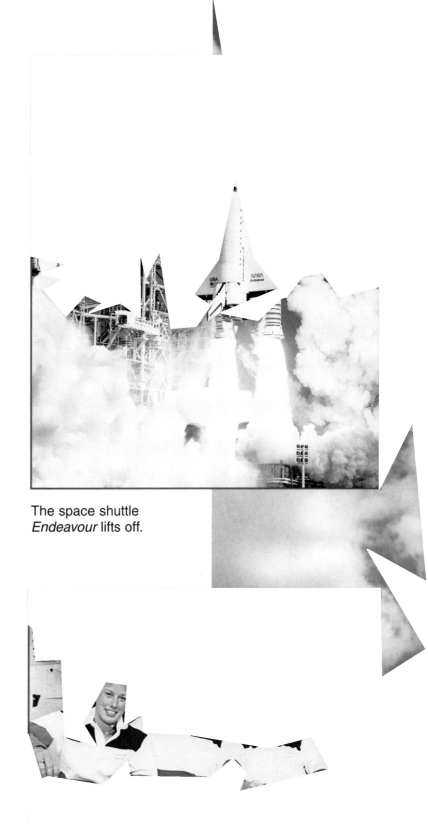

The space shuttle
*Endeavour* lifts off.

While in space, the
*Endeavour* astronauts
pose for a portrait.

77

story began nearly thirty-six years earlier, in a small town in Alabama.

Mae Carol Jemison was born on October 17, 1956, in Decatur, Alabama. While she was still a toddler, Mae and her family moved to the big city of Chicago, Illinois. Mae considers Chicago her hometown because she grew up there.

Mae was the youngest child in her family. She had an older brother, Charles, and an older sister, Ada. Her parents, Charlie and Dorothy Jemison, were helpful and supportive of all of Mae's interests. "They put up with all kinds of stuff, like science projects, dance classes, and art lessons," Mae said. "They encouraged me to do it, and they would find the money, time, and energy to help me be involved."

Other adults were not as encouraging as Mae's parents. When Mae told her kindergarten teacher that she wanted to be a scientist, the teacher said, "Don't you mean a nurse?" In those days, very few African Americans or women were scientists. Many people, like Mae's teacher, couldn't imagine a little black girl growing up to become a scientist. But Mae refused to let other people's limited imaginations stop her from following her dreams.

Mae had always dreamed of becoming an astronaut. Her dream came true in 1987.

Mae loved to work on school science projects. She spent many hours at the public library, reading books about science and space. On summer nights, she liked to lie outside, look up at the stars, and dream of traveling in space. Mae was fascinated by the real-life space flights and moon landings that she watched on television. Mae Jemison knew that she wanted to be an astronaut. Although all the astronauts at the time were white and male, Mae wasn't discouraged.

Science and space were not young Mae's only interests. She also loved to dance. Mae started taking lessons in jazz and African dance at the age of nine. By the time she was in high school, Mae was an accomplished dancer, and she frequently performed on stage. She was also skilled at choreography, the art of creating a dance.

Mae at Stanford University

In 1973, Mae graduated from Chicago's Morgan Park High School, where she was an honor-roll student and excelled in science and math. That fall, Mae entered Stanford University in California. At Stanford, she specialized in African and Afro-American studies, and chemical engineering. Mae continued her dancing and choreography. She also became involved with student organizations, and she was elected president of the Black Student Union.

After receiving her Bachelor of Science degree from Stanford, Mae enrolled at Cornell University Medical College in New York. She had decided to become a doctor. Medical school was demanding, but Mae still found time to participate in student organizations. She served as president of both the Cornell Medical Student Executive Council and the Cornell chapter of the National Student Medical Association.

Mae traveled to several countries as part of her medical training. She studied medicine in Cuba. She helped provide basic medical care for people in rural Kenya and at a Cambodian refugee camp in Thailand.

Mae received her Doctor of Medicine degree from Cornell University in 1981. Like all new doctors, she served an internship, a period of practicing under experienced doctors. Mae completed her internship at the Los Angeles County/University of Southern California Medical Center. Then she started working as a doctor in Los Angeles.

Mae was working as a doctor in this Los Angeles office when NASA selected her for its astronaut program.

Although she had settled into a career as a doctor, Mae wasn't finished traveling yet. She remembered the trips she had taken during medical school, and she still wanted to help people in other parts of the world. Mae decided to join the Peace Corps, an organization of volunteers who work to improve conditions in developing nations.

Mae spent more than two years in West Africa. She was the Area Peace Corps Medical Officer for Sierra Leone and Liberia. She was in charge of health care for all Peace Corps volunteers and U.S. embassy employees in those two countries. It was an important responsibility for someone who was only twenty-six years old.

"I learned a lot from that experience," Mae said. "I was one of the youngest doctors over there, and I had to learn to deal with how people reacted to my age, while asserting myself as a physician."

When her tour of duty in the Peace Corps was over, Mae returned to Los Angeles and resumed her medical practice. She also started taking advanced engineering classes.

Mae sits in the cockpit of a shuttle trainer.

Mae and her survival-training classmates watch a demonstration of how to build a fire.

Mae had not forgotten her dream of traveling in space. Now that she had the necessary education and experience, Mae decided to try and become an astronaut. She applied to the National Aeronautics and Space Administration (NASA), which is responsible for U.S. space exploration. After undergoing background checks, physical exams, medical tests, and interviews, Dr. Mae Jemison was accepted into the astronaut program in June 1987. She was one of only fifteen people chosen from nearly two thousand qualified applicants!

Mae didn't let success go to her head. "I'm very aware of the fact that I'm not the first African-American woman who had the skills, the talent, the desire to be an astronaut," she said. "I happen to be the first one that NASA selected."

Mae moved to Houston, Texas, where she began a year of intensive training at NASA's Johnson Space Center. She studied space shuttle equipment and operations. To learn how to handle emergencies and deal with difficult situations, Mae practiced wilderness- and water-survival skills. Survival training also helps teach cooperation and teamwork. These are important abilities for astronauts who must live and work together for long periods in a cramped space shuttle.

Mae took lessons on how to move her body and operate tools in a weightless environment. On Earth, the force of gravity keeps us from floating off the ground. But in space, there is less gravity, so people and objects drift about. Since there is no "up" or "down" in space, astronauts don't need to lie down to sleep. They can sleep in any position. To keep them from drifting while asleep, they zip themselves into special sleeping bags attached to the shuttle's walls.

During training, Mae got a preview of weightlessness. She flew in a special training jet that simulates zero gravity. The jet climbs nearly straight up, then loops into a steep dive. This is similar to the loop-the-loops on many roller coasters. For thirty seconds at the top of the loop, trainees feel weightless. Their feet leave the floor and they can fly around inside the padded cabin.

At the end of her training year, Mae officially became a mission specialist astronaut. "We're the ones people often call the scientist astronauts," Mae explained. "Our responsibilities are to be familiar with the shuttle and how it operates, to do the experiments once you get into orbit, to help launch the payloads or satellites, and also do extravehicular activities, which are the space walks."

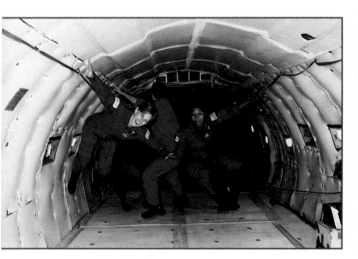

Mae in training (top) clinging to a life raft in water-survival training; (middle) practicing with the shuttle escape pole for emergency bailouts; (bottom) learning to use a parachute.

Bottom left: Mae and astronaut Jan Davis (left) hold onto each other in NASA's "zero-gravity" training aircraft.

This illustration shows how the space shuttle looks during flight. The cargo bay holds Spacelab, the science laboratory where *Endeavour's* astronauts conducted most of their experiments.

In the 1970s, NASA designed the space shuttle as the first reusable spacecraft. A shuttle launches like a rocket, but it returns to Earth and lands on a runway like an airplane. A space shuttle has many uses. It carries both equipment and people into space. Astronauts aboard a shuttle can capture, repair, and launch satellites. Shuttles are often used as orbiting laboratories, where space scientists conduct experiments in a zero-gravity environment. In the future, space shuttles might transport supplies and workers for building space stations.

The *Endeavour* crew on their way to the launch pad.

Although Mae was a full-fledged astronaut, she still had to wait four more years before she went into space. While she waited, Mae worked with the scientists who were developing experiments for her mission. She also trained with her fellow crew members. In her spare time, Mae liked to read, travel, ski, garden, dance, and exercise. She also enjoyed taking care of Sneeze, her white, gray, and silver African wildcat.

On September 12, 1992, the long wait was over. Space shuttle *Endeavour* perched on the launch pad like a great white bird waiting to take flight. Everything was ready for the liftoff.

Mae awoke early to shower and dress. She ate breakfast with the other astronauts. Then, Mae and the crew put on their orange space suits and boarded a van for the short drive to the launch pad. For two-and-a-half hours until liftoff, they lay on their backs, strapped into their seats, as the countdown progressed. At 10:23 A.M., precisely on time, *Endeavour* lifted off on its historic space journey.

Dr. Mae Jemison earned her place in the history books as the first African-American woman in space. Mae said, "My participation in the space shuttle mission helps to say that all peoples of the world have astronomers, physicists, and explorers."

Mae prepares to board the shuttle.

Mae injects liquid into a mannequin's hand. She is testing new medical equipment that is specially designed for a weightless environment.

*Endeavour*'s mission was devoted to scientific research. Mae was responsible for several key experiments. She had helped design an experiment to study the loss of bone cells in space. Astronauts lose bone cells in weightlessness, and the longer they stay in space, the more they lose. If too many cells are lost, bones become weak and can break easily. Scientists hope to find a way to prevent this loss.

Mae explained, "The real issue is how to keep people healthy while they're in space."

Mae investigated a new way of controlling space motion sickness. Half of all astronauts experience space sickness during their first few days in space. They often feel dizzy and nauseated. Astronauts can take medicine to control space sickness, but the medicine can make them tired.

Mae and Jan Davis conduct a zero-gravity experiment. In space, a person's fluids shift toward the upper body. The device Mae is wearing simulates normal gravity and forces the fluids back to the lower body.

To carry out the space-sickness experiment, Mae had been trained in the use of "biofeedback" techniques. Biofeedback uses meditation and relaxation to control the body's functions. Mae wore special monitoring equipment to record her heart rate, breathing, temperature, and other body functions. If she started to feel ill, she would meditate. She concentrated intensely on bringing her body back to normal. The purpose of the experiment was to see if Mae could avoid space sickness without taking medication. The results of the experiment were not conclusive, but space researchers still hope to use biofeedback in the future.

Mae is all wired up for the biofeedback experiment.

Mae was also in charge of the frog experiment. Early in the flight, she fertilized eggs from female South African frogs. A few days later, tadpoles hatched. She then watched the tadpoles carefully. Her goal was to find out if the tadpoles would develop normally in the near-zero gravity of space. "What we've seen is that the eggs were fertilized and the tadpoles looked pretty good," said Mae. "It was exciting because that's a question that we didn't have any information on before."

Mae works with the frog experiment.

Home again. *Endeavour* lands on the runway at the Kennedy Space Center.

Mae with Morgan Park High School's principal, Earl Bryant, at a special homecoming ceremony in her honor.

On September 20, 1992, at 8:53 A.M., *Endeavour* landed at Kennedy Space Center. The crew had spent more than 190 hours (almost eight days) in space. They had traveled 3.3 million miles and had completed 127 orbits of Earth!

After her space mission, Mae returned home to Chicago. Her hometown welcomed her with six days of parades, speeches, and celebrations. Then she went to Hollywood to accept the American Black Achievement Awards' Trailblazer Award for being the first African-American woman in space. In 1993, Mae was inducted into the National Women's Hall of Fame in Seneca Falls, New York.

Mae Jemison had made her childhood dream come true. She was ready for new challenges. A few months after her space flight, Mae took a leave of absence from NASA to teach and to do research at Dartmouth College in New Hampshire. Then, on March 8, 1993, she permanently resigned from the astronaut corps.

Mae formed her own company called The Jemison Group, Inc. The Jemison Group's goal is to develop ways of using science and technology to improve the quality of life. Mae's company makes a special effort to improve conditions in poor and developing countries.

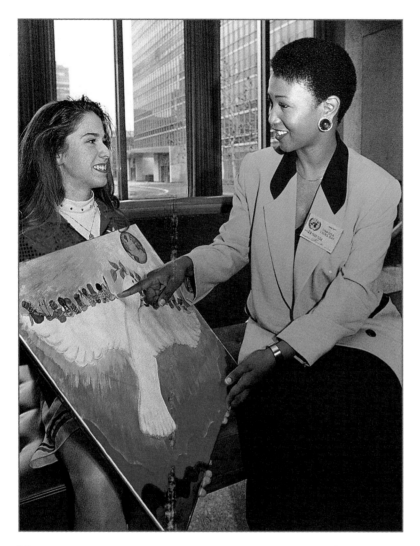

Mae encourages youngsters to follow their dreams. She is shown here with thirteen-year-old Jill Giovanelli, the winner of the International Peace Poster Contest.

The company's first project used satellite communications to provide better health care for people in West Africa. Mae also established an international summer science camp for young people.

Besides her work with The Jemison Group, Mae spends much of her time traveling around the country, giving speeches, and encouraging young people to follow their dreams. Mae Jemison believes in the motto:

"Don't be limited by others' limited imaginations."

# Mae Jemison
## Space Scientist

## Meet the Author

**Gail Sakurai** was born in Detroit, Michigan. As soon as she learned to read, she knew she wanted to be a writer.

Ms. Sakurai gets story ideas from the world around her. Her book about Dr. Mae Jemison, the first female African-American astronaut, grew out of a lifelong interest in space exploration. She says, *"I get the ideas for my books from everywhere—from things I read, from my children, and even from television. I have more ideas than I'll ever have time to use."*

Ms. Sakurai's advice to aspiring young writers is simple. *"Read. Read everything you can get your hands on!"*

# Theme Connections

## Think About It

Biographies are stories about the lives of famous important people. Join with a small group of your classmates and discuss why Mae Jemison is an important person. Here are some things to talk about:

- What did Mae Jemison do that was important? Why was it important?
- Why did Mae Jemison do what she did?
- Did the work of Mae Jemison make a difference to people? Who did it make a difference to? Have you been affected by her work?

## Record Ideas

Imagine you are the director of a play that is based on this selection. Make a list of the sets you will need and write a brief description of each in your Writing Journal. Share your work with two or three classmates and add to your list if you missed any.

## Bring in a Photograph

Work with a classmate to find a photograph or a picture of someone you believe risked, in some thoughtful way, to reach an important goal. Join a small group of your classmates and tell them who the person is, what he or she has accomplished, and how he or she has persevered.

# The Acrobats

Dorothy Aldis
*illustrated by Laura Huliska-Beith*

Flying high on silver bars
Ladies spangled like the sun
Turn just so, and then let go—
And catch another one!
And smile when they come down, and wave,
And are not proud of being brave.

# People Who Must

Carl Sandburg
*illustrated by Laura Huliska-Beith*

I painted on the roof of a skyscraper.
I painted a long while and called it a day's work.
The people on a corner swarmed and the traffic
   cop's whistle never let up all afternoon.
They were the same as bugs, many bugs on
   their way—
Those people on the go or at a standstill;
And the traffic cop a spot of blue, a splinter
   of brass,
Where the black tides ran around him
And he kept the street. I painted a long while
And called it a day's work.

# Two Tickets to Freedom

from *Two Tickets to Freedom: The True Story
of Ellen and William Craft, Fugitive Slaves*
by Florence B. Freedman
*illustrated by Doris Ettlinger*

*Among the many slaves in Georgia in 1848 were a
young couple named William and Ellen Craft. Ellen
was a maid and William a skilled cabinetmaker.
Their lives were not as harsh as those of many
other slaves, but the desire to be free never left
them. However, escaping would be difficult!*

*William had been saving money for tickets to
escape. He had a plan for himself and Ellen, who
was light-skinned enough to pass for white. Ellen
would dress up as an injured man, bandaging her
face to further disguise the fact that she was a
woman, and bandaging her right arm and
hand to prevent anyone from asking her to
write. She would then travel with
William as her slave.*

*Their journey would include a train ride
to Fredericksburg, Virginia, followed by a boat trip to
Washington, D.C., and finally a train ride to Philadelphia,
the first stop on the Underground Railroad.*

*By the time they left the train in Fredericksburg and
boarded a ship for Washington, D.C., William and Ellen felt
sure they were safe. They were unaware that the most
difficult part of their daring escape was just around the
corner. Would they ever make it to Philadelphia?*

In a few minutes, the ship landed at Washington, and there William and Ellen took a carriage to the train for Baltimore, the last slave port they were to see. They had left their cottage on Wednesday morning, the 21st of December. It was Christmas Eve, December 24, 1848, when they arrived in Baltimore.

William and Ellen were more tense than ever. They were so near their goal . . . yet they knew that officials in Baltimore were particularly watchful to prevent slaves from escaping across the border to Pennsylvania and freedom.

William settled his "master" in a first-class carriage on the train and went to the car in which blacks traveled. Before he entered, a Yankee officer stopped him, saying sternly, "Where are you going, boy?"

"Philadelphia, sir," William replied humbly.

"What are you going there for?" asked the officer.

"I am traveling with my master who is in another carriage, sir."

"I think you had better get him out, and be quick about it, because the train will soon be starting," the officer ordered. "It is against the rules to let any man take a slave past here unless he can satisfy them in the office that he has a right to take him along." The officer moved on, leaving William on the platform.

William's heart was beating furiously. To have come so far—and now this! How would Ellen be able to prove ownership? He consoled himself with the thought that God, who had been so good as to allow them to come this far, would not let them be turned aside now.

William hastened into the car to tell his master the bad news. "Mr. Johnson," seated comfortably in the railroad car, smiled at him. They were so near their destination.

"How are you feeling, sir?" asked William.

"Much better," answered his "master." "Thank God we are getting on so nicely."

"Not so nicely, sir, I am sorry to say," William said. "You must leave the train and convince the officials that I am your slave."

"Mr. Johnson" shuddered.

"Good heavens!" he whispered. "Is it possible that we will be sent back into slavery?"

They were silent for a few despairing moments. Then they left the train and made their way to the office.

Ellen summoned her last bit of courage.

"Do you wish to see me, sir?" "Mr. Johnson" asked the man who appeared to be the chief officer.

"Yes," he answered. "It is against our rules, sir, to allow any person to take a slave out of Baltimore into Philadelphia unless he can satisfy us that he has a right to take him along."

"Why is that?" asked "Mr. Johnson" innocently.

"Because, sir," the officer answered in a voice and manner that almost chilled the blood of the fugitives, "if we should allow any gentleman to take a slave past here into Philadelphia, and should the gentleman with whom the slave was traveling turn out to be not his rightful owner, and if the real owner should prove that his slave escaped on our railroad, we should have to pay for him."

This conversation attracted the attention of a large number of curious passengers. They seemed sympathetic to "Mr. Johnson," because he was so obviously ill.

Seeing the sympathy of the other passengers, the officer asked, more politely, "Do you know someone in Baltimore who might vouch for you and assure us that you have a right to take this slave into Pennsylvania?"

"No, I do not," asserted "Mr. Johnson" regretfully. He then added more forcefully, "I bought tickets in Charleston to pass us through to Philadelphia, and you have no right to detain us here!"

The officer was firm. "Right or wrong, I shan't let you go."

William and Ellen looked at each other, but did not dare to say a word for fear they would give themselves away. They knew that, if the officer suspected them, he had the right to put them in prison. When their true identity became known, they would surely be sent back into slavery, and they knew they would rather be dead. They silently prayed to be delivered from this new danger.

Just then, the conductor of the train on which they had come from Washington, came in.

"Did this gentleman and his slave come on your train?" asked the official.

"They did," answered the conductor, and left.

Suddenly the bell rang for the train to leave. The other passengers fixed their eyes upon the officer, "Mr. Johnson," and his slave, their expressions showing their interest and concern.

The officer seemed agitated. Running his fingers through his hair, he finally said, "I don't know what to do." Then looking around, he added, "I calculate it is all right. Run and tell the conductor that it will be all right to let this gentleman and his slave proceed," he told one of the clerks. "Since he is not well, it is a pity to stop him here. We will let him go."

"Mr. Johnson" thanked him and stepped out, crossing the platform as quickly as possible, with his slave close behind. William escorted his master into one of the best carriages of the train and reached his own just as the train pulled out.

It was eight o'clock on Christmas Eve, just eight days after William had first thought of their plan. In the four days before they left Macon, he and Ellen had both been working; they had seen each other only at night, when they talked over each detail of their plan. They had had hardly any sleep for the four days of planning and the four days of the journey. Now that the last hurdle was passed, William realized how terribly tired he was. Knowing that they would be in Philadelphia in the morning, and that there were no important stations between Baltimore and Philadelphia, William relaxed his guard, and fell asleep. It proved to be the wrong time for sleeping.

When the train reached Havre-de-Grace, all the first-class passengers were told to get off the train and onto a ferryboat, to be ferried across the Susquehanna River to take the train again on the opposite side. This was to spare the passengers the jolting of rolling the cars onto the boat. The baggage cars, however, were rolled on the boat to be taken off on the other side. The sleeping William was near the baggage car, so they did not wake him.

When Ellen left the railroad carriage to get on the ferryboat, it was cold and dark and rainy. She was alone, without William, for the first time on the journey. She was frightened and confused.

"Have you seen my boy?" "Mr. Johnson" asked the conductor.

The conductor, who may well have been an abolitionist, thought he would tease this Southern slaveowner.

"No, I haven't seen anything of him for some time; no doubt he has run away and has reached Philadelphia long before now. He is probably a free man by now, sir."

"Mr. Johnson" knew better. "Please try to find him," he asked the conductor.

"I am no slave hunter," the conductor indignantly replied. "As far as I am concerned, everybody must look after his own slaves." With that, he strode away.

Ellen was frightened. She feared that William had been kidnaped into slavery, or perhaps killed on the train. She was in a predicament for another reason. She had no money at all. Although Ellen had been carrying the money up to then, she had given it all to William the night before after hearing that there were pickpockets in Philadelphia who preyed on travelers. A pickpocket would not think of a slave as a likely victim.

Ellen did have the tickets, however. Frightened and confused though she was, she realized that there was no use in her staying there at Havre-de-Grace. She must board the ferry and complete her journey, hoping and praying that she and William would find each other again in freedom.

The ferry ride over, the passengers went back on the train. After the train was well on its way to Philadelphia, the guard came to the car where William was sleeping and gave him a violent shake, saying, "Boy, wake up!"

William started, not knowing for a moment where he was.

"Your master is scared half to death about you," the guard continued. It was William's turn to be scared. He was sure that Ellen had been found out.

"What is the matter?" William managed to ask.

"Your master thinks you have run away from him," the guard explained.

Knowing that Ellen would never think any such thing, William felt reassured and went to his "master" immediately.

After talking with "Mr. Johnson" for a few minutes, William returned to his place, where the guard was talking with the conductor.

"What did your master want, boy?" asked the guard.

"He just wanted to know what had become of me."

"No," said the guard. "That's not it. He thought you had taken leave for parts unknown. I never saw a man so badly scared about losing his slave in my life. Now," continued the guard, "let me give you a little friendly advice. When you get to Philadelphia, run away and leave that cripple, and have your liberty."

"No, sir," replied William. "I can't promise to do that."

"Why not?" asked the conductor, evidently much surprised. "Don't you want your liberty?"

"Yes, sir," he replied, "but I shall never run away from such a good master as I have at present."

One of the men said to the guard, "Let him alone. I guess he'll open his eyes when he gets to Philadelphia."

In spite of William's seeming lack of interest, the men gave him a good deal of information about how to run away from his master in Philadelphia, information which he appeared not to be taking to heart, but which he found useful for both of them later.

On the train, William also met a free black man, who recommended to him a boardinghouse in Philadelphia kept by an abolitionist, where he would be quite safe if he decided to run away from his master. William thanked him, but did not let him know who he and his "master" really were.

Later on in the night, William heard a fearful whistling of the steam engine; he looked out the window and saw many flickering lights. A passenger in the next car also stuck his head out the window and called to his companion, "Wake up! We are in Philadelphia." The sight of the city in the distance and the words he heard made William feel as if a burden had rolled off his back; he felt really happy for the first time in his life.

As soon as the train reached the platform, he went to get "Mr. Johnson," took their luggage, put it into a carriage, got in and drove off to the abolitionist's boardinghouse recommended to him by the free black man.

No sooner had they left the station than Ellen, who had concealed her fears and played her part with so much courage and wit throughout the journey, grasped William's hand and said, "Thank God we are safe!" She burst into tears, and wept like a child.

When they reached the boardinghouse, Ellen was so weak and faint that she could scarcely stand alone. As soon as they were shown their room, William and Ellen knelt down and thanked God for His goodness in enabling them to overcome so many dangers in escaping from slavery to freedom.

That was Sunday, December 25, Christmas Day of 1848.

Ellen was twenty-two years old, and William a few years older. They thought all their troubles were over. They were young, strong, and in love. And they were free.

*Philadelphia was the first stop on the Underground Railroad for William and Ellen. Eventually, they made their way to England, where their children were born. After the Civil War, they returned to Georgia with their family and bought a large plantation. There they established the Woodville Cooperative Farm School for poor families, to which they devoted the rest of their lives.*

# Two Tickets to Freedom

## Meet the Author

**Florence B. Freedman** was born in Brooklyn, New York. She went to school at Columbia University and later became a teacher of English and Hebrew. One of her students was Ezra Jack Keats, illustrator of "The King's Fountain."

Many of Ms. Freedman's books are based on stories she heard or read when she was growing up. *Two Tickets to Freedom* is a true story. To write it, Ms. Freedman researched old newspaper articles, journals, and William Craft's own narrative of what happened.

## Meet the Illustrator

**Doris Ettlinger** grew up in Staten Island, New York. She took painting lessons from local artists, read "How to Draw" books, and copied the comics from the newspaper. She studied illustration at the Rhode Island School of Design, graduating in 1973, and has illustrated professionally ever since. Today Ms. Ettlinger lives on the banks of the Musconetcong River in New Jersey with her husband and two children. Several days a week she teaches art to children and adults. She tells her students that, *"drawing every day improves my skills, just as a musician practices an instrument or an athlete works out."*

# Theme Connections

## Think About It

Why were the Crafts willing to take their risk-filled journey?
Would you have taken the risks they did? Here are some ideas
to discuss:

- Sometimes the consequences of not taking risks are
  worse than the consequences of taking risks.
- Taking control of your life when it is unhappy is
  sometimes worth taking risks.
- Taking risks with someone who is close to you can
  help motivate you.

## Record Ideas

Work with a classmate and, from memory,
list the problems the Crafts encountered
and how they solved each one. Record the
problems in your Writing Journal.

## Create a Wheel of Feelings

How did the Crafts feel as they encountered the various
problems on their journey? Draw a wheel in your Writing
Journal.  Make sure there is enough space between the spokes
of the wheel to write on them. On each spoke write down
the feelings you think the Crafts had at different stages of
their trip.

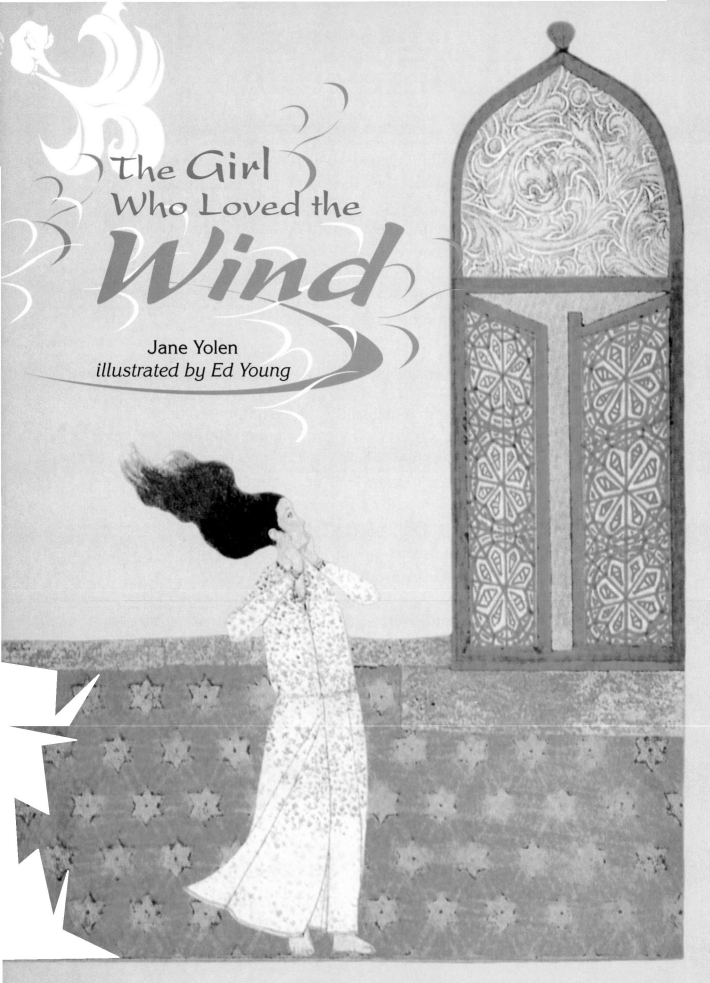

# the Girl Who Loved the Wind

Jane Yolen
*illustrated by Ed Young*

Once many years ago in a country far to the east there lived a wealthy merchant. He was a widower and had an only daughter named Danina. She was dainty and beautiful, and he loved her more than he loved all of his treasures.

Because Danina was his only child, the merchant wanted to keep her from anything that might hurt or harm her in any way, and so he decided to shut her away from the world.

When Danina was still an infant, her father brought her to a great house which he had built on the shore of the sea. On three sides of the house rose three huge walls. And on the fourth side was the sea itself.

In this lovely, lonely place Danina grew up knowing everything that was in her father's heart but nothing of the world.

In her garden grew every kind of fair fruit and flower, for so her father willed it. And on her table was every kind of fresh fish and fowl, for so her father ordered. In her room were the finest furnishings. Gaily colored books and happy music, light dancing and bright paintings, filled her days. And the servants were instructed always to smile, never to say no, and to be cheerful all through the year. So her father wished it and so it was done. And for many years, nothing sad touched Danina in any way.

Yet one spring day, as Danina stood by her window gazing at the sea, a breeze blew salt across the waves. It whipped her hair about her face. It blew in the corners of her room. And as it moved, it whistled a haunting little tune.

Danina had never heard such a thing before. It was sad, but it was beautiful. It intrigued her. It beguiled her. It caused her to sigh and clasp her hands.

"Who are you?" asked Danina.

And the wind answered:

*Who am I?*
*I call myself the wind.*
*I slap at ships and sparrows.*
*I sough through broken windows.*
*I shepherd snow and sandstorms.*
*I am not always kind.*

"How peculiar," said Danina. "Here you merely rustle the trees and play with the leaves and calm the birds in their nests."

*"I am not always kind,"* said the wind again.

"Everyone here is always kind. Everyone here is always happy."

*"Nothing is always,"* said the wind.

"My life is always," said Danina. "Always happy."

*"But life is not always happy,"* said the wind.

"Mine is," said Danina.

*"How sad,"* whispered the wind from a corner.

"What do you mean?" asked Danina. But the wind only whirled through the window carrying one of her silken scarves, and before she could speak again, he had blown out to sea.

Days went by, happy days. Yet sometimes in her room, Danina would try to sing the wind's song. She could not quite remember the words or recall the tune, but its strangeness haunted her.

Finally, one morning, she asked her father: "Why isn't life always happy?"

"Life *is* always happy," replied her father.

"That's what I told him," said Danina.

"Told who?" asked her father. He was suddenly frightened, frightened that someone would take his daughter away.

"The wind," said Danina.

"The wind does not talk," said her father.

"He called himself the wind," she replied.

But her father did not understand. And so when a passing fisherman found Danina's scarf far out at sea and returned it to the merchant's house, he was rewarded with a beating, for the merchant suspected that the fisherman was the one who called himself the wind.

Then one summer day, weeks later, when the sun was reflected in the petals of the flowers, Danina strolled in her garden. Suddenly the wind leaped over the high wall and pushed and pulled at the tops of the trees. He sang his strange song, and Danina clasped her hands and sighed.

"Who are you?" she whispered.

*"Who am I?"* said the wind, and he sang:

*Who am I?*
*I call myself the wind.*
*I've worked the sails of windmills.*
*I've whirled the sand in deserts.*
*I've wrecked ten thousand galleons.*
*I am not always kind.*

"I knew it was you," said Danina. "But no one believed me."

And the wind danced around the garden and made the flowers bow.

He caressed the birds in the trees and played gently with the feathers on their wings.

"You say you are not always kind," said Danina. "You say you have done many unkind things. But all I see is that you are gentle and good."

*"But not always,"* reminded the wind. *"Nothing is always."*

"Is it sad then beyond the wall?"

*"Sometimes sad and sometimes happy,"* said the wind.

"But different each day?" said Danina.

*"Very different."*

"How strange," Danina said. "Here things are always the same. Always beautiful. Happy. Good."

*"How sad,"* said the wind. *"How dull."* And he leaped over the wall and blew out into the world.

"Come back," shouted Danina, rushing to the wall. But her voice was lost against the stones.

Just then her father came into the garden. He saw his daughter standing by the wall and crying to the top. He ran over to her. "Who are you calling? Who has been here?" he demanded.

"The wind," said Danina, her eyes bright with memory. "He sang me his song."

"The wind does not sing," said her father. "Only men and birds sing."

"This was no bird," said his daughter.

"Then," thought her father, "it must have been a man." And he resolved to keep Danina from the garden.

Locked out of her garden, Danina began to wander up and down the long corridors of the house, and what once had seemed like a palace to her began to feel like a prison. Everything seemed false. The happy smiles of the servants she saw as smiles of pity for her ignorance. The gay dancing seemed to hide broken hearts. The bright paintings hid sad thoughts. And soon Danina found herself thinking of the wind at every moment, humming his song to the walls. His song about the world—sometimes happy, sometimes sad, but always full of change and challenge.

Her father, who was not cruel but merely foolish, could not keep her locked up completely. Once a day, for an hour, he allowed Danina to walk along the beach. But three maidservants walked before her. Three manservants walked behind. And the merchant himself watched from a covered chair.

One chilly day in the fall, when the tops of the waves rolled in white to the shore, Danina strolled on the beach. She pulled her cape around her for warmth. And the three maidservants before her and the three manservants behind shivered in the cold. Her father in his covered chair pulled his blanket to his chin and stared out to sea. He was cold and unhappy, but he was more afraid to leave Danina alone.

Suddenly the wind blew across the caps of the waves, tossing foam into the air.

Danina turned to welcome him, stretching out her arms. The cape billowed behind her like the wings of a giant bird.

"Who are you?" thundered Danina's father, jumping out of his chair.

The wind spun around Danina and sang:

> *Who am I?*
> *I call myself the wind.*
> *I am not always happy.*
> *I am not always kind.*

"Nonsense," roared Danina's father. "Everyone here is always happy and kind. I shall arrest you for trespassing." And he shouted, "GUARDS!"

But before the guards could come, Danina had spread her cape on the water. Then she stepped onto it, raised one corner, and waved good-bye to her father. The blowing wind filled the cape's corner like the sail of a ship.

And before Danina's father had time to call out, before he had time for one word of repentance, she was gone. And the last thing he saw was the billowing cape as Danina and the wind sailed far to the west into the ever-changing world.

# The Girl Who Loved the Wind

## Meet the Author

**Jane Yolen's** parents were writers. Jane loved reading, playing fantasy games, and dancing. She also shared her father's love of kites and flying, which shows up in *The Girl Who Loved the Wind*.

Ms. Yolen has written more than 125 books. She often starts writing a book without knowing how it will end. After her first draft, she spends a lot of time editing and revising. Sometimes she edits a book 20 times before getting it the way she wants.

Her advice to young writers is *"read and read. It's the only way you will discover what great stories you want to tell better. Write every day because writing is like a muscle that needs to be flexed."*

## Meet the Illustrator

**Ed Young** was born in Tientsin, China. As a young boy, he made up plays and created many drawings. He was determined to do something artistic with his life.

Mr. Young moved to the United States when he was twenty and became a naturalized citizen. He has been illustrating children's books since the early 1960s. In the 1970s he started writing and illustrating his own books. Many of the books he illustrates are about the folklore of China.

# Theme Connections

## Think About It

- What risks did the father not take? Why?
- What were the consequences of not taking those risks—both for himself and his daughter?
- What risk did the daughter take? Why?
- What were the consequences of taking those risks—both for herself and her father?

## Record Ideas

Make a list of several risks you have taken. Pick two or three and tell what the possible consequences might be both for you and other people. Write your thoughts in your Writing Journal.

## Tell a Story

- Working with a partner, plan a modern-day version of this story.
- Now tell it to another pair of students, and have them offer constructive criticism.
- What did you change in the story?
- Did the other students change the same things?
- What did you change that they didn't?
- What did they change that you didn't?

# Bibliography

### Alice Ramsey's Grand Adventure

**by Don Brown.** Come along for a ride in Alice Ramsey's Maxwell touring car when she attempts to be the first woman to drive across America. It won't be an easy trip.

### The Bobbin Girl

**by Emily Arnold McCully.** Rebecca is only ten years old, but she is old enough to be her family's breadwinner and old enough to join in a protest for worker's rights.

### El Chino

**by Allen Say.** Billy, a Chinese American, risks everything to become a bullfighter in Spain.

### The Enchanted Tapestry

**by Robert D. San Souci.** Li Ju begins a dangerous search for his mother's handmade tapestry, held by the fairies of Sun Mountain.

## Follow the Drinking Gourd

**by Jeanette Winter.** Peg Leg Joe teaches slaves a simple folk song that isn't as simple as it appears. Is it really a map to freedom?

## Knee-knock Rise

**by Natalie Babbitt.** On a dare, Egan decides to climb Knee-Knock Rise. Will he find the dreaded Megrimum?

## Nim and the War Effort

**by Milly Lee.** The newspaper drive for the war is on, and no matter what the consequences are, Nim is determined to prove that she is the school's hardest worker and the greatest patriot.

## Sky Pioneer: A Photobiography of Amelia Earhart

**by Corinne Szabo.** When women were expected to stay at home, Amelia Earhart took to the sky. Her spirit of adventure is contagious. Catch it!

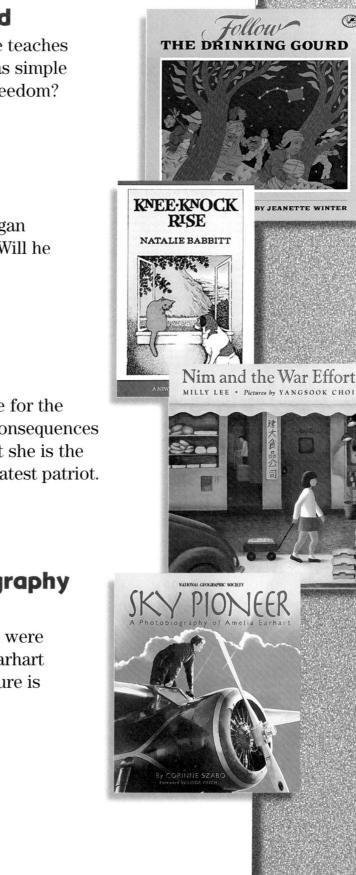

**W**hat do these people have in common? Josie has her own hot dog stand on a busy street corner. Angeline buys used designer jeans and sells them in her shop. Nancy has started a company that makes educational computer games. Don't say they're all women. That's true, but it's not the point. The point is that they all run their own businesses instead of working for someone else. Would you like to do that? It isn't easy. You'll learn why in this unit. But for many people it's the only way to go.

# Eddie, Incorporated

from *Eddie, Incorporated*
by Phyllis Reynolds Naylor
*illustrated by Charmie Curran*

The South End Middle School was composed of sixth, seventh, and eighth graders instead of the usual junior high arrangement. Every noon, the students had an hour off for something called activity period. During this time they ate their lunch and afterwards they could walk around, talk with teachers, use the library, and go outside and throw frisbees.

Eddie called a business conference during activity period. While their other sixth-grade friends were shooting baskets over on the concrete, Eddie, Dink, and Elizabeth sat on the wall at the driveway entrance and had a meeting.

It was understood from the beginning that they were partners. They would all three be bosses, so nobody could tell them what to do.

"We've got to have advertising," said Eddie.

Elizabeth lifted her face toward the warm May sun and closed her eyes for a moment. She wore huge, round, blue-tinted glasses, and her hair was pulled up in a large topknot.

"What we need," she said, "is to rent a plane that would fly all over Detroit trailing a banner that said, 'Anselmino's Aluminum Recycling Now Open for Business.'"

She even looked like an executive.

"Elizabeth can do advertising," said Eddie, and knew she'd think of something, even without the plane. "We also need someone in charge of supply——to find out where the cans are and go after them."

"I could use Dad's garbage can carrier and go around collecting," Dink said. He was wearing a tee-shirt with Godzilla on the front. He didn't look like an executive, but he did look as though he could walk over half of Detroit pushing a one-hundred pound load.

"You've got it," said Eddie. "Vice-president in charge of supply."

"Hey, Eddie," Billy Watson called. "Let's shoot a few baskets."

"Not now," said Eddie. "We've got business."

Eddie himself was in charge of the factory, which was half the Anselmino's basement. He set up a card table with a clock and a pen and a notebook on it. He propped up a long piece of rain gutter under the basement window as a chute, a packing box to catch the cans, a tub to rinse them in, a hair dryer to dry them, a sledge hammer to flatten them, and a box of leaf bags to bind them up in five-pound bundles.

All week long Elizabeth went about the neighborhood tacking handmade posters on telephone poles. The announcement read:

*Tired of litter?*
*Sick of junk?*
ANSELMINO'S ALUMINUM
RECYCLING COMPANY
*needs your old cans*

And then it listed Eddie's address and phone number.

Dink had painted a big OPEN sign on the back of a dart board to set up outside the house. The Anselmino Aluminum Recycling Company would begin its first day of business on Saturday, May 17, at nine o'clock.

"I'll be here at eight-thirty, in case there's a line," Elizabeth said to Eddie on Friday.

"And we ought to put in a night deposit box so people will have some place to put their cans after we're closed," Dink suggested. He said he would make one and bring it with him on Saturday.

Even Eddie's brother Joseph was interested in the company.

"How much can you get for aluminum cans, Eddie?" he asked at dinner.

"Seventeen cents a pound."

Joseph figured it out on the calculator he had wedged between his leg and the seat of his chair. "Only five hundred and eighty-eight pounds and you'll have a hundred dollars," he said, and went on to figure the interest.

"What are you going to do with the profits?" Eddie's other brother, Roger, asked Eddie. "Have you thought of investing it somewhere? The bank gives five and one half percent."

Actually, Eddie had been thinking of putting it in the back of his top dresser drawer under the extra shoelaces, but he said he'd consider investing.

"And what about Dink and Elizabeth?" Mr. Anselmino asked. "Are you putting them on salary, or do they share the profits?"

Eddie wasn't sure.

"If they're on salary," his father said, "that means you pay them a certain amount each week regardless of how much the company takes in. If the company loses money, you'll have to pay them out of your allowance or something. But if the company makes money, they still get only their salary and you get all the rest."

It wasn't difficult to decide that one. Eddie, Dink, and Elizabeth were a team. It would be share and share alike. Even if they made a hundred dollars the first day, they'd split it three ways.

"We're sharing the profits," he said, and realized he was beginning to sound like Roger. It was a good feeling, especially when he understood what he was talking about.

"Who's going to pay for the leaf bags you took out of the tool shed?" asked Mrs. Anselmino.

"We'll take it out of our earnings," Eddie told her. They hadn't even opened for business and already they were sixty-three cents in debt.

He woke at five the next morning and looked out the window to see if a line was forming yet. The street was still dark and empty. He knew he wouldn't sleep anymore, so he got up, dressed, and went out on the porch to wait.

The paper boy came by, followed by his dog. The mutt was holding something in his mouth that looked familiar. Eddie went down the steps and took it away from him. It was one of the advertisements for the Anselmino Aluminum Recycling Company.

"Hey, where'd he get this?" Eddie called after the boy.

The paper boy shrugged. "I don't know. It was blowing around on the street back there."

Eddie went down to the corner. The poster had been ripped off the telephone pole. There was still a piece of it left. He walked over to the next street. That poster was there, but someone had drawn two tanks on it, having a war, with smoke and bombs all over the words. At the next telephone pole, someone had crossed out Eddie's telephone number and scribbled in the number for the fire department instead.

He went back home and sat on the steps. This neighborhood didn't have too many old cans; it had too many rotten children. Anselmino's Children Recycling Company, that's what it ought to be. They ought to go around collecting bratty kids in Dink's garbage cart, weigh them in, tie them in sacks, and send them off to Siberia.

Mrs. Anselmino found Eddie still on the porch at seven o'clock and made him come in for breakfast. She put a plate of scrambled eggs before him and a sausage and an English muffin and then, on the spur of the moment, she poured him a half cup of coffee and filled the cup up with cream.

"Now," she said, "you're ready for business."

He was beginning to feel good again.

Dink and Elizabeth arrived at eight-thirty. Dink had brought a night-deposit box made out of an ice cream container. On the curb at the end of the driveway he placed the dart board sign saying, OPEN.

At five minutes till nine, they took their places——Dink outside the basement window, Elizabeth at the bottom of the chute, and Eddie at the card table desk.

On the top of the first page of his notebook, Eddie wrote, "The Anselmino Aluminum Recycling Company" and, as an afterthought, added, "Incorporated," though he wasn't sure what it meant.

Underneath, he made six vertical columns with a ruler. At the top of the first column he wrote, "Date." At the top of the second, he wrote "Number of cans." At the top of the third, "Number of pounds." At the fourth, "Income," the fifth, "Expenses," and at the top of the final column he wrote "Profit." Then, after a moment, he added, ". . . or Loss."

Nine o'clock came, nine-fifteen, and at twenty after, Dink yelled, "Somebody's coming!"

There were footsteps on the driveway outside, and the sound of the mailman's voice. He wanted to know where the aluminum deposit was, and Dink directed him to the open window.

The sleeve of a blue uniform came through the window and deposited one empty iced tea can in the rain gutter.

*Clunk-ity . . . clunk-ity . . . thunk.*

It was a very lonely sound. The iced tea can lay all by itself in the bottom of the packing box, and the blue uniform disappeared.

Elizabeth picked up the can and dropped it in the water in the wash tub, placed it under the hair dryer for a minute, and then flattened it with the sledge hammer.

"One," she said, as she set it over against the wall.

Eddie made a mark in the second column of his notebook beside May 17.

About ten o'clock, Mr. Clemmons came over with an armload of cans he had picked up in the alley. He dropped them down the chute one after another: *clunkity, clunkity, thumpity, bang, thud.*
It was a beautiful noise.

"Hey, thanks a lot!" said Dink outside the window.

Now it was more like a factory. Elizabeth had barely taken all the cans out of the packing box when Dink's mother came around to the window and deposited a few cola cans and seven ginger ales. There were cans in the packing case at the bottom of the chute, cans floating about in the wash tub, cans under the hair dryer, and cans waiting to be smashed.

"This is more like it," said Eddie.

Things slowed a little over the lunch hour. Mrs. Anselmino brought down some salami sandwiches, and they took turns eating and standing out on the driveway to direct people to the deposit window.

Billy Watson and some boys from the South End Middle School rode over on their bikes, stuck their heads in the window and yelled crazy things. One of them rolled a rock down the chute. But after they went away, Elizabeth's father arrived with two grocery sacks full of cans.

"Way to go!" whooped Dink from outside as he poured the cans down the rain gutter.

Eddie and Elizabeth were working as fast as they could.

About three o'clock the hair dryer began to smell funny, and Eddie decided that maybe it needed a rest, so they finished drying the cans with a towel.

At four, old Mrs. Harris came by pulling a little wagon. It was piled high with cans, and she stooped down outside the window and began dropping them one at a time down the chute.

Eddie and Elizabeth stared. There were baked bean cans and creamed corn cans and scalloped potato cans and about twenty fruit cocktail. Only one of the cans was aluminum; the rest were tin, and the baked bean can still had a frankfurter in the bottom.

"Why didn't you stop her, Dink?" Elizabeth called up after the woman had left.

"I didn't have the heart," he said. "She pulled that wagon four blocks, so I just thanked her, and she said there were more cans where those came from."

At five o'clock, Eddie took the OPEN sign and put it behind the house. He closed the basement window and put the night deposit box in front of it. Then he and Dink and Elizabeth went back to the basement to tally up the day's profits.

There were one-hundred and thirty-six cans. Eddie brought down the bathroom scale to see how many pounds that would be. They began putting the flattened cans on the scale one at a time.

The marker barely moved. Three cans . . . four cans. . . .

"Maybe the scale is broken," said Elizabeth.

Around ten cans, they could tell that the marker had moved halfway between zero and one. It took twenty-one cans to make a pound.

Carefully they divided the cans into little heaps of twenty-one each. Six piles of cans with ten left over. Six pounds of cans at seventeen cents a pound.

Eddie went to his desk and figured it out. One dollar and two cents. He entered it under "income." Then he remembered the sixty-three cents they owed for the leaf bags and put that in the column marked "expenses." One dollar and two cents minus sixty-three cents left a profit of thirty-nine cents. And thirty-nine cents divided between Eddie, Dink, and Elizabeth was thirteen cents apiece.

"At least you didn't go in the hole," Mr. Anselmino said at dinner that evening.

"And people know where to bring the cans now," said Roger.

"And he paid off his debt to me the very first day," said Mrs. Anselmino.

Joseph had not brought his pocket calculator to the table that evening, but Eddie could tell, by the way he pressed his fingers against the table top one at a time, that he was figuring something out in his head. "Thirteen cents a day, six days a week, fifty-two times a year, at five and a half percent . . ." he was saying to himself.

But Eddie wasn't interested in what he could make if the Anselmino Aluminum Recycling Company lasted a year. He was wondering if it would last a month. Eight hours a day for only thirteen cents was just a little more than one-and-a-half cents an hour, which meant he'd have to work a day and then some just to afford a stamp to mail his income tax. Bosses had more problems than anybody.

# Eddie, Incorporated

## Meet the Author

**Phyllis Reynolds Naylor** was born in Anderson, Indiana. Reading was always important. Her mother spent hours reading to her—everything from Sherlock Holmes mysteries and author Mark Twain to *Collier's Encyclopedia*.

By the time she was in first grade, Ms. Naylor was already writing stories. At ten, she wrote a whole series of mysteries. At sixteen she sold her first story to a magazine.

Ms. Naylor says she's not happy unless she writes every day. Working on several projects at the same time, she always has at least five books "waiting in the wings." She writes her first draft in long hand, revises her work many times, then edits her stories to make sure every word makes sense. She keeps ideas in three-ring binders lined up in her living room.

## Meet the Illustrator

**Charmie Curran** has always liked to draw. She received a degree from the Vesper George School of Art in Boston, where she met her husband, Michael. They have two children, two dogs, two zebra finches, one cat, and eleven assorted chickens. Ms. Curran now lives and works out of her studio in Bow, New Hampshire, in collaboration with her husband. They have donated many illustrations in support of the arts and the community.

# Theme Connections

## Think About It

Eddie and his friends had a good idea for a business, but any business faces difficulties. Anticipating problems and having a plan for overcoming them is important. Form small groups to talk about what you have learned about business. Here are some things to think about.

- Is there any way that Eddie could collect enough cans to make a reasonable hourly wage?
- Why did the Anselmino Aluminum Recycling Company need to advertise? What are some other (inexpensive) ways they could advertise?

Look at the Concept/Question Board to see if there are questions that you can answer now. If the selection or your discussion raised new questions about business, post them on the Concept/Question Board. Maybe the next selection will help answer the questions.

## Record Ideas

Did you learn new things from this selection? What important information or ideas do you want to remember? Record them in your Writing Journal.

## Research Ideas

- Many companies are now in the recycling business. Investigate them and research problems that interest you, or plan your own recycling company.
- Some businesses can actually be harmful to people or the environment. Should these businesses be banned? Choose a business that you think might be harmful and consider the pros and cons. Maybe you could think of a way to make the business safer.

# Lemonade Stand

Myra Cohn Livingston
*illustrated by Bob Barner*

Every summer
under the shade
we fix up a stand
to sell lemonade.

A stack of cups,
a pitcher of ice,
a shirtboard sign
to tell the price.

A dime for the big,
A nickel for small.
The nickel cup's short.
The dime cup's tall.

Plenty of sugar
to make it sweet,
and sometimes cookies
for us to eat.

But when the sun
moves into the shade
it gets too hot
to sell lemonade.

Nobody stops
so we put things away
and drink what's left
and start to play.

PRICE
BIG 10¢
SMALL 5¢

LEMONADE

# Elias Sifuentes
## Restaurateur

from *All in a Day's Work: Twelve Americans Talk About Their Jobs*
by Neil Johnson

I do it all. I open the restaurant in the morning and I close it up at the end of each day. From the minute that I open the door I do everything that has to be done until I close the door. There are a thousand things that have to be done in a restaurant.

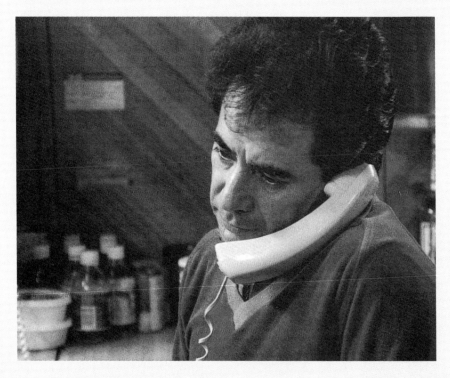

*Elias Sifuentes has run a Mexican restaurant for almost ten years. After having other jobs and working part-time in Mexican restaurants for many years, he and a friend decided to start their own.*

I used to work at a General Electric factory. I was a punch-press operator. I was making good money, but working there frustrated me because I like to work with people, talk to people. And there, there was nobody to talk to. The only time I got together with others was during lunch or during meetings. And I said to myself, "I like the money. I like the benefits. But this is not what I want to do all my life."

I've worked part-time in Mexican restaurants for most of my life being a waiter, cook, dishwasher. Not because I was hungry for money, but because I told myself, "Someday I'm going to do something for myself and I want to learn the whole trade." While I was at GE, the restaurant where I was working part-time was closed down. So my partner and I got together, and I said, "What are you going to do?" He said, "I don't know." I said, "Let's get a place of our own! I'll do the cooking. You be the front man. What else do we need?" He liked the idea, and so we put the idea to work, and it works.

We started from scratch. In the beginning, we didn't get a paycheck. The only money we got was to buy groceries. My partner was kind of frustrated. Whatever we were making was going to pay our bills. I told him, "That's what it is. That's the way it goes. I like to have a payday, but we just can't do it right now." When we expanded the place, we got more customers, more business. We felt better because it finally started to pay off. We were very pleased. We saw more traffic and we started putting money in our pockets. We felt better. One hundred percent. The success has continued ever since.

In the beginning I was kind of shaky and afraid because I knew very little spoken English. I could more or less write in English. And to learn all the trade— that's a big step. In Mexico I took a year of business administration in college, so I had my year's training. It's not a whole lot, but it helped me when I needed it. I learned about supervising, expenses, administration. How to buy, how to spend, how to control, all these kinds of things.

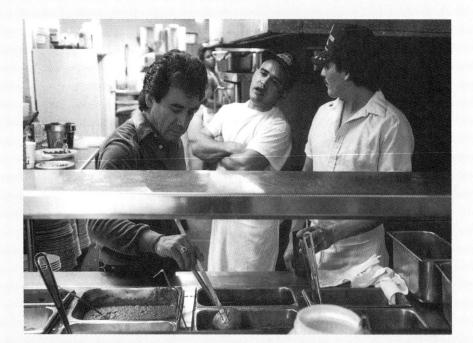

But now I am learning on the job. I believe you learn a lot better when you exercise what you are doing. To me, I have no other choice but to learn—be forced to learn to do the job. Until now, I have been fortunate to do a good job. There are a good number of people depending on me, and I haven't let them down yet. My twenty-eight employees depend on me to be smart enough to continue the business for all of us—so all of us can make a good living. A lot of places come and go. Even big companies with big money and good managers—they are gone. Fortunately we have managed to stay.

To stay in business, I have to be aggressive. I have to fight. If I go by another Mexican restaurant and I see a line of people, I say to myself, "They are doing something right." If I go to my place and see nobody there, I say, "I am doing something wrong." So then I have to do something different. I must be more conscious of my customers and give them more attention. That's what I do best—pay attention to my customers. Talk to them. Meet them. Let them know who I am.

When customers complain, they keep me more aware. They open my eyes. I don't mind having a complaint once in a while. Nobody likes to have those, but if I do, I want to be sure that the same customer doesn't have the same complaint twice. I feel bad when a customer comes and tells me that he waited too long and never got service. I feel bad when a customer comes to tell me that a waiter has been rude. When a customer tells me that the food doesn't have enough seasoning, I feel bad. But I face the customer. It doesn't matter what happens, they always come to me. They say they want to see me. I say, "Fine, no problem." I take all kinds of complaints, which can get me down a lot.

I usually come to work at eight o'clock in the morning. Normally, I stay until two o'clock in the afternoon, doing the supervising, the purchasing, seeing the salesmen, seeing the advertisers. Then I go to my house to take a shower, and I come back at five o'clock. I stay until closing time at ten o'clock. We usually leave the place at eleven or twelve, after cleaning up.

When customers walk in my door, I receive them in the friendliest way I can. I see to it that they get service properly from my busboy, from my waitress, even from myself. If anything takes longer than it's supposed to, that is what I am there for——to take care of that kind of problem. Afterward, when the customer is finished, I come to the table again—— maybe two, three more times. "Is everything OK? Everything satisfactory?" That's my job in the front of the restaurant. Then back in the kitchen, I see that everything comes out properly. I do that myself every morning. I taste everything, believe me! Chips, hot sauce, dressing, beans, Spanish rice, cheese sauce, you name it. I taste everything to see it is prepared right, before we open the doors. That keeps me going through lunchtime. Sometimes we stay so busy that I forget to sit down and have a meal.

A man who had come up from Mexico asked me the other day about opening a restaurant. He said to me, "If you did it, I can do it. " I said, "Yes, you can do it." Then he said, "You tell me how." I said, "Wait a minute. You just told me you can do it. You don't need my advice. You can do it! But if you don't have your heart in it, forget it."

# Elias Sifuentes
## Restaurateur

## Meet the Author and Photographer

**Neil Johnson** lives in Shreveport, Louisiana. His articles and photographs have appeared in magazines and newspapers such as *Time, USA Today,* and *Louisiana Life.*

When Mr. Johnson decided to write about people at work, he looked for people who were enthusiastic, willing to talk, and didn't mind having their pictures taken. Elias Sifuentes fit all those things and more.

About photography, Mr. Johnson says, *"Photography . . . allows us to see things that cannot be put into words."*

# Theme Connections

## Think About It

Elias Sifuentes had a well-paying factory job but did not want to do it for the rest of his life. He followed his dream to do something else.

- What risk was Elias taking when he left his job to start a restaurant? What would you have done in his place?
- Restaurants often fail even though they have plenty of customers and charge regular prices. Their costs can be more than their income. What costs are involved? How could costs be reduced without lowering quality?

Look at the Concept/Question Board to see if there are questions there that you can answer now. If the story raised new questions that you want to find answers to, post them on the Concept/Question Board.

## Record Ideas

What did you think of this story? Would you like to be like Elias Sifuentes? Why or why not? Record your ideas in your Writing Journal.

## Research Ideas

- The money needed to start up a company is called **capital.** Capital could come from your own savings, but there are other sources also. Research additional sources. Find out about venture capital, loans, and stock.
- Did you know that most big fast food chains started small? How did some become world-wide giants while others remained small? Examine the various fast food chains you see advertised on television, in magazines, or on signs. Determine which advertisements you think are most effective and why.

# ICE CREAM CONES:
## A NEW SCOOP

from *What If?*
by Dian Dincin Buchman
and Seli Groves
*illustrated by Barbara Bruno*

In 1904 the city of St. Louis, Missouri, put on one of the biggest fairs ever held anywhere.

Charles Menches was one of the many people who were there to sell refreshments to the fairgoers. He sold ice cream, and the hotter it got, the more dishes of ice cream he sold. At the end of a busy day, he always had fewer dishes left than he started with. Some broke when they were being washed. Some dropped to the floor and were cracked. And some just disappeared. But Menches never worried about that: His supplier always turned up with a new supply every day.

On one especially hot July day, Menches opened his stand prepared to face a very busy day. He needed lots of new dishes, but the supplier was late. Menches was down to a very low number of plates before noon. What, he wondered, would he do when the demand for ice cream increased with the arrival of the large noontime crowd?

His friend in the stand next to his, a man named Ernest Hamwi from Syria, was selling Zalabia, a sort of flat, crisp wafer that was popular in the Middle East. Menches thought he'd buy one of them for his lunch while he tried to think of a way to handle his disappearing dish problem. As he held the Zalabia, he noticed how easily it folded. It reminded him of how colored sheets of paper were rolled into cones to hold candies as birthday party favors when he was a little boy.

He thought, "*What if* I rolled the Zalabia into cones and put the ice cream into them?"

The idea was a fabulous success. People not only could eat the "dish" in which the ice cream was served, they could also walk around and enjoy the fair while enjoying their ice cream treat.

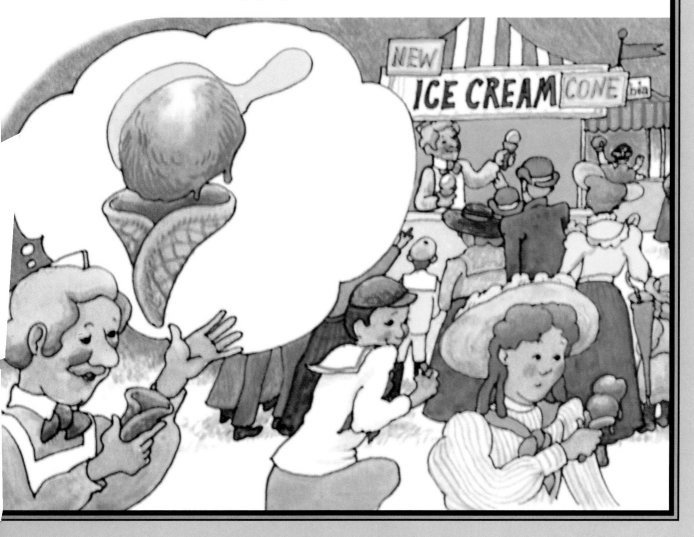

# ICE CREAM CONES: A NEW SCOOP

## Meet the Authors

**Dian Dincin Buchman** was born in New York, where she lives today. She is a radio show producer and interviewer. Many of her shows are about health-related topics, including food, natural health, and nutrition. She also loves to travel and has been through Europe and much of the Far East.

**Seli Groves** was also born in and now lives in New York. She began writing at an early age. She says that whenever her parents gave her a gift, *"they always included a book. My mother got me my own library card when I was six. I read all the children's books at the Brooklyn [New York] Public Library."*

## Meet the Illustrator

**Barbara Bruno** is a writer, artist, and photographer. Her Master of Arts degree is from Philadelphia College of Art. She has worked on several craft features for *Cricket Magazine.* She has also illustrated several books.

Ms. Bruno lives in New Jersey with her husband and her dog, Junkyard.

# Theme Connections

## Think About It

Ice cream cones were developed about 100 years ago as the solution to a problem. There are still plenty of consumer needs to fill and new problems arise frequently.

- Businesspeople are thinking up new ideas for products and services all the time. What are some clever ideas you have noticed?
- How do you get new ideas? What do you see a need for?

Look at the Concept/Question Board to see if there are questions that you can answer now. If the selection or your discussion raised new questions about business, post them on the Concept/Question Board.

## Record Ideas

What product do you wish you had that would make your life easier? Can you think of any way it could be made? Record ideas in your Writing Journal about what products you think might help you or someone you know.

## Research Ideas

- Think about a product you use often. Research how and when it was invented. Perhaps you could think of a way to improve it.
- Make a list of problems you faced during a given day. If the problems were solved, note how they were solved. If the problems were still there, jot down some possible solutions.

# FINE Art

*Buffalo Newsboy.* 1853. **Thomas LeClear.** Oil on canvas. 24 × 20 in. Charlotte A. Watson Fund, 1942, Albright-Knox Art Gallery, Buffalo, New York.

*Poultry shop trade sign.* Date unknown. Marble relief. Museo Ostiense, Ostia, Italy. Photo: SCALA/Art Resource, NY.

*Incantation.* 1946. **Charles Sheeler.** Oil on canvas. 24 × 20 in. The Brooklyn Museum, Brooklyn, New York. John B. and Ella C. Woodward Memorial Funds.

*Market Scene.* Mid-20th century. **Rodrigue Mervilus.** Oil on canvas. Private Collection. Photo: SuperStock.

# Food from the 'Hood:
## A Garden of Hope

by Marlene Targ Brill

Sometimes horrible events turn into the most hopeful dreams. That's what happened to students at Crenshaw High School in South Central Los Angeles, California. In May 1992, riots destroyed the neighborhood surrounding their school. Businesses went up in flames. Hundreds of shopkeepers were left with nothing but ashes. Families, some too poor to afford gas money, were forced to travel from the city to the suburbs just to buy food.

Students in Tammy Bird's biology class felt awful. "This is where we all grew up," said Carlos Lopez. "The corner store in my neighborhood burned down. That was where we hung out."

Carlos and his classmates refused to let riots wreck their lives. They talked about different ways to help rebuild their community. Nothing seemed quite right. Then Ms. Bird remembered the weed-infested patch behind the football field. Perhaps the school would give them the quarter-acre plot of land for a garden. As a bonus, Ms. Bird offered extra credit to attract student gardeners.

Carlos and 38 of Ms. Bird's other students decided that planting was an important step toward restoring their neighborhood. The garden would be one green spot among the ashes. With Los Angeles's warm, sunny climate, crops could grow year round. Everyone agreed that their harvests should go to people unable to buy food.

Within weeks, the teenagers cleared the overgrown lot and planted seeds for collard greens, squash, tomatoes, and herbs. They grew vegetables organically, without chemicals that might hurt their bodies or the environment. Each day, they took turns watering and weeding the shoots during free time and before and after school. Adults from outside the community worked with the students as part of the city's overall plan to rebuild the riot-torn downtown.

The teenagers soon realized the community needed more than food to survive. It needed shops where people could easily buy everyday goods. Most of the burned-out stores had owners who lived outside the neighborhood. The money they made left South Central Los Angeles at the end of the workday. Students believed their community needed new business owners who were willing to put money back into the burned-out community. One adult volunteer, Melinda McMullen, suggested that the garden become that kind of business.

"We all wanted to give something back to the community, and this was a way to do it," Carlos remembered.

Melinda helped the students organize their business. First, they hunted for an office to house the company. They discovered an unused rabbit room behind the animal science lab and gave it a good scrubbing. Except for a few escaped rats eating electric wires, the room seemed perfect.

Then students met at lunchtime and after school to hammer out what the company would be like. Each volunteer became a student owner with an equal voice in making decisions. After several meetings, the owners agreed that the number-one reason for their business was to better their community. They wanted to prove that businesses could be kind and still make money, too. They pledged to create jobs for more teenagers. And they promised to use skills they learned from the garden to better the future for themselves and those around them.

Student owners named the company in much the same way as they planned—with respect for everyone's ideas. First, they brainstormed what the name should say about the business. They wanted a name that told people about the company's products in a general way. For now, products included organic foods. Who knew what the future would bring?

Everyone insisted that the name reflect who they were as people. This was a student-owned company, so the name should be catchy and fun. Moreover, students came from the inner city and were proud to live there. They represented many cultures, especially African-Americans, Latinos, and Asian Americans. The right name would celebrate these different groups working and living together.

For several hours, owners shouted out whatever name seemed to fit. Ms. Bird wrote 72 choices on the blackboard. Some sounded hip, such as *Food from the 'Hood,* and others unusual, such as *Straight Out 'the Garden.* Then everyone voted until five names remained. Over the next two weeks, students tested the five names on friends in class, at home, and throughout the neighborhood. They talked with strangers of all races, ages, and occupations.

Food from the 'Hood won thumbs-up. The name told about the products, which were different foods. And the name said where the company and its owners were from— the *'hood,* which was short for "inner-city neighborhood."

The only missing piece was the many cultures behind the business. To represent the different races, student artist Ben Osborne drew a company logo with white and brown hands reaching toward sun-lit buildings. He painted the logo and snappy name in bright colors on a mural behind the garden.

"People usually smile or laugh when they hear our company name," said student founder Ivan Lopez. "But they never forget us."

Slowly, a small garden turned into the nation's first student-run natural food company. Food from the 'Hood harvested its first crop two months after forming a business. They gave all the vegetables to a neighborhood homeless shelter. "Giving food to the needy really brought out the holiday spirit in us," said student owner Jaynell Grayson.

Now Melinda had another idea. The student owners proved they could grow a healthy garden and brighten the community. Why not sell some of the vegetables to raise money to help owners pay for college?

"We found the best way to give back to our community was to get a higher education," remembered Jaynell.

"We all got hooked on gardening. Then we decided to make money off of it. Then the scholarship idea kicked in," Carlos added.

In the summer of 1993, students took a supply of vegetables to the Santa Monica, California, farmer's market. Excited customers swarmed around the Food from the 'Hood table like bees. Customers couldn't buy fast enough. Within 30 minutes, the company sold $150 worth of vegetables. Student owners were amazed at their easy success.

Making enough money to build a scholarship fund proved more difficult, however. After one year in business, sales totaled only $600. Three graduating owners split the sum, which was a good start but not nearly enough to send anyone to college. "That hardly covered college book fees," Ben Osborne said.

After summer break, student owners met again. This time they talked about finding another way to raise money. A customer at a farmer's market suggested that they offer a factory-made product with the company's name on it. The product could sell more widely in stores than at a local farmer's market.

One student studied what buyers liked and disliked in new products. He found that people were more willing to try new salad dressings than other new products. "We thought, since we already grow lettuce, why not sell the topping?" Jaynell said.

Students experimented with salad dressing recipes in Ms. Bird's science class. They tasted different mixes of ingredients for the right balance. The dressing had to include plenty of basil and parsley because these were grown in their garden. Then students sent the formulas to outside food labs to test the ingredients. "Our community has a problem with heart disease, so we wanted a healthy, low-salt choice," Jaynell said.

After six months of testing mixtures, students agreed on a creamy Italian recipe. Ben designed a colorful label modeled after the garden mural. Then everyone voted on the name for their new line of dressing. The winner, Straight Out 'the Garden Creamy Italian Dressing, combined the runner-up company name with the dressing flavor.

Ms. Bird continued to supervise Food from the 'Hood at school. Melinda kept her ears open for different sources of money and aid. Other adult help came from unusual places.

Norris Bernstein, who ran the successful Bernstein Salad Dressings, read about Food from the 'Hood. After talking with student owners, Bernstein became hooked on their strong sense of pride and independence. He helped students connect with large chain stores that would sell their dressing.

Another surprise visitor was Prince Charles from England. Carlos heard that the prince loved organic gardening, and he was visiting California. So Carlos wrote the British consul and asked if the prince would like to see Food from the 'Hood. "It was just something to do, just to see if it would really happen, and it really did," Carlos said later. The prince not only accepted, but he also ate lunch in the garden and later donated a van to help transport vegetables, herbs, and flowers to farmer's markets.

The city gave Food from the 'Hood $50,000. Some of the money went to supply an office to house the growing company. Students selected carpeting, a large meeting table, and furniture for five work stations. They ordered a telephone, answering machine, and computers.

Most money went toward making the first batch of salad dressing. Food from the 'Hood hired businesses to print labels, manufacture large amounts of salad dressing, and distribute the finished product to stores. "We wanted to work with other companies from poorer areas of Los Angeles. We especially looked for businesses run by minorities," student owner Mark Sarria said.

Food from the 'Hood chose women-owned company Sweet Adelaide to make and bottle the dressing. Skid Row Access, staffed by former homeless people of color, decorated banners. And herbs and spices came from small vendors rather than larger grocery store suppliers.

Some of the most difficult problems involved working together. Student owners took months to create a plan for dividing money the company earned. Finally, everyone agreed to a point system. Each owner earned points for hours spent in the garden and office.

Food from the 'Hood stands for good grades and going to college. Therefore, student owners received points for grades and for helping others improve their schoolwork. Owners learn to take care of each other. They share tips about how to study, complete college forms, and take college exams. For many, Food from the 'Hood is like family.

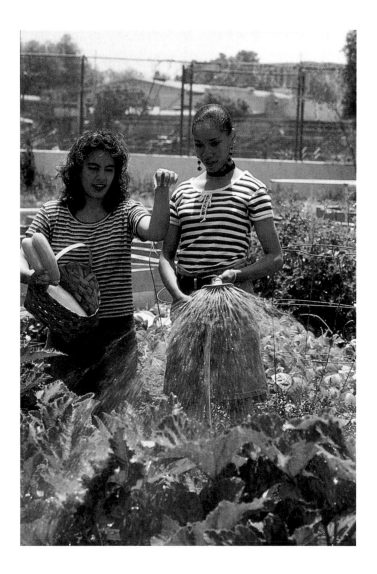

Although an adult watches over the office full-time now, student owners run every other part of the business. They produce and sell vegetables and salad dressing. They keep records, train new workers, pay bills, and answer telephones. Most importantly, they grow the garden, the heart of the business.

Hard work has paid off. Food from the 'Hood has added another salad dressing, Straight Out 'the Garden No-Fat Honey Mustard. More than 2,000 grocery stores carry the two dressings in 25 states. By 1996, the company awarded student owners a total of $27,000 to fund college.

Teachers claim that students improve in reading, writing, public speaking, and math after joining Food from the 'Hood. Many student owners discover talents they never knew they had. Sandra Raymond hated to talk in class before selling dressing and answering the office telephone. Now she feels confident enough to go into business. Similarly, Ben Osborne intends to study art in college as a result of designing the logo, mural, and salad dressing label.

"We showed that a group of inner-city kids can and did make a difference. We learn to take responsibility for our actions, how to sort out what's important, and how to be leaders instead of followers," Terie Smith, student founder, said.

Food from the 'Hood has become so successful that other schools asked to copy the program. In 1996 a high school group from Ithaca, New York, began using the name on applesauce. "We met with them in Washington, D.C., to talk about their applesauce idea, and we were very impressed," Terie said. Now three flavors of Food from the 'Hood East's Straight Out 'the Orchard are sold in Ithaca and are headed for New York City and other areas. Schools in Chicago, Illinois; Hawaii; and Oakland, California, hope to sell products that will help put kids through school.

The real success, however, is the garden, the center of giving. Half the total crop goes to community groups. Student owners vote which organizations receive the food. The idea is to help a balance of African-American, Latino, and Asian groups that reflects the company's—and community's—population.

New students apply to Food from the 'Hood each year. About 40 percent work other jobs in addition to going to school, but find time to garden. After more than five years, the business is here to stay. A small group of inner-city teenagers have proven that anyone can achieve success if they try.

"What comes from that garden is hope," said Carlos. "From anything—even the riots—amazing things can grow."

# Food from the 'Hood:
## A Garden of Hope

## Meet the Author

**Marlene Targ Brill** was born in Chicago, Illinois. She loved books from a very young age. Her parents read constantly, and she remembers being jealous of her older brother who had a room filled with books and records.

Ms. Brill had an active imagination. A favorite pastime was sitting in the window, watching people pass by, and making up stories about where they were going and what they were doing.

Brill says she loves all kinds and aspects of writing, especially research. She says, *"I feel like an explorer, delving into old newspapers, tracking down historical documents, and locating famous and not-so-famous people to interview. To me, research is an endless treasure hunt with many pots of gold."*

# Theme Connections

## Think About It

The efforts of the high school students in this selection helped their community a great deal. Are you too young to help your community? Here are some things to think about.

- What are some businesses that could improve the community in which you live?
- How important is marketing to business success?
- How is starting a business like Food from the 'Hood similar to or different from doing volunteer community service work?

Look at the Concept/Question Board to see if there are questions that you can answer now. If the selection or your discussion raised new questions about business, post them on the Concept/Question Board.

## Record Ideas

What needs do you see in your community that you could help with? Would it take a lot of money to do it? Would it be important to make a lot of money? Record your ideas.

## Research Ideas

Food from the 'Hood was started with very little money. Research the ways money is needed and used in a business such as this. Make a diagram to show the way money is needed and used.

# BUSINESS IS LOOKING UP

Barbara Aiello and Jeffrey Shulman
*illustrated by Diane Paterson*

*Renaldo Rodriguez, a visually impaired eleven-year-old, needs money to buy a special type of calculator for the blind. He decides he can earn the money by starting a business and shares his idea with his best friend, Jinx.*

"Jinx!" I shouted when she answered the phone. I sure was excited about my business idea. "It's me! Renaldo. Renaldo Rodriguez!"

"Renaldo, you're the only Renaldo I know," Jinx said. "And you don't have to holler! I can hear you."

I explained the whole idea to her——"R.R. Stepcards" I called it. That was a pretty clever name, even I have to admit. I told her how I would make and sell cards for people who had stepfamilies: birthday cards, get well cards, Valentine cards——the list was endless!

"What do you think, Jinx? Am I going to be Woodburn's first millionaire?"

There was silence on the other end. I could tell Jinx was thinking about it. She always thinks about things before she gives her opinion. And she always thinks about what other people might think. "Opposing viewpoints," she calls them. Jinx does a lot of thinking.

"Well," she finally asked, "have you done any marketing research?"

"Marketing research?"

"Have you thought about your investment?"

"Investment?"

Jinx was on a roll. I felt doomed.

"Oh, how will you advertise?"

I felt it coming, but I couldn't stop it. "Advertise?" I said. "Just listen to me," I thought to myself, "Renaldo Rodriguez, the human echo!"

Research? Investment? Advertising? "Jinx," I said, "this is starting to sound like work! Explain this stuff to me."

I knew Jinx was excited. I could hear the excitement in her voice. "Look," she began, "marketing research is the first thing you do. You find out if someone else has already thought of your idea. You find out if there's such a thing as a stepcard. If there's not, then you can figure out your investment. That's how much money you want to spend to get the business started."

"Spend?" I said. "But I want to *make* money, Jinx."

"I know," Jinx said in her most patient voice. "But you can't get something for nothing. We will have to buy markers and paper, maybe even paints and stencils, too. That's our investment."

"*Our* investment? When did it become *our* investment?"

"Renaldo, this is an excellent idea," Jinx continued. "But there's a lot to do. You're going to need a partner." And I didn't even have the time to say "A partner?" before Jinx jumped in again. "Hmmmm . . . I do like the sound of it," she said. "Yes, 'R.R. and J.B. Stepcards.' I like the sound of it very much."

And you know what? So did I. With J.B. as my partner, I was more excited than ever——so excited that I couldn't get to sleep that night. I turned my pillow to the cold side a hundred times until I gave up trying to sleep. I got out my stylus and slate and started to write: "R.R. and J.B. Stepcards. For Your Favorite Stepfriend." There were stepfathers, stepmothers, stepbrothers, stepsisters, stepgrandmothers——the list went on and on. "For All Occasions." There were birthdays, anniversaries, graduations, holidays—and so many more. I started counting our profits. I couldn't help it.

"Excuse me, Mr. Businessman," Josue said, hiding a big yawn. "Mom already came in here. She made me stop reading. We're supposed to be asleep, you know."

Josue was right. Mom doesn't let us read or write after lights out. But, you see, I don't have to sneak under the covers with a flashlight the way Josue does.

"I'm not reading," I told Josue. "This, my little brother, is marketing research—I think."

"It looks like reading to me. It's not fair. I ought to tell on you!" Josue climbed out of bed to get a better look. "Just what kind of business is this anyway?"

"None of *your* business," I said firmly. And I closed my slate. I wasn't taking any chances on someone stealing the business idea of the century, certainly not a nosy little brother. I turned my pillow over for the last time.

"Let's go to sleep."

The next day was Saturday, and with lots of kids from Woodburn, Jinx and I headed for the mall. We take turns delivering the "Woodburn Flyer" to the stores at the Woodburn Shopping Center. The "Flyer" is the free newspaper that tells about all the things happening at Woodburn. Then it's time for fun.

But this Saturday was different. Today, there were no video games, no french fries, no window-shopping. Today, we were all business.

I knew we were near Calloway's Cards and Gifts when I smelled the tempting aroma of cheese, tomato sauce, and special toppings. Polotti's Pizza Palace was just next door to the card store.

"I don't think I can do the marketing research on an empty stomach. How about a business lunch?" I was tapping my cane toward the sweet smell of Polotti's.

"Renaldo," Jinx said sternly, "we don't have much time."

"Okay. Okay," I said. "Give me your arm." Jinx was right. We really didn't have much time. "It will be faster for me to walk alongside you—and less temptation, too."

There must have been a thousand different kinds of cards in Calloway's, and each one was cornier or mushier than the last. One thing about those cards, though—they really cracked us up!

"Look at this one, Renaldo," Jinx said.

"*To My Daughter and Her Husband on This Special Day,*" Jinx read. She described the card to me. "It's big," she said, passing it to me.

"It's almost the size of our spelling notebook," I said, feeling around the edges of the card.

"It has two pink hearts with bows on them. Two white doves are holding the ends of the ribbons in their mouths. It looks like the words *Happy Anniversary* are coming right out of their beaks," Jinx giggled.

I could feel the raised lines of the hearts, the bows, and the birds. "Yuk," I said, "it sounds pretty corny to me."

"Listen to this, Renaldo."

*To My Daughter and Her Husband on This Special Day:*
*'Like two white doves are lovers true,*
*Like two pink hearts forever new.*
*I hope this day will always view*
*A ribbon of happiness just for you.'*

"Double yuk," I said. "Who buys this mush?"

"Here's another one, Renaldo," Jinx said. "*Congratulations on Your New Baby!* It has a picture of a stork with a baby in a diaper hanging in its mouth."

"It must look so silly," I said, trying hard not to giggle too loudly.

173

"It gets worse." Jinx was cracking up. "When you open up the card, the stork drops the baby—plop!—right on somebody's doorstep!"

"It sounds like a wet diaper to me!" I squealed. Jinx was laughing, too. But then she suddenly stopped. I could tell she was really thinking.

"But, Renaldo," she said in a serious voice, "somebody buys these cards, and"——she was getting very excited——"there are no stepcards!"

Now I was getting excited, too. We did a high-five right there in Calloway's. "We're going to be rich!" we both shouted.

"C'mon, Renaldo," Jinx urged, "let's go home and get to work."

"Be sure to save an extra large pepperoni and sausage for Woodburn's youngest millionaires!" I shouted when we passed Polotti's.

Getting to work was not as easy as it sounded.

Jinx and I had to buy the paper for the cards. We put our money together for an investment of twelve dollars and thirty-two cents. ("That's a lot of french fries," I thought.) We had to decide what kind of cards to make. We had to think of designs for the front of the cards and messages to go inside. We had to find a way to let people know about "R.R. and J.B. Stepcards."

Let's face it: We had a lot to learn about starting a business.

When I have more questions than answers, I always turn to the expert——my Mom. "Mom," I said when she got home from work, "Jinx and I need to speak to an old hand in the business world."

"Good luck finding one," she replied as she started to take off the running shoes she wears to work.

"No, Mom," I explained, "I meant you."

"Oh," she said, looking up. "What can this 'old hand' do for you?"

My Mom knows about business, especially bad businesses. She works in an office helping people who bought things that don't work or aren't safe. I figured if she knew all about bad businesses, she could tell us how to start a good one.

Jinx and I explained our business idea. "How do we get started?" Jinx asked.

"How do we make lots of money?" (I guess you can figure out who asked that one!)

Mom thought for a while. Then she spoke slowly. "Jinx, Renaldo, starting and running a business is not so easy. It's more than just making money. A successful business needs a good product to sell or a useful service to offer. And a successful businessman—or businesswoman—thinks about the customer all the time. Ask yourself: 'What do they want?' 'How can my product or my service help them?' "

Jinx and I were trying to listen to all of this, but it wasn't easy. We *did* have a lot to learn.

"Now, you two have a good product," Mom continued. "I'm proud of you for coming up with this idea. But a good idea is not enough. You need to plan carefully."

"What do we do, Mrs. Rodriguez?" Jinx asked.

"Well," Mom said, "you need to figure out how much money you'll need to get started and where the money will come from. You need to decide who will do the work and, believe me, a business *is* work. Now, if you're still interested in 'R.R. and J.B. Stepcards,' let's make a plan!"

"Always ask the expert," I shouted. I could hear the rubber soles of Mom's shoes make that familiar squeegy sound. Mom wears business suits and running shoes every day to work. Dad says she's dressed for success from her head to her knees——but her feet are dressed for failure! That always makes me laugh.

With Mom's help we really got started. Jinx and I used our "investment" to buy paper, paints, markers, and stencils. We worked every day after school. We took turns with the stencils to make the designs. We'd take a small roller and dip it into a bright color of paint. When we'd smooth the roller over the stencil, there was a butterfly or flower or other designs. Jinx said they looked great!

I liked making up the words for our stepcards.
I thought of some pretty good ones, if I must say so myself.

177

*To My Stepfather:*
*'Getting to know you hasn't been half bad.*
*I'm glad Mom picked you to be my Stepdad!'*

Well, I didn't say they were great cards.

*To My Stepsister:*
*'You have two families, I know that's true.*
*But I want you to know that I love you, too!'*

All right, so Renaldo Rodriguez has a mushy side. Don't rub it in!

At the end of just one week, Jinx and I had 34 cards ready to go.

"To go where?" I asked.

"Where else?" Jinx said. "Why, the Woodburn School and Community Center!" It was time to advertise, and Woodburn was the place to start.

The Woodburn School was the oldest school building in the city. It almost closed the year before. There just weren't enough kids to fill it up, I guess. That's why the school board decided to add a Community Center. Now there was a day-care room for little kids and an activity center for older people, too. Woodburn is like a little city all its own.

The first thing on Monday morning Jinx and I marched down to Woodburn and showed our cards to Mr. Mohammadi, the assistant principal. Boy, was he excited!

"A sound idea," he said. "A very sound business idea. And you'll get a real education in the bargain. A real education. How can I help?"

We explained that advertising "R.R. and J.B. Stepcards" was the next part of our business plan.

"Let's see now." Mr. Mohammadi was thinking out loud. "You can put advertisements in the school newspaper, posters in the Senior Center, flyers to go home. . . ." Mr. Mohammadi was pacing the floor and spouting new ideas faster than . . . faster than . . . well, faster than Jinx and I could write them down.

"This is going to be a snap," I predicted. "I should have started a business years ago. Think of all the time I've wasted in school!"

That stopped Mr. Mohammadi in his tracks. "Just a little business joke," I gulped.

If you want to start a business, take it from me: advertise! With Mr. Mohammadi's help, Jinx and I spread the word about "R.R. and J.B. Stepcards." Believe it or not, within one week, we sold 17 of our cards and had orders for 20 more. That's 37 cards! We'd make back all the money we spent on supplies. We'd even have some left over.

"Now that we'll have a little extra money, why not buy some stickers and glitter?" Jinx suggested. "Let's make the cards even prettier."

I was thinking about my calculator. I wanted to buy it as soon as I could. "But, Renaldo," Jinx said, "if we make our cards prettier, we'll sell more and make more money."

That made sense. Then I could buy the calculator and a new pair of soccer shoes.

"Don't forget," Jinx reminded me, "we have to pay to use the copying machine." We had to make copies of the advertisement Mr. Mohammadi was going to send home with the kids.

"And we need copies to take to the Senior Center, too," I told Jinx. I remember Mom saying, "You have to spend some money to make money." We thought that advertising was the best way to get more sales.

We thought right! Every day more orders came in the mail.

This was going to be a snap.

Jinx and I had to work every afternoon that week to fill the orders. And every day more orders came in.

Jeremy Kendall's stepsisters had their birthdays coming up, so he ordered two cards from "R.R. and

180

J.B. Stepcards," along with a special card for his stepmother. Mrs. Rothman (from the Senior Center) told us her son had just married a woman with twin boys, and she needed birthday cards for her stepgrandchildren. Roger Neville's stepfather was in the hospital, so he wanted a special get well card. And Joanne Spinoza's mother, Lena, wanted a stepcousin Valentine.

Phew! Jinx and I could hardly believe how well our business was going. We just didn't expect how happy people would be with our cards.

"You know, Jinx," I said, as I lined up the paint jars, "it's nice to give people something special."

Jinx agreed. "Jeremy told me that our card really helped him tell his stepmother how much he liked her."

"No kidding?"

"You know what else? He said she cried a little when she read it, and then she said she really liked him, too."

"Hey," I said, "making people happy is a pretty good way to make a living."

181

# BUSINESS IS LOOKING UP

## Meet the Authors

**Barbara Aiello** was eight years old when her mother had to spend several weeks in a hospital. While she was away, Barbara made a magazine for her filled with neighborhood news, a short story, a pet column, and want ads. That was the beginning of her writing career. In addition to being a writer, Ms. Aiello is also a teacher who has spent many years working in special education.

**Jeffrey Shulman** teaches English at Georgetown University in Washington, D.C., and has been writing children's books since 1986. *Business Is Looking Up* is Mr. Shulman's first and favorite book. He enjoys telling his daughters stories. *"I like to make up the stories as I go along. It keeps my imagination pretty busy."*

## Meet the Illustrator

**Diane Paterson** has illustrated several books for children, including *The Christmas Drum* and *Marmee's Surprise*. She has also illustrated several books she wrote herself, such as the children's books *Someday* and *Smile for Auntie*. Ms. Paterson lives in southwest Florida with her husband, her dog, and over 50 orchids.

# Theme Connections

## Think About It

R.R. and J.B. Stepcards targeted a certain group of consumers. Some businesses become very successful that way. Here are some things for you to think about.

- How did R.R. and J.B. Stepcards know there was a need for their cards? What are other special groups of consumers could you design greeting cards for?
- Why was it important for R.R. and J.B. Stepcards to advertise? What are some other ways they could have reached people?

Look at the Concept/Question Board to see if there are questions that you can answer now. If the selection or your discussion raised new questions about business, post them on the Concept/Question Board.

## Record Ideas

Several different aspects of starting a business were presented in this story. In your Writing Journal, record any new ideas you have that might be useful to your unit activity.

## Research Ideas

- Think of a product you could market to a small group of consumers and then come up with a way to advertise it.
- Together with your unit activity group, decide what market you plan to appeal to and what adjustments in your plan you may need to make for that.

# Birth of a Baby Food

from ***The Problem Solvers***

by Nathan Aaseng

One Sunday evening in the summer of 1927, Dan and Dorothy Gerber were getting ready to go out for the evening. They found it was taking them longer than they had hoped. Dorothy had to feed their seven-month-old daughter, Sally, before they left. Dan impatiently eyed the clock as Dorothy began to strain the peas.

Dorothy was tired of mashing vegetables through a strainer three times a day, seven days a week. She suggested that Dan try hand-straining the baby food himself. The container of peas, the strainer, and the bowl ended up in Dan's lap, and he discovered for himself what a slow, messy, frustrating process straining vegetables was. Within 24 hours, Dan was looking for a better way to make baby food.

Fortunately, the materials for a solution were near at hand. Dan and his father, Frank Gerber, owned a vegetable canning factory in their small town of Fremont, Michigan. Dorothy knew that the plant already had a machine that could puree tomatoes. She wondered if any of the equipment there could also strain baby food.

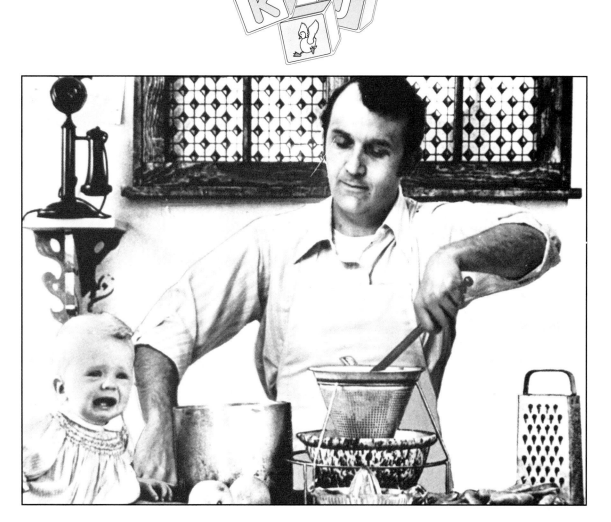

Before the advent of precooked baby food, parents had to
strain vegetables by hand, a lengthy and often frustrating process.

When Dan went to work the next morning, he spent
much of the day adapting some of the plant machinery to
the task of straining peas. The more the Gerbers thought
about it, the more certain they were that other parents
hated the tedious straining process as much as they did.
Why not design machinery to do the job in the factory and
eliminate the task from the family kitchen?

The plan, however, had to be approved by the majority
owner of the factory, Dan's father. Frank Gerber knew the

risks involved in making products for babies. If the company ever made a mistake that caused trouble for a baby's delicate digestive system, the Fremont Canning Company could be ruined. Since the plant was doing well, it would have been easy for Frank to stick with what he was doing.

But the elder Gerber had never been one to stand still. He had risked using new processes before. With both his son and daughter-in-law arguing in favor of making strained foods, Frank Gerber gave Dan his approval.

Cautious with the family money, Dan took his time in laying the groundwork for his project. First he researched the market. Strained baby food was not a novel idea. Some brands were already on the market, but they were not selling well. These specialty products sold only in drugstores, and they cost so much that few people could

Tired of making baby food at home, Dorothy Gerber urged her husband Dan to try to find a better way to make it.

Dan Gerber

afford them. National surveys showed that many people across the country were exasperated with straining baby food. If the Gerbers could maintain a high-quality product and keep it reasonably priced by selling large quantities in grocery stores, they were certain to be successful.

The next step was coming up with a good product. Frank and Dan spent nearly a year trying out various recipes and straining techniques. Babies of Fremont Canning Company employees, including Sally Gerber, sampled the concoctions and their responses were recorded.

In the fall of 1928, the Gerbers introduced their first five baby foods: peas, spinach, prunes, carrots, and vegetable soup. Dan then devised a clever plan to get the product into grocery stores. He placed an advertisement in *Good Housekeeping* magazine, offering to sell six cans of baby food for $1.00 to people who would send him the name of their local grocer. Armed with the directory of names this gave him, Dan approached the grocers and asked them to stock his products based on his evidence of the demand for baby food.

Recognizing the importance of a strong visual identity for their product, the Gerbers set up a contest for artists to submit pictures of a healthy, happy baby. One of the contestants, Dorothy Hope Smith, sent in a charcoal sketch with an attached note saying she would be happy to finish the picture if it was what the Gerbers wanted. Dan and

The familiar image of the smiling Gerber baby is a trademark—a word, name, symbol, or device used by a manufacturer to identify its products and distinguish them from other products. Only the Gerber Products Company can legally use the picture of the Gerber baby.

Frank liked the sketch just as it was, and Smith's rough drawing became the famous Gerber baby.

Gerber baby food set off a storm of demand far greater than Dan had ever imagined possible. Within six months of beginning production, Gerber strained products could be found on grocery shelves across the country. The baby food did not stay long on the shelves, either. The Fremont Canning Company sold more than a half million cans of baby food during the first year of business.

Success breeds imitators, and the baby food market was no exception. Just four years after Dan Gerber broke new ground in this market, he faced more than 60 competitors. The company kept ahead of the competition by establishing a reputation as baby experts. Dorothy Gerber answered letters from consumers who wrote in with a variety of child-rearing concerns. Before long the company hired a nationally known dietition and other experts who wrote pamphlets and booklets on the care and feeding of babies.

In 1930, Gerber hired dietician Dr. Lillian Storms to develop and test recipes for the company.

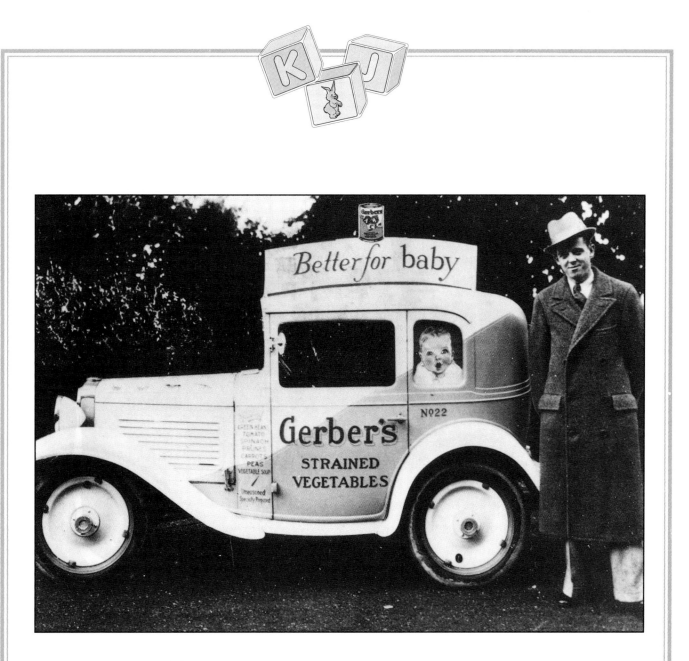

In 1941 the name of the company was changed from the Fremont Canning Company to the Gerber Products Company. Since that time, most United States parents have been happy to let food companies handle the inconvenience of mashing food for babies. Many families have given the task to Gerber, which now makes more than 187 varieties of baby foods.

Few people have been as successful as the Gerbers in "killing two birds with one stone." Not only did they get rid of one of their most dreaded chores, but they were able to make a fortune in the process.

# Birth of a Baby Food

## Meet the Author

**Nathan Aaseng** grew up in St. Louis Park, Minnesota. Since grade school, he had wanted to be a writer, but he thought writing was a hard field to get into. He studied and worked in biochemistry instead.

Aaseng took a year off work to try writing. He remembered something his parents had taught him—shame is not in failure, but in aiming too low.

Says Aaseng, *"I am becoming a writer. My books so far are all part of the learning process. I look forward to being able to make my words say so much more."*

# Theme Connections

## Think About It

The Gerbers did not create prepared baby food, but they made it a successful business. Here are some things to think about.

- Prepared baby food is an example of a product that people could make for themselves, but they instead are willing to pay others to make for them. What other examples can you think of?
- The Gerbers convinced consumers to buy their product instead of someone else's. How did they do this?

Look at the Concept/Question Board to see if there are questions that you can answer now. If the selection or your discussion raised new questions about business, post them on the Concept/Question Board.

## Record Ideas

 What product do you know of that you think could be improved? How would you convince others to buy your product? Record your marketing and advertising ideas in your Writing Journal.

## Research Ideas

- Plan a new business that provides a product or service people now make or do for themselves. Identify what you would do and write out a plan for making it into a profitable business.
- Think of a product or service you or someone you know currently uses that could be improved. Describe the product and how you would change it, and develop strategies for convincing consumers your product or service is better.

# Salt

Harve Zemach
*illustrated by Margot Zemach*

**L**ong ago there lived a merchant who had three sons. The first was Fyodor, the second Vasily, and the third Ivan—Ivan the Fool.

This merchant was rich. He sent his ships over the ocean in all directions to trade goods in foreign lands. Once he loaded two ships with precious furs, wax, and honey, and sent them sailing with his two elder sons. But when Ivan asked for the same, the merchant refused, saying: "You would do nothing but sing songs to the moon, and try to make the fishes dance, and come home without your head."

However, when he saw how much his son wanted to go, he gave him a ship with the very cheapest cargo of beams and boards.

Ivan prepared for the journey, set sail, and soon caught up with his brothers. They sailed together for a day or two, until a strong wind came up and blew Ivan's ship away into uncharted seas.

The wind blew Ivan and his crew to the north and to the south. At last they reached an island. Ivan stepped out upon the shore and found a path which led to the top of a mountain. There he discovered that this mountain was not made of rock, nor of sand, nor of stone, but of salt— pure Russian salt.

Without delay he ordered his sailors to throw away all the boards and beams, and to load the ship with salt. As soon as this was done, Ivan set forth once more.

After a long time or a short time, either nearby or far away, the ship arrived at a large city. Ivan went into the city to bow before the king and request permission to trade his merchandise. He took a bundle of the salt with him. The king greeted him in a friendly manner and heard his request.

"And what kind of goods do you sell?" asked the king.

"Russian salt, Your Majesty," said Ivan, showing him the contents of his bundle.

The king had never heard of salt. The people of his kingdom ate all their food without salt. When he saw what Ivan showed him, he thought it was only white sand.

"Well, little brother," he said to Ivan, "we have all we need of this. No one will pay you money for it."

Ivan turned away feeling very disappointed. Then he thought to himself: "Why don't I go to the king's kitchen and see how the cooks prepare the food and what kind of salt they use." He went and watched the cooks running back and forth, boiling and roasting and pouring and mixing. But no one put a single grain of salt in the food.

Ivan waited his chance and then secretly poured the right amount of salt into all the stews and sauces.

When the first dish was served to the king, he ate of it and found it more tasty than ever before. The second dish was served, and he liked it even better.

Then the king called for his cooks and said to them: "In all the years that I have been king, you have never cooked me such a delicious meal. How did you do it?"

The cooks answered: "Your Majesty, we cooked the same as ever. But the merchant who asked your permission to trade was watching us. Perhaps he added something to the food."

"Send for him!" commanded the king.

Then Ivan, the merchant's son, was brought before the king. He fell on his knees and confessed his guilt.

"Forgive me, Your Majesty," he begged. "I put Russian salt in all the stews and sauces. That's the way we do it in my country."

"And what is the price of this salt?" asked the king.

Ivan realized his advantage and said: "Not very much—for two measures of salt, give me one measure of silver and one of gold."

The king agreed to this price and bought the entire cargo. Ivan filled his ship with silver and gold and made ready to sail for home.

Now the king had a daughter, a beautiful princess. Attended by her maidservants, she went down to the port to see the Russian ship. Ivan the Fool just then was strumming a tune. The melody reached the ears of the princess, and its sweetness entered her heart.

It was not long before Ivan and the beautiful princess stood together before the king to receive his blessing. To the sound of trumpets and the cheers of the king's subjects, Ivan and the princess departed from the city and sailed forth on a favorable wind.

For a long time, for a short time, Ivan and the princess sailed the sea. Then his elder brothers appeared across his path. They learned of his good luck and were very jealous.

They boarded his ship, seized him, and threw him into the sea. Then they divided the booty; Fyodor, the eldest brother, took the princess, and Vasily, the second brother, took the ship full of silver and gold.

Now it happened that when they flung Ivan from the
ship, one of the boards that he himself had thrown into the
sea was floating nearby. He grabbed hold of this board and
for a long time was tossed upon the waves. Finally he was
carried to an unknown island. No sooner had he landed on
the shore than along came a gloomy giant with an
enormous mustache, from which hung a huge pair of
mittens, drying after the rain.

"What do you want here?" asked the giant. Ivan told him
everything that had happened.

The gloomy giant sighed and said: "Come along, I will
carry you home. Tomorrow your eldest brother is to marry
the princess. Sit on my back."

The giant lifted Ivan, set him on his back, and raced across the sea. Soon Ivan could see his native land ahead, and moments later they arrived. The giant put him down, saying: "Now promise not to boast to anyone about riding on my back. Don't try to make fun of me. If you do, I shall grab you up and toss you back into the sea."

Ivan, the merchant's son, promised not to boast, thanked the giant, and went home.

He arrived just as the wedding procession was about to enter the church. When the princess saw him, she cried aloud and tore herself away from Fyodor, the eldest brother.

"This is the one I must marry," she said, "and not the other."

199

"What's that?" asked the father.

Ivan told him everything—how he had traded the salt, how he had won the favor of the princess, and how his brothers had thrown him into the sea.

The father got very angry at his elder sons, called them scoundrels, and married Ivan to the princess.

There now began a joyful feast. The guests ate and drank and made merry. The men began to boast, some about their strength, some about their riches, some about their beautiful wives. And Ivan the Fool happily boasted too: "Listen to this! I really have something to boast about! A giant carried me piggyback across the sea!"

As soon as he said these words, the giant appeared at the gate.

"Ah, Ivan!" said the gloomy giant. "You promised not to boast about me. Now what have you done?"

"Forgive me!" cried Ivan. "It was not really I that boasted, but my happiness."

"Come, show me what you mean," said the giant. "What do you mean by happiness?"

Then Ivan took up his mandolin, and played and danced the best he knew how. And his playing and dancing was so filled with happiness that all the guests danced and clapped their hands. And soon the gloomy giant let himself smile and kept time to the music with his feet.

"Well, Ivan," he said at last, "now I know what happiness is. You may boast about me all you like."

So the wedding feast continued, and the giant departed, and Ivan the Fool and the beautiful princess lived happily ever after.

# Salt

## Meet the Author

**Harve Zemach** was born in New Jersey. He was a philosopher and a social science teacher. While in college, he met Margot Zemach in Vienna, Austria, and they were married two years later.

Harve did not plan to be a writer. He was a teacher. But Margot really wanted to draw illustrations for children's books. She finally convinced him to write a book so she could illustrate it. He wrote a story about a boy in Vienna, and the book was a success. Harve kept teaching, but after that he also wrote a book every year for Margot to illustrate.

## Meet the Illustrator

**Margot Zemach** was born in Los Angeles, California. By the time she was five, she was involved with the theater. Her mother was an actress and her stepfather was a director and dancer. Margot watched from backstage where she also drew pictures and made up stories.

*"I have always drawn pictures, all my life. It seems necessary for me to draw. It really is where I live. I was a poor file clerk, a messy confused messenger girl, a very bad salesgirl, and I cannot add. Thank goodness I can draw."*

# Theme Connections

## Think About It

This is a folktale read mainly for enjoyment, but there is a message about succeeding in business.

- What did the situations with Ivan's salt and the Gerbers' baby food have in common?
- What is the message about business in this selection?
- What kinds of things are truly valuable? What did Ivan think? What did the king think? What did the giant think?

Look at the Concept/Question Board to see if there are questions that you can answer now. If the selection or your discussion raised new questions about business, post them on the Concept/Question Board.

## Record Ideas

What is valuable to you? Which character has the same value? Record your ideas in your Writing Journal.

## Research Ideas

- Trading by ship required a lot of time on the sea. Find out more about ancient trading. What trade routes did merchants use? Did they go over land? If so, how? Was it dangerous?
- World trade depends on foreign exchange. Find out more about currency used in other countries and how exchange rates work.

# Bibliography

## Brother Anansi and the Cattle Ranch: El Hermano Anansi y el Rancho de Ganado

**by James De Sauza.**   Anansi is a trickster. So what kind of a business partner does a trickster make?

## The Dream Jar

**by Bonnie Pryor.**   Valechaka wants to contribute to her family's dream and income, but what can she do to earn money?

## Henry Reed's Baby-Sitting Service

**by Keith Robertson.**   Henry and Midge are teaming up to try and make some money. Will their baby-sitting business be a success?

## The Kid's Guide to Money: Earning It, Saving It, Spending It, Growing It, Sharing It

**by Steve Otfinoski.**   Read this book and find out how to make the most of your money!

## Madam C. J. Walker: Self-Made Millionaire

**by Patricia and Frederick McKissack.**
Meet Madam C. J. Walker, a 19th-century
entrepreneur who made a million!

## Market!

**by Ted Lewin.** Smell the smells, check out
the wares, and meet the people who do
business in the markets all over the world.

## Max Malone Makes a Million

**by Charlotte Herman.** Max and his friend
Gordy are frustrated by their attempts to get
rich while their neighbor does so with ease.

## Uncle Jed's Barbershop

**by Margaree King Mitchell.** No matter
how tough things got for Uncle Jed, he was
determined not to quit until he had his very
own barbershop.

# From Mystery to Medicine

**P**eople have always wondered about diseases and how to cure them. The more we know, the more there is to wonder about. How does the immune system work? How do antibiotics kill germs inside us without killing us at the same time? What are cancer cells? You probably have questions of your own. This unit will give you a chance to research them. Don't expect final answers. Medical science is always "work in progress."

# Medicine:
# Past and Present

by André W. Carus

illustrated by Jim Roldan

## EARLY MEDICINE

Imagine you are living in Italy a few hundred years ago. One day, your friend next door gets sick. His mother and brother become ill the following day, and that night all three of them die. Neighbors all around you are sick—and dying. You don't know who might be next. It could even be you or your parents.

In those days, this nightmare is what life was like. In the middle of the fourteenth century, an epidemic called the Black Plague swept across Europe, Asia, and Africa. It killed about 75 million people, wiping out more than a third of Europe's population. While the disease spared some towns and villages, it killed nearly everyone in others. There was little warning, and those who caught the disease were dead within a few days.

Getting sick was always scary, not just during epidemics like the Black Plague. Death was never far away. People could fall ill and die at any moment, and no one would know why. Most people did not live to be very old. The average life expectancy was only thirty or forty years, about half what it is now in the United States.

For most of human history, people did not know what caused diseases. They could not see germs, so they didn't realize germs existed. Even after germs were discovered, it took a long time to connect them up with various diseases. It took even longer for people to understand how to keep germs from making people sick.

Before people knew about germs, they had other ideas about what caused diseases. Mostly, these ideas involved some kind of magical powers. It is easy to understand why people would believe such ideas. Diseases were terrifying and mysterious. Often there seemed to be no pattern to them. Why did some people die young and others get old? Why did some wounds get infected and others heal? Why did epidemics kill some people and not others? Without knowing about germs, it was easy to believe anything that might make a difference and possibly save a life.

So, it was a new idea when a few people suggested, in Greece about 2,500 years ago, that the human body is predictable and that diseases have natural causes and reasonable explanations. Hippocrates is the best known of these people. Because this basic idea is so important, he is called the Father of Medicine. Hippocrates was sure that he could find reasons for illness by closely studying the human body and observing diseases. He also thought that people could understand the way the body worked.

We now know that Hippocrates was on the right track. But when he lived, and for a long time afterwards, his idea was no more than a guess. And often it didn't seem like a very good guess (Hippocrates had lived nearly 2,000 years before the Black Plague and his beliefs still had very little support). So most people went on believing their old ideas and attempting to use magic to cure diseases. Sometimes the things they did had good results, even though the ideas about why these things worked were wrong. For example, when the ancient Chinese used herbs and the ancient Egyptians used moldy bread on wounds, they found that infections healed. Some Native-American people knew that chewing willow tree bark would help reduce pain. And many people knew that a doctor could help just by soothing patients and taking good care of them.

**2500–300 B.C.**
Chinese practice acupuncture and the use of herbal treatments to remedy illnesses.

**460–377 B.C.**
Hippocrates learns through observation and examination of patients. Living in Greece, he is a great medical teacher and creates the Hippocratic oath, a code of medical ethics still in use today.

**A.D. 1220–1280**
Venetians first use eyeglasses to correct poor vision.

But Hippocrates' basic idea went on being not much more than a guess for a long time. Around 1600, things began to change. An Englishman named William Harvey discovered that blood in human and animal bodies doesn't just sit there. It moves, or circulates, all through the body every few minutes. And the heart is the pump that makes it move. This was an important breakthrough because it made sense of many things that had long been known about the heart and blood, but had never been pulled together. So it was an important step toward making Hippocrates' guess look more reasonable. A lot of seemingly mysterious and unrelated facts turned out to have a simple and natural explanation.

**1334**
The Plague spreads across Europe. Three fourths of the European and Asian populations die in a twenty-year period.

**1628**
The English doctor, William Harvey, discovers blood is circulated throughout the body by the heart. He realizes the heart works like a pump to keep the blood in constant motion.

# DISCOVERING GERMS

The discovery of germs and how they cause diseases took much longer. The first step was to realize that there *were* animals so tiny that they couldn't be seen by the naked eye. This step was taken by a Dutchman named Anton van Leeuwenhoek in 1674. After he heard of microscopes that magnified small objects, he made himself a very powerful one. He used it to look at water from a nearby pond and was amazed to find tiny animals swimming around in it. No human being had ever seen them before! He found many different kinds of microbes, as these tiny animals are called today, and became famous for this discovery. Ever since 1300, people had sometimes thought that such tiny living things might cause diseases. But Leeuwenhoek did not know of this idea. He did not suspect that the microbes he saw could cause the diseases that kill people. But now people knew that microbes really existed.

**1674**
Anton van Leeuwenhoek studies life under the microscope and is able to achieve 160 times magnification.

**1735**
English surgeon Claudius Amyan successfully completes the first surgery to remove the appendix.

Another big step was taken around 1800 by an English doctor named Edward Jenner. He believed Hippocrates' guess; he was sure that diseases had natural causes. One particularly terrifying disease at that time was smallpox, which killed most people who got it. The few who recovered were left with scars on their faces and bodies but never got the disease again. Jenner guessed that the body developed some means to fight the disease, so that if it were invaded by smallpox again, the infection could not survive. He tried to think of a way of getting the body to develop these antibodies (as they are now called) to attack the disease without having to get smallpox first.

He knew that among cattle there was a disease called cowpox, which was similar to the human disease of smallpox. Humans could also get cowpox, but it rarely killed them and left no permanent scars. Jenner heard it said among country people in some parts of England that if you got cowpox, you would never get smallpox. Jenner

**1753**
James Lind discovers that lemons and limes can cure scurvy, a vitamin C deficiency. Sailors, who frequently suffer from this disease on long ocean voyages, welcome his findings and drink lime juice.

**1780**
Benjamin Franklin invents a bifocal lens.

decided to find out if this was true. He guessed that once the body developed antibodies to cowpox, the same antibodies would be able to fight off smallpox. He infected some people with cowpox, waited until they recovered, and then tried to infect them with smallpox. (This test was dangerous. Such experiments wouldn't be tried today!) The people didn't get ill. They had developed the antibodies, and they would not catch smallpox. They were immune to the disease.

So, Jenner had discovered a way of preventing smallpox. For the first time ever, doctors could do something to prevent a disease. And they had evidence that whatever caused smallpox could be defeated by something the body developed for itself. But they still didn't know what actually caused the

disease. For centuries, people had been guessing that microbes, or germs, caused smallpox. No one made the actual connection between germs and disease until Louis Pasteur, a French chemist, conducted some experiments in the mid-1800s.

**1796**
Edward Jenner experiments with cowpox vaccinations against smallpox.

**1860**
The French scientist Louis Pasteur demonstrates the presence of airborne bacteria.

## MAKING THE CONNECTION

While Pasteur was doing his experiments, other scientists were discovering many different microbes. One kind of very small microbe, shaped like a rod or stick, was called bacterium, after the Greek word for stick. Pasteur carefully followed these discoveries and learned a lot about different types of bacteria. But before he could make the connection between these bacteria (or germs) and diseases, he had a more difficult job. Pasteur had to dispel, or prove wrong, an old belief that was standing in the way of his research.

Many people believed that living things could grow from nonliving things. They thought that rats grew from pieces of cheese, rotting meat turned into worms, and animals grew out of water. This idea, called spontaneous generation, seems silly to us now. But, it is easy to see why people believed it. When Anton van Leeuwenhoek discovered microbes under his microscope, no one had an explanation for how they got into the water. So it seemed likely that the water must have turned into these animals. Pasteur thought this idea was wrong. He conducted several experiments to make sure.

**1860**
Florence Nightingale establishes the Nightingale School for Nurses, the first of its kind in the world. An English nurse, Nightingale was the founder of modern nursing.

**1881**
Louis Pasteur vaccinates animals against anthrax.

In a previous series of experiments, Pasteur had learned that certain bacteria made wine spoil. When he heated the wine, the bacteria were killed. (This process of heating to kill bacteria became known as pasteurization.) In another set of experiments, Pasteur heated a flask of water to kill all the bacteria. He took samples of the water and showed under the microscope that the water contained no microbes. He then opened the flasks so that dust could get into the water. He took another sample of the water, looked at it under the microscope, and found bacteria in it. This proved that the bacteria was carried into the water by the dust particles. The bacteria had not grown out of the water.

Once people believed that all living things came only from other living things, it was easier for Pasteur to prove that diseases were caused by living things. While conducting his experiments on wine, Pasteur had wondered if bacteria might also cause diseases in humans.

**1885**
Louis Pasteur develops a vaccine for rabies.

**1886**
Louis Pasteur creates a process of sterilization known as pasteurization.

Pasteur began conducting experiments on animals with anthrax, a disease common in sheep and cattle. While looking under the microscope at blood samples from the sick animals, Pasteur discovered bacteria that were common to all of the infected animals. He knew that if he could inject healthy animals with this bacteria, and they got anthrax, it would prove that the bacteria caused the disease. Pasteur injected healthy rabbits and guinea pigs with a solution that contained the bacteria. All the animals became sick and died, proving the bacteria caused the disease. Using this information, Pasteur was able to develop a vaccine for anthrax.

**1893**
Daniel Hale Williams performs
first successful heart surgery.

**1895**
Wilhelm Conrad Röntgen
discovers X-rays.

# FIGHTING GERMS

Pasteur's work made people aware that bacteria, or germs, caused diseases and infections. Joseph Lister, a Scottish surgeon who was a friend of Pasteur's, began to sterilize all his equipment before an operation to get rid of germs. He made sure that only clean gloves were used by his assistants. He disinfected wounds with carbolic acid to kill germs. Sure enough, his patients rarely died of infections, and other surgeons began to use his methods.

**1899**
The drug aspirin is first used to relieve pain.

**1929**
Alexander Fleming discovers mold contains a substance that will kill bacteria. He names it penicillin.

Although doctors could take steps to prevent germs on the outside of the body from spreading or infecting people, they had no way to kill the germs once they were inside the body. This important step in fighting diseases took place less than fifty years ago when Alexander Fleming discovered a substance that would kill bacteria. Quite by accident, Fleming noticed that one of his lab experiments on bacteria was contaminated with mold. Instead of just throwing the ruined experiment away, Fleming studied it carefully. What he found was extraordinary. The mold destroyed the bacteria. Fleming then tested the mold on other types of bacteria and found it had the same effect on many of them. Years of testing confirmed Fleming's observations. The substance Fleming found was penicillin, modern medicine's first antibiotic. Since its discovery, penicillin has saved hundreds of thousands of lives. Many infections that once killed people are now easily treated.

**1939**
Howard Florey uses penicillin, extracted from mold juice, to treat a patient for the first time.

**1953**
Jonas Salk develops a polio vaccine.

It is only within the last hundred years that most people in the United States have come to believe that Hippocrates' guesses are true. All medical research now assumes that the human body is part of nature, and that diseases have explanations just like everything else in nature. As the natural causes of diseases are discovered, scientists are able to find ways of stopping those diseases. More and more diseases can be prevented or cured. There has been tremendous progress in the last hundred years.

**1958**
Swedish doctor Ake Senning invents the first cardiac pacemaker.

**1975**
Smallpox is eliminated through a mass vaccination sponsored by the World Health Organization.

But there is a great deal that we don't know. We still cannot cure many diseases. We don't understand why some people get cancer or heart disease. Millions of people, however, are involved in research on these diseases and on the drugs to cure them. They all accept that Hippocrates was right. But, his idea is still just a guess. And while we think there must be natural causes for these diseases, we don't know what they are. When someone gets cancer today, we are almost as mystified and helpless as people were about any disease a few hundred years ago. If you become a doctor or a medical researcher you may be one of the heroes, like Jenner or Pasteur, who have dispelled some of that fear.

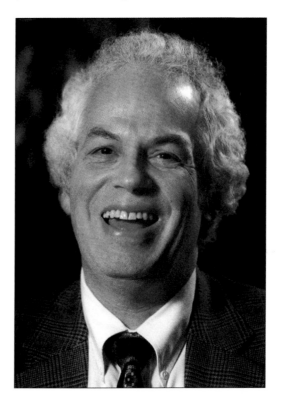

**1985**
"Keyhole" surgery is created, named so because it is less invasive.

**1997**
Stanley Prusiner is awarded a Nobel Prize for his discovery of prions, the cause of several serious brain diseases.

# Medicine:
## Past and Present

## Meet the Author

**André W. Carus** was the boss at the time
the editors were putting together this book. They
had trouble finding a short article about the history
of medicine. Their boss at the time was André
Carus. The editors knew Mr. Carus had studied
history, so they asked him to write an article. Said
Mr. Carus, *"Writing is hard, but it's satisfying to
get something down on paper. Running a company
never gives you a sense of completion like that."*

## Meet the Illustrator

**Jim Roldan** received a box of crayons, his
first memorable gift as a child. He drew pictures
of cartoon characters, animals, comic book
heroes, dinosaurs and spaceships. He studied art
at the Rhode Island School of Design. After a few
years of working in a graphic design studio, Mr.
Roldan started his own business illustrating
advertisements, magazines, posters, books, and
cartoon characters. He currently lives and works
in New Hampshire, where he shares a house with
his wife and their two cats.

# Theme Connections

## Think About It

You have just read a lot of information about people and events important in the history of medicine. Here are some things for you to think about in starting your discussions about medicine.

- What part did superstition play in early medical knowledge? Why?
- What do you think is the most important discovery in the history of medicine?
- What was the most surprising thing you learned through this selection?

Look at the Concept/Question Board to see if there are questions that you can answer now. If the selection or your discussion raised new questions about medicine, post them on the Concept/Question Board.

## Record Ideas

If you could go back in time, what questions or comments would you have for important figures mentioned in this selection? Write your ideas in your Writing Journal.

## Research Ideas

- You learned that Louis Pasteur had the idea that germs were alive and that he developed a vaccination for anthrax. Find out more about Pasteur and his life.
- Some diseases have been nearly wiped out by the use of vaccinations. Find out what some of these diseases are, how and when the vaccinations were developed, and how widespread cases of these diseases are today.

# The Microscope

**Maxine Kumin**
*illustrated by Robert Byrd*

Anton Leeuwenhoek was Dutch.
He sold pincushions, cloth, and such.
The waiting townsfolk fumed and fussed
As Anton's dry goods gathered dust.

He worked, instead of tending store,
At grinding special lenses for
A microscope. Some of the things
He looked at were:

mosquitoes' wings,
the hairs of sheep, the legs of lice,
the skin of people, dogs, and mice;
ox eyes, spiders' spinning gear,
fishes' scales, a little smear
of his own blood,

and best of all,
the unknown, busy, very small
bugs that swim and bump and hop
inside a simple water drop.

Impossible! Most Dutchmen said.
This Anton's crazy in the head.
We ought to ship him off to Spain.
He says he's seen a housefly's brain.
He says the water that we drink
Is full of bugs. He's mad, we think!
They call him *Dummkopf,* which means dope.
That's how we got the microscope.

227

# Sewed Up His Heart

███████████████████████████████████████████████

from *Sure Hands, Strong Heart:*
*The Life of Daniel Hale Williams*
by Lillie Patterson
*illustrated by Leslie Bowman*

July 9, 1893, was hot and humid in Chicago. The
scorching heat wave wrapped the city like a sweltering
blanket and blistered the sidewalks. Rising
temperatures sent thermometers zooming toward one
hundred degrees.

The heat and high humidity took a heavy toll on young
and old, animals and people. Horses pulling carts and
streetcars dropped in their tracks. People fainted from heat
prostration and sun strokes. No relief was in sight.

Doctors and hospitals were kept busy. The new Provident
Hospital was no exception. Dr. Dan kept close watch on his
patients. Making his rounds, he looked as immaculate as
always, despite the heat. After his late-afternoon rounds
were over, he retired to the closet-like room he used for
his office.

Suddenly, a young student nurse burst into the room, her
long starched skirt rustling as she ran.

"Dr. Dan!" she gasped. "An emergency! We need you."

Without a word Dr. Dan dropped the report he was
reading and hurried to the room set aside for emergency
cases. The lone hospital intern, Dr. Elmer Barr, came
running to assist.

228

The emergency case was a young man. He had been brought in by his friend, who gave sketchy information. The patient's name: James Cornish. His age: twenty-four years. His occupation: laborer. The illness: he had been stabbed in the chest.

The frightened friend tried to explain what happened. James Cornish had stopped in a neighboring saloon on his way home from work. The heat and a few drinks caused an argument among the customers. A fight broke out. When it ended, Cornish lay on the floor, a knife wound in his chest.

"How long was the knife blade?" Dr. Dan asked as he began his examination. This would give a clue to the depth and seriousness of the wound.

The victim had not seen the knife blade. Nor had his friend. Action in the fight had been too fast and furious.

Dr. Dan discovered that the knife had made an inch-long wound in the chest, just to the left of the breastbone. There was very little external bleeding. Nevertheless, Cornish seemed extremely weak, and his rapid pulse gave cause for concern. The X ray had not yet been invented, so there was no way to determine what was happening inside the chest.

Dr. Dan knew from experience that such cases could develop serious complications. James Cornish must be kept in the hospital, he decided. And he must be watched closely.

That night Dr. Dan slept in the hospital. He did this often when there were serious cases. As he had feared, Cornish's condition worsened during the night. He groaned as severe chest pains stabbed the region above his heart. His breathing became labored. A high pitched cough wracked his sturdy frame. The dark face on the pillow was bathed in perspiration.

Dr. Dan watched the wounded man carefully all night. The next morning, as he took the patient's pulse, he voiced his concern to the intern. "One of the chief blood vessels seems to be damaged," he said to Dr. Barr. The knife must have gone in deep enough to cut the internal mammary artery, he explained. The heart itself might be damaged.

James Cornish showed symptoms of lapsing into shock.

Both doctors knew that something had to be done, and done quickly. Otherwise Cornish would surely die within a matter of hours.

*But what?*

The only way to know the damage done would be to open the chest and look inside. In 1893, doctors considered this highly impracticable. For surgery, the chest was still off limits.

Standing beside the patient's bed, the barber-turned-doctor faced the situation squarely. Later he would recall how he weighed the risks of that moment. Thoughts tumbled through his mind as furiously as flurries in a wintry Chicago snowstorm.

He knew that medical experts repeatedly warned against opening the thorax, the segment of the body containing the heart and lungs. Heart wounds were usually considered fatal. As a medical student, Dr. Dan had read a quote from an eminent physician-writer. "Any surgeon who would attempt to suture a wound of the heart," the surgeon wrote, "is not worthy of the serious consideration of his colleagues."

So far, doctors had followed this cautious advice.

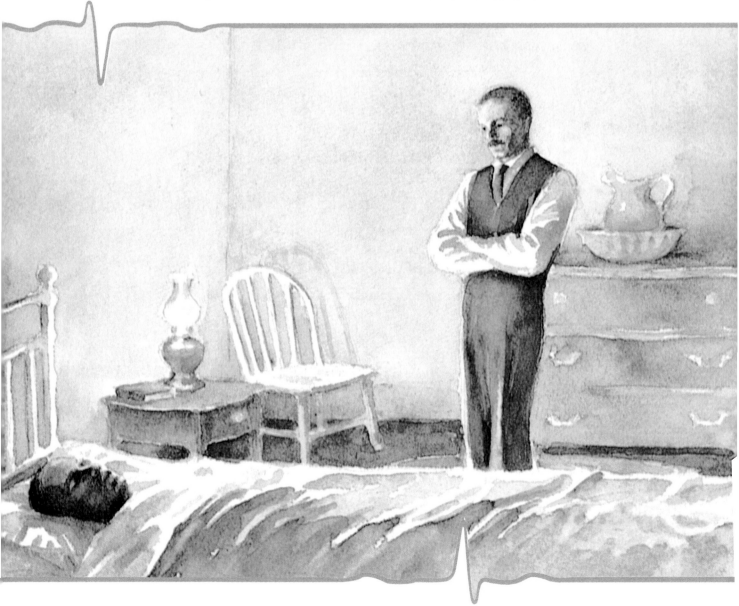

The risks were there for him and for Cornish. If he did not attempt an operation, Dr. Dan reasoned, the patient would die. Nobody would blame the doctor. Such cases often died.

On the other hand, if he opened the chest and Cornish died anyway, there would be certain condemnation from medical groups. His reputation as a surgeon would be questioned, perhaps lost.

The odds were against both him and Cornish. But Daniel Hale Williams had never allowed the odds to intimidate him.

Dr. Dan lifted his chin, the way he did when he faced a challenge. The storm of doubts suddenly swept away, leaving his mind clear and calm as a rain-washed April morning.

The surgeon quietly told his decision to the intern. Two words he spoke. "I'll operate."

The word spread quickly through Provident hospital. Like a small army alerted to do battle, student nurses rushed to get the operating room ready and prepare the patient. They knew Dr. Dan's strict rules regarding asepsis, or preventing infection. The instruments, the room, furniture; everything that came in contact with the patient must be free of microbes that might cause infection.

Meanwhile, Dr. Dan sent a hurried message to a few doctors who often came to watch him operate. The intern, a medical student, and four doctors appeared. Dr. George Hall of Provident's staff was there. So was Dr. Dan's friend, Dr. William Morgan. The circle of watchers gathered in the operating room; four white, two black.

Dr. Dan scrubbed his hands and arms thoroughly. Then, with a nod toward his colleagues, he walked over and looked down at Cornish, now under the effects of anesthesia. Strong shafts of sunlight slanted through a window, giving the doctor's curly red hair a glossy luster. His thin, sensitive mouth drew taut with concentration.

The surgical nurse, proud of her training, stood at attention.

*Scalpel!*

A loud sigh escaped one of the doctors when the light, straight knife touched Cornish's bare skin. After that there was silence from the onlookers.

None of them knew what would happen next. How would the body react when air suddenly hit the chest cavity? Would vital chest organs shift too far out of place? Dr. Dan could not benefit from the experiences of other doctors. No paper had been written, no lectures given to guide him. Dr. Dan was pioneering in an unexplored territory. He was on his own.

The surgeon worked swiftly. He had to. The surgeon of 1893 did not have a variety of anesthetics or artificial airways to keep the patient's windpipe open. Blood transfusion techniques were unknown. Penicillin and other infection-fighting drugs had not been discovered.

Quickly, Dr. Dan made the incision, lengthening the stab wound to the right. Expertly, he cut through the skin and the layers of fat beneath it. Now he could see the breastbone and the ribs. He made another cut to separate the rib cartilage from the sternum.

Long years of studying and teaching human anatomy gave his every movement confidence. Working with precision, he made his way through the network of cartilages, nerves, blood vessels. A few inches from the breastbone he cut through the cartilage to make a little opening, like a trapdoor.

Bending his head close to the patient's chest, he peered through the opening he had made. Now he could examine the internal blood vessels.

Now he could see the heart!

The tough bundle of muscles throbbed and jerked and pulsated, sending food and oxygen through the body. Dr. Dan examined the pericardium, the fibrous sac that protected the pear-shaped heart and allowed it to beat without rubbing against other parts of the body.

At each step, Dr. Dan reported his findings to the group of observers. The vital pericardium was cut——a tear of about an inch and a quarter in length. He probed further. Yes, there was another puncture wound, he reported, about one-half an inch to the right of the coronary artery. Had the knife moved a fraction of an inch, Cornish would have bled to death before he reached the hospital. Also——Dr. Dan paused——the left mammary artery was damaged.

As the problems were ticked off, the atmosphere in the room grew more tense. The temperature rose above one hundred degrees. Yet not one doctor reached to wipe the perspiration that poured down hands and faces. No one took note of the time. It seemed as though the moment were somehow suspended in history, awaiting results.

Dr. Dan kept on talking and working. The small wound in the heart itself should be left undisturbed, he advised. It was slight. The tear in the pericardium was a different matter. That had to be repaired.

Now the surgeon's hands moved with a rhythm born of knowledge, practice, and instinct. Strong hands; flexible enough to pluck tunes from guitars and violins. Sure hands; steady enough to string high telephone wires. Quick hands; made nimble from years of cutting hair and trimming beards and mustaches.

These hands now raced against time to save a life. Dr. Dan tied off the injured mammary artery to prevent bleeding.

*Forceps!*

Now he had to try to sew up the heart's protective covering. Meticulously, he irrigated the pericardial wound with a salt solution of one hundred degrees Fahrenheit. There must be no chance of infection after the chest was closed.

Using the smooth forceps, he held together the ragged edges of the wound. Against his fingers the fist-sized heart fluttered and thumped like a frightened bird fighting to fly free.

*Sutures!*

Despite the rapid heartbeats, the master surgeon managed to sew up the torn edges of the pericardium. For this he used a thin catgut. After that he closed the opening he had made, again using fine catgut.

Another kind of suture would be used for the skin and cartilages, he informed the circle of watchers. He changed to silkworm gut, using long continuous sutures. This allowed for quick entry if infection or hemorrhage developed later. Over the outer sutures he applied a dry dressing.

The operation was over. James Cornish was still alive.

Dr. Dan straightened his aching back. Only then did he stop to wipe the perspiration from his face.

Like figures in a fairy tale suddenly brought to life by magic, the circle of doctors began to move and talk. They rushed to congratulate the surgeon. "Never," said one, "have I seen a surgeon work so swiftly, or with so much confidence."

Each of them dashed from Provident to spread the news. Daniel Hale Williams had opened a man's chest, repaired the pericardium, closed the chest; and the patient's heart was still beating.

How long would Cornish live? Worried watchers waited in suspense. Had the doctor repaired the heart but killed the patient?

During the hours that followed the operation, Dr. Dan scarcely left Cornish's side. Alarming symptoms developed, and he made careful notes. The patient's body temperature rose to 103 degrees. His pulse raced at 134 beats a minute. Heart sounds became muffled and distant. Seizures of coughing shook his frame.

Dr. Dan shared his fears with Dr. Barr. Fluid had collected in the pleural cavity. This meant another operation.

He waited a few more days to give Cornish more time to gain strength. Three weeks after the first operation, Cornish was again rolled into the operating room. As before, Dr. Dan made an incision, this time between the seventh and eighth ribs. Through this opening he drew five pints of bloody serum.

Thanks to his careful adherence to antiseptic surgical techniques, there was no infection, and there were no further serious complications. Fifty-one days after James Cornish entered Provident with little chance of living, he was dismissed——a well man.

A news reporter from Chicago's *Inter Ocean* newspaper came to Provident to interview the surgeon and get the story first-hand. He found Dr. Dan more anxious to talk about his interracial hospital and the program for training nurses than to talk about the historic operation. The reporter had to coax details from him.

Nevertheless, the reporter's story came out with an eye-catching headline: "SEWED UP HIS HEART!" Another heading read: "DR. WILLIAMS PERFORMS AN ASTONISHING FEAT. . . ."

The *Medical Record* of New York later carried Dr. Dan's own scientific account of the techniques and procedures he had used during the operation. His case created worldwide attention, for it was the first recorded attempt to suture the pericardium of the human heart.

His pioneering operation gave courage to other doctors to challenge death when faced with chest wounds. Dr. Dan's techniques were copied by other surgeons, step by step.

The phrase "Sewed Up His Heart" became closely associated with the name of Daniel Hale Williams. The historic operation on James Cornish helped to advance the progress toward modern heart surgery.

# Sewed Up His Heart

## Meet the Author

**Lillie Patterson** grew up on Hilton Head, South Carolina. She spent most of her time with her grandmother who was a great reader and singer. *"From my grandmother I captured a sense of the power of words. It was natural that I would follow a career in library media services, and later in writing."*

Ms. Patterson became a children's librarian and a popular storyteller. She also helped to develop radio and television shows for children.

When she gets an idea for a book, Ms. Patterson spends a great deal of time doing research. She finds as much information as possible. Then she rereads everything until she feels she has captured "the spirit" of her subject.

## Meet the Illustrator

**Leslie Bowman** grew up in Connecticut. She started drawing when she was about four years old. She says she never wanted to be anything but an artist. She got lots of encouragement, especially from her mother who was a painter herself.

Ms. Bowman started illustrating children's books in 1986. Since then she has illustrated several books and also worked for *Cricket Magazine.* She says, *"When I work on the illustrations for a book, I read the story over and over until I see the pictures in my head. Then I do sketches of what I see."* She does any research she needs, like finding out what clothes people wore at the time of the story. She adds these details to her sketches, and from these she produces her final illustrations.

# Theme Connections

## Think About It

Dr. Daniel Hale Williams lived in a time when the field of medicine was still fairly undeveloped. When faced with a difficult dilemma, Dr. Dan became responsible for a significant medical advancement. Here are some things for you to think about.

- What can you infer about Dr. Dan's character? Do you think Dr. Dan's behavior would have been different if he were worried about being sued? Explain.
- How did the fact that the events in the story took place over a hundred years ago affect the situation? How would things be different today?
- Which condition do you think was the most important in this story—courage, patience, medical knowledge, or luck? Explain.

Look at the Concept/Question Board to see if there are questions that you can answer now. If the selection or your discussion raised new questions about medicine, post them on the Concept/Question Board.

## Record Ideas

In your Writing Journal, record any new information or questions you have after reading this selection. Also jot down any personal reactions or insights you have had in response to the information.

## Research Ideas

- During Dr. Williams's time, opening the chest cavity was discouraged. Today, heart surgery has become much more scientific. Find out more about trends, procedures, or instruments used in heart surgery today.
- A great deal of research is done on how to keep the human heart healthy. What are some things that can be done for a healthy heart?

# Surgeons Must Be Very Careful

Emily Dickinson
*illustrated by Robert Byrd*

Surgeons must be very careful

When they take the knife!

Underneath their fine incisions

Stirs the culprit,——Life!

# The Germ

Ogden Nash
*illustrated by Robert Byrd*

A mighty creature is the germ,
Though smaller than the pachyderm.
His customary dwelling place
Is deep within the human race.
His childish pride he often pleases
By giving people strange diseases.
Do you, my poppet, feel infirm?
You probably contain a germ.

# The Bridge Dancers

Carol Saller
*illustrated by Gerald Talifero*

Mama gives the comb a yank through the mess of Callie's long, wild hair, and Callie gives a yell like you've never heard before. That's not to say I've never heard it before; I've heard it plenty. Callie says when she grows up she's going to the city to live, where she'll start a new style. All the ladies will come to her and pay a lot of money to get their hair tangled up in knots, and she'll get rich and never comb her hair again.

I'm not a lot like Callie. My hair doesn't fly around much, and I like it combed, and I don't often think about leaving this mountain. Callie's going to be thirteen soon. I'm only eleven, and I've never even been across the bridge.

When Callie's all combed, we go down the path to the bridge. It's our favorite place to play when our chores are done. The dirt path is steep from our house down the twisty old hill. We like to run down fast, bouncing off the little trees in a crazy zigzag, but when we reach the edge of the gorge, the path levels off and we run alongside it. To folks way down below on the river we must look like two little pokeberries, up high on the mountain's edge.

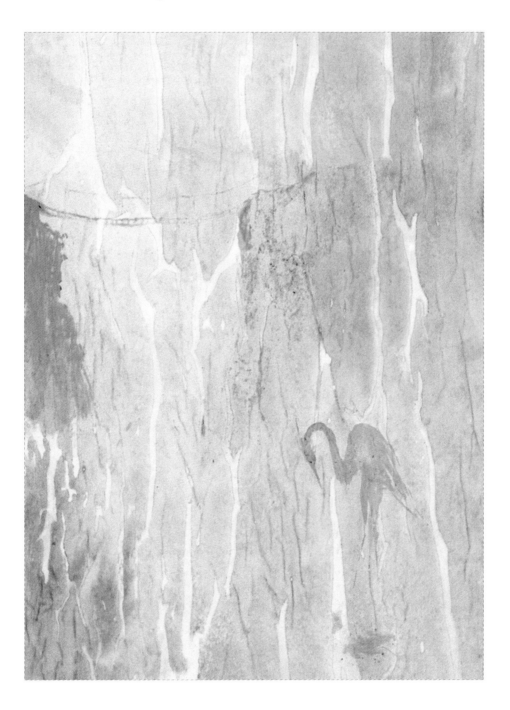

What we call the bridge isn't the real bridge, where horses and buggies can get across, that's a few miles off along the path. Our bridge is just a shaky old skeleton, a tangle of ropes and boards that ripples and swings in the breeze. Our house is the closest one to this bridge. The next nearest is the Ketchums' place, another mile up the mountain. Most of our neighbors live across the gorge; Mama says there are seven houses within the first half hour's walk. Mama often has to cross the bridge, but we're not allowed.

On this day, the wind is strong and the bridge is rocking like a boat in a storm. We make clover chains and toss them into the gorge, watching them blow away and then down, down. We count the seconds till they hit the water far below. Callie stays by the edge, but I spy some yellow-eyed daisies growing up the hill a ways, and I know Mama will want them. If you boil daisies——stalks, leaves, and all——it makes a tea that's good for coughs, or a lotion for bruises and sores. Mama doctors most of the folks on this mountain, and we always keep a store of dried plants for medicine. I pull the best ones and put them in my apron pocket.

Later, when the sun is behind the mountain and I'm getting cold and hungry, I start back up the path, but Callie doesn't want to go. "Maisie! I dare you to stand on the bridge!" she calls, just like she does every time we're here. I don't answer, but I stop and turn to look. She knows the thought of it scares me.

Now she skips up the hill a little ways and stands on her toes like a dancer, her skirt ballooning in the wind. In the gloomy light of sundown she is ghostlike and beautiful. "Announcing . . . Calpurnia the Great!" She twirls and leaps and strikes a pose with one toe pointed forward: "Calpurnia——the Daring Bridge Dancer!"

I laugh. I'm pretty sure she's only teasing. Callie dances toward the bridge, humming a tune that she imagines sounds like a circus. When she gets to the part of the bridge that sits on land, she holds onto one post and points her foot out

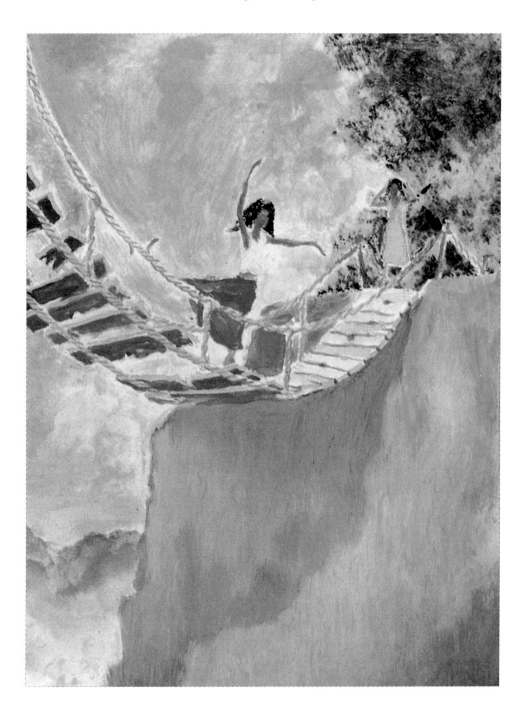

toward the gorge, leaning back in a swoop. Then she grabs both posts and slides both feet out onto the bridge. She starts to slip, but before I can cry out, she turns back, laughing. My heart is jumping. I'm getting ready to run and pull her away from the bridge when she skips aside quick as lightning and starts chewing a piece of clover. In a second I see why.

Mama is huffing down the path. She's lugging her doctoring bag and has to watch her step. If she'd seen Callie fooling around on the bridge we'd both have caught it. "Girls, I've got to attend to Mrs. Gainie," Mama says, putting her bag down for a rest. "She thought the baby would come last night, but tonight's the full moon. It'll come tonight." She looks us over and frowns across the gorge. "I might be gone till sunup, so get yourselves some supper, and don't forget to bolt the door, you hear?" She points at some dark clouds moving fast across the sky. "Hurry on up. I've already made a fire——there's a storm blowing." We nod. She starts for the bridge.

"Mama?" I call, and she stops and turns. "Is Mrs. Gainie going to be all right?" Mama nods. "She's a strong woman." She reaches for the bridge rail with one hand.

"Wait!" I call.

Mama stops again. "What is it, Maisie?"

"Have you got the tansy I picked?" I ask. Tansy is supposed to help a baby come, but if it doesn't do that, at least it keeps the bugs away.

Mama says, "I've got it, but I don't expect to need it this time." She smiles at me. "I'll mind my steps on the bridge, Maisie." Mama knows I'm afraid.

When Mama crosses the bridge, I never let go of her with my eyes. She's a big, heavy woman, and when she steps off the land part, the whole bridge from one side to the other dips into a sharp V with Mama at the bottom point. She goes slow, holding the ropes with one hand and her bag with the other, and she walks in a careful rhythm, giving the bridge time to bounce just right between steps. Callie says, "She won't fall if you look away," but I never look away. On the other side it's already dark, but we can just see Mama turn and wave. We wave back, and Mama disappears around the side of the mountain down the path to the Gainies'.

"Come on, Callie," I say, starting up the path. I know that there's supper to get and more wood to gather and plenty else to do. But Callie isn't of a mind to work. She throws her blade of grass to the wind and runs ahead of me, her arms flung wide. "Burst into jubilant song!" she cries. "The everlasting chains are loosed and we are free!" Callie gets a lot of big words from reading the Bible. "Let us soar into the heavens, never to be enchained again!"

With that, she scampers off the path into the brush, and is soon just a flutter of white in the dusk, dancing and dodging among the trees. I feel the first drops of rain, and in a moment Callie is back.

"Maisie, I know what let's do," she says, blocking the path. She has to raise her voice now against the wind.

"What?" I ask with a frown. Callie's smile looks like it's hiding a bad idea, and I'm not sure I want to know.

"Let's get the ax and split a log for the fire," she says, wrapping her skirt around her and skipping along beside me. "There's a big storm coming. Let's have a fire that will last us all night."

I'm not sure. A fire would be good on a cold, stormy night, and I know there's only kindling left in the box. But Mama's the one who chops the wood. She takes down that big old ax from its pegs high on the wall and tells us to stand away. She's never told us not to touch it, but I have a feeling that we're not supposed to. I shake my head. "Callie, I don't hardly think you could even lift that ax. You're likely to get yourself killed." But my words blow away with the wind, and Callie is already halfway up to the house. I start to run, too, but I've never yet stopped Callie from doing what she wants to do. I figure the best I can do is be there when she needs help.

When I get to the door, Callie has the lantern lit and is dragging the rocking chair over to the wall. "Don't stand on that—it's too tottery!" I cry, and I run to hold the rocker while Callie climbs up and waits for the wobbling to stop. When the chair is still, she reaches up both hands to lift the ax from its pegs. It's heavy, all right; I can see by the way Callie's muscles stand out on her arms. Just when she's got it lifted off the pegs, the wind blows the door shut with a powerful "bang!" and we both jump with fright. The rocker pitches, and Callie falls.

For a long moment it seems like nothing happens. My thoughts stop; even my heart seems to stop. Then Callie is crying out with pain and fear. It's her leg, cut deep by the ax. She clutches hold of my arm, tight, and gasps with the force of the pain. "Maisie, hurry and get Mama!" she whispers. "Callie . . ." I start to say, thinking about the wind, the dark, the bridge. Callie sees how I don't want to go, and she looks at me, begging with her eyes. "Maisie, I'm sorry——but you've got to go! You're the only one who can help me!"

I don't want to think about what Callie is saying. Instead I grab one of the clean cloths Mama uses for straining her herb medicines, and with shaky fingers, tie it tight around Callie's leg. I take a quilt from the bed and put it over her, then run to the kindling pile and throw an armload of sticks on the fire. Callie is crying; the wind is crying. I light another lantern and wonder how I can cross the bridge, in the night, in the storm.

Outside, the wind and trees are whipping at the sky. I hold my skirt in one hand, the lantern in the other, and stumble in the quivery light down the path to the bridge. With my whole heart I wish there was some other way to fetch Mama. I think of Mama with her jars and packets, her sure hands and her healing ways. She'll stop the bleeding with a poultice of yarrow; she'll make an herb tea that will help Callie sleep. But Mama is far across the valley——how will I ever cross that bridge . . . Near the bottom of the hill, I can hear it before I see it, ropes groaning and boards creaking, as it tosses in the storm.

I stand at the edge of the gorge, my lantern lighting the first few steps of the rain-slicked bridge. The fear in me is so powerful it stings my eyes, and I know I don't have the courage for even the first step. But I remember what Callie said——"Maisie, you're the only one who can help me"——and I step onto the bridge with both feet.

The bridge pitches and plunges. I grab for the ropes, and the lantern flies from my hands. "No!" I shriek, as it rolls away and drops into the darkness. On my hands and knees, I crawl back to the edge of the gorge, sobbing in the terrible black night, crying for Callie, crying for Mama. How can I cross the bridge . . . how can I help Callie . . . think what to do, Maisie, think what to do. With my face near the ground, I make myself take slow breaths. I can smell clover, damp with rain.

Suddenly, I know what to do. I pick myself up and start back up the path, feeling my way in the darkness, guided by the small light in the house at the top of the hill. I remember all the times I've watched Mama with her bag, with her poke leaves for burns, her chickweed for tummyache. It's the yarrow plant that stops someone bleeding, and I can make the poultice myself. Near the top I begin to run.

When I burst in through the door, I see that Callie's face is pale. "Maisie——Mama!" she says, weakly. "There, Callie, don't fret; it's going to be fine," I comfort her. "I know what to do. Mama will come later, but I know just what to do."

My hands shake a little as I set the kettle on to boil——the fire is still burning strong. Then I go to Mama's cupboard of crushed and dried plants. I find some yarrow and wrap it in a clean muslin cloth to make the poultice. My fingers are sure now——Mama does it exactly so. Then I take a handful of dried feverfew and put it in a pot, for tea. Callie is moaning, so I sit by her and talk. "Yarrow is just the thing——and I remember I picked this myself! It has such pretty little flowers, and so many funny names: thousand-leaf, angel flower, bunch-a-daisies, sneezewort. It won't take but a minute, once that water's boiled. Don't you worry, Callie. Maisie can take care of you."

When the water is boiling, I pour some into the teapot with the feverfew and put it near the window to cool. Then I put the wrapped-up yarrow into the kettle and put the kettle back on the fire——not too long, just long enough for the water to soak in and soften the yarrow. Then I scoop out the poultice with a ladle, and after a minute, while it's still hot, I put it carefully on Callie's leg. I know it will hurt, so I keep talking. "Listen to that rain! It's really starting to pour now. You know, this is a pretty bad cut, Callie, and it hasn't stopped bleeding yet. This poultice will stop it. Can you smell how sweet?" But Callie yells when the poultice touches her leg.

When the tea is cool, I pour some into a cup, and hold up Callie's head for her to drink. "That's good," I tell her. "This will ease the pain. Maybe you can sleep a little; sleep till Mama comes." I rest her head in my lap, leaning my back against the wall. Rain thrashes the roof as I stroke her hair, all tangled and wild. I talk on and on, about ox-eye daisies and Queen Anne's lace, chickweed and tansy, the names like song words, lulling her to sleep at last.

When Mama came home early the next morning, she found us sleeping on the floor. She unwrapped the cloths and washed out the cut——Callie hollered like anything——and said I'd done just what she'd have done herself. She never scolded about the ax——she knew there was no need——but she did ask why I hadn't come to fetch her. I was ashamed, telling Mama how I'd been too afraid to cross the bridge. "You've got good sense, Maisie," she answered. "I guess there's more than one way to cross a bridge."

It's been three months since Callie was hurt, and she's healed as much as she ever will. There's a fearsome scar on her leg, but Callie says that when she goes to live in the city she'll wear long pants like the men and no one will ever know.

Ever since I took care of Callie, Mama has let me help her with the doctoring. From the time I was little, I've helped her find and dry the flowers, but now I go along and watch when she tends to sick folks. When Callie talks about the city, I sometimes think I might visit her there. But for me, I think the mountain will always be my home. I like the way the mountain needs Mama. Someday I think it's going to need me, too.

# The Bridge Dancers

## Meet the Author

**Carol Saller** is a writer and editor who lives in Chicago, Illinois. She gets ideas for some of her stories from her two sons, John and Ben, who love to read.

When she's not working, Ms. Saller enjoys quilting and finding recipes for her husband to cook.

*The Bridge Dancers* is Ms. Saller's first book.

## Meet the Illustrator

**Gerald Talifero** was born in Detroit, Michigan. Today he lives in Santa Barbara, California, where he works as an artist, designer, musician, and teacher.

Gerald Talifero is a multimedia artist who works in watercolor, pencil, and ink. In addition to art, he also works with troubled and disadvantaged children. His goal is to help children *"explore and develop their inner resources by outwardly coming in contact with nature."* Mr. Talifero and his "children" enjoy sailing, scuba diving, biking, and mountain climbing.

256

# Theme Connections

## Think About It

You have just read an exciting story in which a young girl used herbal treatments. Here are some things for you to think about.

- How was Maisie's treatment of Callie's cut the same as a doctor's would be? How was it different?
- What did Maisie's mother mean when she said there's more than one way to cross a bridge? Have you ever had to "cross a bridge" in a different way? Explain.
- Would you want someone to treat you with herbal remedies? Why or why not?

Look at the Concept/Question Board to see if there are any questions that you can answer now. If the selection or your discussion raised new questions about medicine, post them on the Concept/Question Board.

## Record Ideas

 What did you learn about herbal medicine? How have your ideas about herbal medicine changed after reading this selection? Record your ideas in your Writing Journal.

## Research Ideas

- Herbal medicine is thousands of years old, but it is just now gaining in popularity. How are herbal medicines different from the manufactured medicines doctors prescribe?

# The New Doctor

from *You Can Hear a Magpie Smile*
by Paula G. Paul
illustrated by Roberta Collier-Morales

Manuelita's house seemed unusually quiet as Lupe
approached it. She wasn't sure why at first, then she
realized that it was because she did not hear Noche
screeching, cawing, and chattering. Maybe Manuelita was not at
home. Lupe ran the last few steps up to the front and knocked
on the door.

Still no sounds came from inside the house, but soon the door
opened noiselessly, and Lupe saw Manuelita standing in front of
her. Noche was perched on her shoulder, his long tail hanging
down her back. Manuelita said nothing, but stepped aside for
Lupe to enter.

"I thought you weren't home," Lupe said.

"In a few more ticks of the clock, we would not have been,"
Manuelita said.

As Lupe walked into the kitchen, she saw several small cloth
bags lying on the table and a large knapsack beside them.
Manuelita began gathering up the bags and putting them inside
the knapsack.

"You are going to gather herbs," Lupe said. She had seen
Manuelita make these preparations before.

Manuelita nodded. She turned toward the cupboard to check
the contents of a glass jar. Noche almost lost his balance with
the turn and fluttered his wings to keep his position on
Manuelita's shoulder. He seemed to know that Manuelita was

going out and was making sure he stuck close beside her so that she would not leave him behind.

"You will look for summer herbs along the river? May I go with you?" Lupe asked eagerly.

"No," Manuelita answered. "I am going into the mountains."

"The mountains?" Lupe asked puzzled. There was a bigger variety of herbs along the river than in the mountains.

"Yes," Manuelita answered. "I will need more osha."

"But I just brought you some. Remember? I gathered it when Maria and I were lost, and——"

"Yes," Manuelita said. "But I will need more. Much more. There is nowhere else in the whole country that osha is as plentiful and as strong as it is in these mountains here."

Lupe wondered why Manuelita thought she would need so much of the herb. She thought of all the things it was used for. The root could be boiled for upset stomach and headaches, or ground to a powder and mixed with flour to paste on the chest of someone who had a cold, or placed on a sore spot on the body to aid healing. The green leaves could be cooked with meat or beans and eaten regularly, just to stay healthy.

Maybe Manuelita thought there was going to be a lot of sickness in the village. But with the new doctor's popularity, many people would no doubt go to her with their complaints. Manuelita must know that, too. It didn't make sense.

Oh, well, Lupe thought, at least Manuelita doesn't seem unhappy. She is still going about her work as usual. She is being her old dependable self. Maybe that is a good sign.

Still, Lupe wanted to be with her friend.

"I will go with you into the mountains," she said. "I will have to ask Mama, of course, but I'm sure if she knows you are going, she will——"

"No." Manuelita's voice was firm. "I must go alone."

"But——"

Manuelita reached toward Lupe and held her shoulders. "I will go alone," she said, looking deep into Lupe's eyes, "but when I come back, you must come to me."

Lupe searched Manuelita's face, trying to understand. "Yes, of course, I will come," she said.

"Then go and play now. There is still time for that."

Lupe thought that was a strange thing for Manuelita to say, but Manuelita said many strange things. She didn't have time to ask her about it, however, because Manuelita had finished packing her knapsack and was ushering her out the door.

As Lupe started through the brush toward the village, she looked back to see Manuelita, carrying the knapsack and with Noche clinging to her shoulder. The bird was not making a sound but was acting as if he dared not be naughty for fear he would be left behind.

By the time Lupe reached the village, her friend Maria had found someone else to play hopscotch with her. They were too far along with the game to add a newcomer, so Lupe walked away from the sandy spot, looking for something else to do.

She walked past the school and saw several children on the playground, but she didn't feel like joining them. She just kept walking, and before she realized it, she found herself in front of the new temporary clinic building.

There didn't seem to be any cars around it, and the only activity going on was at the noisy construction site for the permanent building nearby. Lupe decided to walk up to the temporary building and peek inside for another look. Since the front door was open just a crack, she tried to see through it. At first, she couldn't see too clearly, so she leaned closer to the door. Just as she did, the door opened from the inside, and Lupe tumbled forward, sprawling on the floor and looking at a pair of sandals. The feet inside the sandals were webbed by gossamer-thin nylon hose.

"Well, what have we here?" said a voice from above. Lupe looked up and saw that both the feet and the voice belonged to Dr. Johnson. The doctor came down to her knees and looked at Lupe. "Are you hurt?" she asked.

"No!" Lupe said. She jumped up quickly and dusted herself off.

"I didn't mean to make you fall. I opened the door to get a breath of fresh air, and I had no idea you were leaning against it."

Lupe ducked her head to hide her burning cheeks.

"Oh, look," the doctor said. "You've scraped your knee on the threshold. Let's see what we can do about that."

Dr. Johnson led Lupe into the examination room. She took her to the sink and washed the knee with warm soapy water, then rinsed and dried it. Next, she took a bottle of red liquid from a shelf and dabbed some of the liquid on the scraped spot. The red medicine caused Lupe's knee to burn furiously, but she did not cry out, and she swallowed hard to keep the tears from her eyes.

The treatment was very much the same as Manuelita would have given. She would have washed the area and dried it. Sometimes she even used the fiery red medicine you could buy at the grocery store, but more often, she would dab on a plaster made from the osha.

"There," Dr. Johnson said, putting the bottle of medicine away. "You have been my first patient, and you have come even before the clinic is officially open. It is to open tomorrow, you know. And I've spent all day today trying to get things organized and put away." The doctor sat down at her desk and faced Lupe. She smiled and said, "Now tell me, what can I do for you? Did you come for something special?"

"Nothing special," Lupe said, her voice very low.

"Perhaps you were just curious."

Lupe nodded her head.

"I can understand," Dr. Johnson said. "You have never had a clinic here before, and I suppose you wanted to see what it is like. I would have been the same way at your age. I was curious about just about everything—always poking my nose into something, and often getting into trouble."

Lupe looked up at the doctor, surprised. She was trying to imagine her as a little girl, poking her nose into things. The doctor was laughing at her memories, and the short curls on her head bounced as she laughed. Lupe found herself laughing with her.

"What is your name?" Dr. Johnson asked.

"Lupe Montano."

"I'm Dr. Eleanor Johnson. Did I meet you at the reception? I'm sorry I don't remember, but there were a lot of people there."

Lupe shook her head. "I wasn't there," she said. Lupe let her eyes roam around the room. Dr. Johnson had placed many things on the shelves and counters. There were bottles and jars which Lupe thought must contain medicines, but she didn't know what all the strange-looking tools were for.

"What are those for?" Lupe heard herself asking. She was surprised at her own question. She hadn't meant to ask anything, but her curiosity was stronger than her shyness.

"This?" Dr. Johnson asked, picking up a piece of cloth attached to ropes and dials. "This is for taking blood pressure. Look, I'll show you how it works." The doctor wrapped the cloth around Lupe's arm. She put something in her own ears and placed the end of it to Lupe's arm also.

"When I listen here"——Dr. Johnson pointed to the thing in her ears——"and look at this" she pointed to the dial——"it helps me find out a little about your body, and maybe whether you are well or sick."

"What do you hear with that?" Lupe asked, pointing to the thing in the doctor's ears.

"This is a stethoscope, and I can hear your heartbeat," the doctor said, and she let Lupe listen to her own heartbeat.

"We will also have X rays, and on certain days of the week, we will have people come here to help me with them. An X ray takes pictures of the inside of your body."

Lupe had heard about X rays in school, although she had never seen one. Taking a picture, from the outside, of the inside of a person's body seemed more like witchcraft to her than anything Manuelita had ever done.

She looked up at the shelves full of bottles. "You have many remedies," she said. "It must have taken you a long time to mix them all."

"Oh, I didn't make them myself." The doctor laughed.

"Then where did you get them?" Lupe asked.

"Why, I bought them, from companies that sell medicines. There are many companies that know how to make medicines much better than I could."

Lupe looked at her silently. She wondered how she knew the medicines were good if she did not make them herself.

"I'll have a lot of advantages to share with you," Dr. Johnson said. "You won't have to travel all the way to Albuquerque when you are sick, or rely on home remedies you make yourself, that don't work most of the time. I'm looking forward to bringing that to all of you, and I'm looking forward to being your friend."

Dr. Johnson reached her hand toward Lupe's, but Lupe pulled her hand away and jumped up from her chair.

"I've got to go now," she said. "I forgot to tell my mother where I would be."

Lupe ran out of the building and down the road toward her house. She did not want to be friends with the new doctor, because the new doctor could not be Manuelita's friend. The new doctor would not want to have anything to do with a person who mixed her own medicines and did not know how to take pictures of people's insides.

Manuelita was gone for several days. Lupe began to worry about her. Manuelita had gone out searching for herbs and stayed far into the night and even overnight before, but never had she been gone this long. Lupe was also concerned because so many people had been going to the clinic. She was afraid they had abandoned Manuelita completely.

Worst of all, Lupe felt disloyal and guilty about the amount of time she, herself, had spent at the new clinic. She couldn't seem to help herself, though. She was fascinated by all the new medicines and strange instruments and, although she did not like to admit it, by the new doctor herself.

One day, when she couldn't talk Maria into going with her, Lupe decided to walk over to the clinic alone. She told herself she only wanted to see how the new building was coming along and perhaps catch a glimpse of Alonzo working with the big machines she'd heard him talk about. But before long, she was seated on the ground in front of the temporary mobile-home clinic, watching people coming and going. Occasionally, if it was someone she knew well enough, she would ask what their ailment was before they went in and what the treatment had been as they came out.

Manuelita had been right. The new doctor's medicine was often very different from hers.

Finally, when the sun was quite low on the horizon, Dr. Johnson herself came to the door. She took off her white coat and held it across her arm. She was wearing a summer dress made of a pretty blue material. It looked nice with her sandals.

"Hello, Lupe," she said. "Someone told me you were out here. Would you like to come in?"

Lupe shook her head.

"Oh, you needn't be shy," Dr. Johnson said. "You seem to be very interested in medicine. Wouldn't you like to talk? I enjoy talking to you."

"It's getting late. It will soon be time for supper," Lupe said, and she ran toward home.

The next time Lupe saw the doctor was in the grocery store. Lupe had gone there to get some flour for her mother to make *tortillas*. A few of the village men were standing around inside the store talking, and Dr. Johnson was talking to Mr. Baca, the owner of the store. She held a can of something in her hand and read the label.

"I don't know," she said. "I do hate to use this. I don't like these poisons, but the bugs are getting to be a problem at the clinic, and I've got to do something."

"You could try calabasilla leaves," Lupe blurted out.

"What?" Dr. Johnson turned around with a surprised look on her face. "Oh, hello, Lupe. I didn't know you were here. Seems you're always surprising me."

"I can bring you some leaves," Lupe said.

"Some what?"

"Leaves. Dried calabasilla leaves. If you sprinkle them around the edges of the rooms, it will keep the bugs out."

"Really? I've never heard of that."

"Works good," said one of the villagers in the store.

"Sure does," said another.

"Lupe knows," said still another.

"I'll bring you some tomorrow," Lupe said. She put the money for the flour on the counter.

Dr. Johnson had a funny look on her face, as if she didn't believe the dried leaves would work. But if she said anything in reply, Lupe didn't hear her over the noise of Mr. Baca's ancient cash register.

Lupe walked out of the store as quickly as she could. She would go back to the clinic just one more time, to deliver the leaves, she told herself. That would be her way of repaying Dr. Johnson for fixing her scraped knee. Every time Lupe thought of that incident, her heart sank. What would Manuelita think if she ever found out that her friend, Lupe Montano, had been the new doctor's first patient!

The day after Lupe had seen Dr. Johnson in the grocery store, she and Maria went down to the sandy spot to play hopscotch. While they were playing, Lupe heard a familiar cawing sound and looked up to see Manuelita walking through the brush toward her house. Noche, as usual, was perched on her shoulder.

"Manuelita's back!" Lupe said to Maria.

"Are you going to stop the game and go see her?" Maria asked, sounding disappointed.

"No," Lupe said. She stood on one foot and bent to pick up her pebble, then hopped to the end of the series of squares and circles. No matter how glad she was that Manuelita was back, she knew she wouldn't have time to go see her. It was getting late, and she still had to take the calabasilla leaves to Dr. Johnson.

When the game was over, Lupe went home to get the dried leaves. Maybe the doctor doesn't really want them, Lupe thought. She certainly didn't act as if she were anxious to have them. But Lupe was anxious to show her how well they worked, so she went to the pantry and took a jar from a shelf. It was too bad, she thought, to take the last jar, and one that Manuelita had given her family at that. But Lupe knew she could always gather the leaves from the sprawling gourd vines herself, when she found the time. They grew profusely along the river and on the mesas.

Lupe told her mother what she planned to do before she left the house.

"That's very nice of you, Lupe," Mama said. "It is always a good thing to welcome a newcomer with a gift."

When Lupe reached the clinic, there was no one in the waiting room. She was glad, because she didn't want to meet anyone who might say something to Manuelita about her being there. That was one of the reasons she had waited so late to come. She was surprised, however, to hear voices coming from inside the office as she walked up to the door. Two men's voices were speaking rapidly and excitedly in Spanish, and Dr. Johnson's voice was pleading in English.

"Please, please," Lupe could hear the doctor say. "Speak more slowly. My Spanish is not good. I can't understand you."

Lupe walked quietly into the office and saw Uncle Pedro and Cousin Josefa's husband.

"Lupe!" Dr. Johnson said as soon as she saw her. "Maybe you can help. Something's wrong, and these two men are too excited to speak English. Can you tell me what they're saying?"

Lupe questioned the men, who answered her in breathless Spanish. Lupe turned to the doctor.

"It is my Cousin Josefa," she said. "They want you to go to her."

"Josefa?" The doctor seemed puzzled for a moment. "Oh, yes. The woman who is going to have a baby!"

"Yes," Lupe answered. "The men say it is time. They are very excited."

"Of course," Dr. Johnson said with a little laugh. She gathered some things into a bag. "I daresay your cousin will be much calmer than these men are. Come on," she said, motioning to the men. "I'll have to go to her. I have no more facilities for delivering a baby in this temporary building than you'll have at home."

The men followed the doctor out to her car, and everyone, including Lupe, got in. No one seemed to expect Lupe not to go, and she certainly hated to miss the excitement. Maybe it was a good thing she did go along, she decided. She was the one who had to direct the doctor to her cousin's house.

When they arrived, the men took the doctor by one arm each and led her into the house. Cousin Josefa was in a bedroom near the front of the house. Lupe waited in the living room with the family while Dr. Johnson went inside to examine Josefa. That was exactly as Manuelita would have done it, Lupe thought. Soon, the doctor came out of the bedroom. She was smiling.

"Josefa is in fine shape," she said. "It will only be a short wait before the baby is born."

In a little while, Dr. Johnson went back to see about Josefa again.

"She is doing very well," the doctor said when she came out of the bedroom, but her smile had vanished.

The next time the doctor went in to examine Josefa, she looked even more concerned when she emerged.

"She is doing very well, physically, but something is making her unhappy. She kept asking for someone named Manuelita. Is that her friend? Or perhaps her mother?"

"I can get her for you," Lupe said quickly.

"No! No!" said Uncle Pedro.

Just then Josefa called from the bedroom. "Is that Lupe's voice I hear? Let me talk to her."

Dr. Johnson turned to Lupe. "I don't know," she said. "You really shouldn't. . . . "

"Lupe! Let me talk to Lupe!" Josefa called.

Dr. Johnson's brow wrinkled into a frown. She bit her lower lip. "Oh . . . very well," she said. "Come with me." She led Lupe into the bedroom.

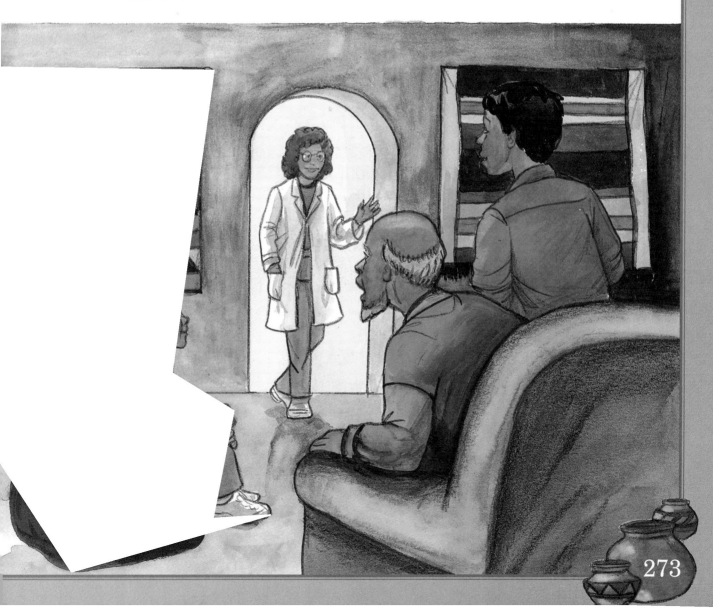

"Lupe!" Cousin Josefa said happily from her bed. "The little curandera." She spoke to Lupe softly in Spanish. She could also speak English very well, as could her husband and Uncle Pedro, but, as with most people in the village, when she was excited or had something very special to say, Spanish seemed the best language for saying it. When she had finished talking, Lupe turned to the doctor and told her what Cousin Josefa had said.

"Josefa says that her father, my Uncle Pedro, wants you to help with the baby because he thinks only the new modern ways are good enough for his grandchild, but she says she wants Manuelita to help her, because she is sure Manuelita knows all the right things to do. She says perhaps you know too, but with Manuelita she is certain."

"Who is Manuelita?"

"A curandera."

"A what?"

"A curandera."

"Oh, yes," Dr. Johnson said. "I seem to remember . . . a healer. Yes, I've heard of them. Sometimes associated with witchcraft, aren't they? No, I won't have that."

"Manuelita does not use witchcraft," Lupe said. "That is what Uncle Pedro thinks, but it is not true."

Josefa, who had heard the conversation, began to cry.

"Now, now," Dr. Johnson said, turning to her. "You mustn't be upset."

"I have seen that your kind of medicine is good, but Manuelita's is good, too," Lupe said. "Perhaps you could learn from each other."

"Superstition has no place at a time like this," Dr. Johnson answered.

Josefa was crying softly. "Lupe is a little curandera," she said in English. "She knows the good way."

"You, a curandera?" Dr. Johnson asked. "What does she mean?"

"Manuelita has taught me many things," Lupe said.

"Well, I guess that explains your interest in medicine. Lupe, I welcome you to come talk to me as often as we can find the time. Maybe I can undo some of the wrong ideas you may have."

"But——" Lupe started to protest.

"We don't have time to talk about it now," Dr. Johnson said. "Josefa's baby will be here soon."

Josefa was still crying. "It is only that I want the best for my baby," she said.

"The best thing for you and the baby both is for you to remain calm."

But Josefa only cried harder and clutched at her middle. Dr. Johnson spoke as if she were talking to herself. "She was handling it so well at first."

"Maybe Manuelita could at least help you," Lupe insisted.

"I could use some help," Dr. Johnson said, "but a curandera . . . no." She looked again at the sobbing Josefa.

Dr. Johnson's not going to give in, Lupe thought. She watched as the doctor fussed around Josefa, holding her hand and talking to her softly.

"It's not going to be a good birth if she is so upset," Dr. Johnson said to no one in particular. She turned to Lupe. "Maybe it wouldn't hurt anything for this, this Manuelita just to be here. . . . All right, Lupe, go get the healer."

Lupe ran from the house as fast as she could, still clutching the jar of calabasilla leaves she had forgotten to give to Dr. Johnson. She was breathless when she reached Manuelita's house, but she managed to explain what was happening and to tell her that the new doctor was with Josefa.

She was surprised at how fast the elderly Manuelita was able to get to Josefa's home. Noche flew ahead, circling and returning to Manuelita and Lupe, screeching and talking nonsense. As usual, he was left outside when Manuelita entered the patient's house.

Uncle Pedro stood up to protest as soon as he saw Manuelita.

"What's she doing here?" he asked.

Manuelita did not look at Uncle Pedro, or speak to him. He tried to follow Manuelita into the bedroom, but she slammed the door in his face, almost catching his nose between the door and the wall.

Lupe could hear many noises coming from the bedroom while she waited in the living room with the men.

"The doctor will see that it is done right," Uncle Pedro said, over and over again, to reassure both himself and his son-in-law.

The noises in the bedroom ceased. The silence was brief, interrupted by the cry of a tiny voice. Both of the men jumped from their seats. Dr. Johnson opened the bedroom door.

"Josefa and her husband have a beautiful daughter," she said.

She let everyone go into the room for a few minutes to see Josefa. First Josefa's husband went in, then Uncle Pedro, then Lupe.

Lupe saw Cousin Josefa holding her baby and smiling, and Manuelita standing beside them. Dr. Johnson walked toward Manuelita and held out her hand.

"Thank you," the doctor said. "I . . . I guess I have a lot to learn."

Manuelita took the doctor's hand in hers, but she did not speak.

# The New Doctor

## Meet the Author

**Paula G. Paul** grew up on a farm in Texas. Her family had no electricity, no television, no telephone, and the nearest town was 30 miles away. She was very good at entertaining herself and finding things that interested her. Even today she says, *"I am a person who is never bored."*

Ms. Paul says this about writing: *"The most important thing a person needs to be a good writer is perseverance, because it's not always easy. Even though we may be full of stories, what we need to learn is how to tell those stories in a way that is easy to read and understand. You have to learn how to tell the story. You have to believe in yourself."*

## Meet the Illustrator

**Roberta Collier-Morales** admits that while she loved to draw, dance, sing, and play the piano as a child, she had a difficult time learning to read. She encourages others who are having problems with certain subjects to seek help and talk about what they are experiencing. *"The important thing is not to give up on yourself,"* she says. Ms. Collier-Morales studied art at Colorado State University, graduating in 1971. She is currently continuing her education in graduate school and lives with her two children, her parents, and her pets.

# Theme Connections

## Think About It

In this story, problems arise when two sides cannot or will not try to understand each other. Here are some things for you to think about.

- Both Manuelita in this story and Maisie's mother in "The Bridge Dancers" practice traditional medicine. What similarities do you see in these women and their backgrounds? What differences do you see?
- If you were Dr. Johnson starting a clinic in the area Manuelita served, how would you handle the situation? Explain.
- Is it possible for traditional and modern medicine to both be accepted forms of treatment? Explain.

Look at the Concept/Question Board to see if there are questions you can answer now. If the selection or your discussion raised new questions about medicine, post them on the Concept/Question Board. Maybe the next selection will help answer the questions.

## Record Ideas

What was your reaction to the conflict in this story? Write your ideas and thoughts in your Writing Journal.

## Research Ideas

- Research some of the plants used in herbal medicines. Where do they grow? Do any grow around your home? How do they grow? What plant parts are used in medicines? What ailments are they used to treat?
- What can be learned about health and illness from different kinds of traditional medicine? Make a list of illnesses Manuelita could treat that were mentioned in both this selection and in "The Bridge Dancers." Find out more about treating these conditions traditionally and with modern medicine.

# FINE Art

*Louis Pasteur in His Lab.* 1885. **Albert Edelfelt.** Oil on canvas. Musée d'Orsay, Paris, France. Photo: ©Erich Lessing/Art Resource, NY.

*Medicine, hexagonal relief from the Campanile.* Mid-13th century. **Andrea Pisano.** Museo dell'Opera del Duomo, Florence, Italy. Photo: Nicolo Orsi Battaglini/Art Resource, NY.

*The Shop of the Druggist.* **Pietro Longhi.**
Accademia, Venice, Italy. Photo: SCALA/Photo
Resource, NY.

*Interior of a Hospital with Doctors Tending
Patients.* **Gaddiano Manuscript 247.** Biblioteca
Laurenziana, Florence, Italy. Photo: SCALA/Art
Resource, NY.

# Susan La Flesche Picotte

from *Homeward the Arrow's Flight*
by Marion Marsh Brown
*illustrated by Diane Magnuson*

*Susan La Flesche Picotte was the first female
Native-American doctor in the United States.
After completing medical school she returned to her
home and began work as the doctor at the
reservation school. In this excerpt, her first
weeks as not only the school doctor but doctor
for the whole reservation are told.*

Susan wrote a letter of application on the very night that she told Rosalie, her sister, she wanted the position of reservation physician. Then she waited anxiously for a reply.

At last the letter arrived. She tore it open eagerly. "Well, finally," she sighed. She carried it to the kitchen where her mother was preparing supper. "I got the appointment," she said. "I don't get any more money though."

Her mother looked up. "So much more work and no more pay?" she asked.

"That's what the letter says: 'As there are no funds available except for your present salary as physician to the government school, we will be unable to pay any additional monies for your additional services as reservation physician.' Well, anyway I have the title. Now to see what I can do with it."

That same night, the first snow of the winter fell. Susan was soon inundated with a siege of colds, grippe, and pneumonia. It was as if the first snowstorm had been a signal for winter illnesses to attack.

She had laid her plans carefully before entering into her new contract to do two jobs for the price of one. She would spend mornings at the school and make house calls in the afternoons. The only problem, she soon discovered, was that there weren't enough hours in the day.

"I don't know why babies always want to get born in the wee hours of the morning," she said to Rosalie, stopping at her sister's house one day on the way to school. She'd been up since midnight and would not have time to go home before she was due at school. She was glad to have a place to clean up and get a cup of coffee.

"Sue, you can't go on this way," her sister said. "You'll ruin your own health."

Susan sighed. "But what else can I do, Ro?"

It was a bad winter, one of the worst Nebraska had seen in many a year. The north wind blew in icy gusts, finding its way around poorly fitted window frames and under ill-hung doors into the Omahas' houses. Many of the houses were getting old and they had not been kept in repair.

When Susan rode up to one in which a windowpane was out, the hole stuffed carelessly with old rags, anger flared in her. Inside, she knew, lay a child on the verge of pneumonia.

"Tom," she said, when she had entered, "there's no excuse for that." She pointed at the window. "When you get your next allotment, buy a piece of glass and some putty and replace that pane."

"You just like Iron Eye," he said, and Susan detected resentment in his tone. "Always try to tell us how to live."

Susan bit her tongue and went about her task of examining the sick child. Was it hopeless, she wondered, trying to teach them? But her father, Iron Eye, had never given up.

One morning when she started for school, the wind was particularly vicious. Reluctantly, she turned Pie, her horse, into it. When they reached the schoolgrounds, she put him immediately into the shed that was provided for bad days. As she turned to the schoolhouse, she noted that the sky looked ominous. It took all her strength to wrench the door open against the wind. "I think we're going to get snow," she called to Marguerite as she entered.

Marguerite turned back, and Susan saw the worried look on her face. "Oh, dear, I hope not. Charlie's sick again. He has an awful cough, Sue, and he was so hot last night, I know he has fever. And he went out to look after the stock this morning. I was hoping you could go by and see him this afternoon."

"Of course I'll go. A little snow won't stop me," Susan replied with a smile, hoping to cheer her sister.

As the morning progressed, the wind howled and the snow grew heavier. In a moment's lull in her work, Susan glanced out the window and discovered she could no longer see the row of trees that formed a windbreak for the school building. She felt a little tug of concern. Some of the children lived quite a distance from school. Perhaps they should be getting home.

It wasn't long until the teachers were consulting her. "Do you think we should dismiss school? If it keeps this up . . ."

"I think it would be wise to get the children on their way. It certainly isn't getting any better."

So an early dismissal was agreed upon.

Susan was helping the teachers bundle the children into coats and overshoes, tying mufflers over mouths and noses, and giving instruction to the older ones to keep tight hold of the hands of younger brothers and sisters, when the outside door burst open and a man stumbled in. He was so caked with snow that at first she didn't recognize him.

$$7 \atop +3 \qquad 7 \atop +5 \qquad 8 \atop +1 \qquad 8 \atop +3 \qquad 4 \atop +5 \qquad 17 \atop +1$$

*Six apples plus eight apples =*

"Dr. Susan!" he cried. "Come quick! My Minnie . . ."

"Oh, it's you, Joe," she said. "Has your wife started labor?"

He nodded. "But she's bad, Doctor. Not like before."

"Come on in and warm up, then go home and put lots of water on the stove to heat. I'll be along shortly."

Joe didn't linger. As soon as the children were on their way and she had straightened up her office, Susan sought out Marguerite. "I'll have to wait to see Charlie until after I deliver Minnie Whitefeather's baby. Joe says she's having a bad time, so I may be late."

"All right. Be sure to bundle up," Marguerite said. "It looks like the storm's getting worse."

"That I will. I always come prepared!" Susan assured her. She pulled her stocking cap down over her ears and donned the heavy wool mittens her mother had knit for her.

"I hope you'll be all right," Marguerite said. "It's a long way over there."

"Don't worry. You can depend on Pie!" Susan waved a cheery good bye and plunged out into the storm. She had to fight her way to the shed. Already drifts were piling high. "I hope the children are all safely home by now," she thought. Her pony was nervous. "Good old Pie," she said, patting the sleek neck as she mounted. "When you were a young one and we went racing across the hills, you didn't think you were going to have to plow through all kinds of weather with me when you grew old, did you?"

The Whitefeathers lived on the northernmost edge of the reservation. Susan turned Pie onto the road, and he plodded into the storm. "Good boy!" she said encouragingly. But she couldn't hear her words above the violent shrieking of the wind. Nor, shortly, could she tell whether they were following the road; she could only trust Pie.

It seemed to her that the storm grew worse by the minute. Suddenly Pie stopped, turning his head back as if asking Susan what he should do. She tried to wipe the caked snow from her eyes to see what was wrong and found that her fingers were stiff. But she saw Pie's problem. A huge drift lay across their path. "We'll have to go around it, Pie." She pulled him to the left until they reached a point where the drift tapered off. Pie moved around it, and Susan thought, "Now can we find the road again—if we were on the road?" She pulled on the right rein. But she couldn't tell whether they were going north, for now the storm seemed to be swirling around them from all directions.

Soon another drift blocked their way. But this time Pie wallowed through with a strange, swimming motion. How did he know he could get through that one and not the

other, she wondered. Suddenly, having maneuvered the drift, the pony stopped.

"Get up, Pie! We have to go on!" she urged. He did not move. She slapped the stiff reins on his neck, but to no avail. She tried kicking his sides with feet she discovered were numb. "We'll freeze to death! Go on!" Still Pie refused to move.

At length she dismounted. If she could walk on her numb feet, perhaps she could lead him. Stumbling, she made her way to Pie's head.

Then she saw, and she caught her breath in terror. For Pie stood with his head directly over a bundle in the snow—a bundle that she knew instantly was a child.

"Oh, my!" she cried. She lifted the bundle into her arms. It was a boy, one of the little ones they had turned out of school to find his way home. "What were we thinking of?" Susan railed at herself. "Jimmy! Jimmy!" she cried, shaking the child. She scooped the snow off his eyelids. He stirred, and then his eyelids lifted. "Jimmy! It's Dr. Sue. You were asleep, Jimmy. You have to wake up now." She hoisted him in front of her on the pony, and holding him close to give him warmth from her body, she beat on his arms.

The minute she was back in the saddle, Pie moved on. "Pie! Bless you. You probably saved Jimmy's life."

As Pie pressed on, she continued to talk to Jimmy, working on him as she talked—rubbing his hands, cradling his face against her. "We have to warm up your nose," she told him. He began to cry. "You mustn't cry. Your tears will make cakes of ice!"

She strained her eyes ahead, but she could see nothing against the driving snow. She had no idea how long they had been in this frozen white nightmare. Surely if they were going in the right direction, they should have reached the Whitefeathers' by now. "Pie's going to take us to where it's nice and warm," she soothed Jimmy. And to herself she said, "If he doesn't, it's the end of all of us, you and me and him. And maybe Minnie Whitefeather too."

She tried to keep the child awake, finding to her consternation that she herself was growing drowsy.

knew that to go to sleep was a sure way to freeze to death.

She must have dozed briefly, for she started when Pie suddenly stopped. She roused herself to urge him on. "Get up, Pie! We can't stop now! We have Jimmy!" She beat on his sides, but he refused to move. The snow had again caked her eyelids, and she pawed at it with unfeeling fists. She supposed they'd come to another drift Pie couldn't manipulate.

As she blinked hard to see, she was suddenly aware of a sound that was not born of the storm. Pie had whinnied. She even felt the ripple of his neck. What did it mean?

Then she saw! They were by the side of a building, sheltered from the wind. It was a barn!

"Pie! Pie! You did it!" she cried.

As she tried stiffly to dismount with Jimmy, strong arms were supporting her. It was Joe.

"We—so glad you here, Dr. Sue. We afraid you not make it."

"So was I," Susan said. "Please take care of Pie. We wouldn't be here except for him."

Susan did not get to Marguerite and Charlie's that night, but she did deliver a baby girl. Nor did she get to her sister's home for the two days following, for the storm raged on fiercely through the night, wrapping the reservation in a tight white cocoon that could not be penetrated. There was no way to return Jimmy to his home or to let his parents know that he was safe. Susan agonized over this, but there was nothing she could do.

There were two other Whitefeather children, and Susan noticed that they came to have their hands washed before a meal. She noticed other things: the family's clothes were clean, and the blankets on the beds were clean. "You're doing well with your little family," she praised Minnie.

Minnie smiled. "Remember the summer you were home from school when you rode around trying to teach people to wash their hands before meals? We believed you— about germs and all."

"And now you're teaching your children," Susan said approvingly. "That's fine, Minnie. It means the upcoming generation will have a better time of it."

When Susan eventually got to Charlie and Marguerite's, she found Charlie in bed in the throes of a violent chill. His cough was frightening. She left medicine and tried to reassure him, but as her sister saw her to the door, she shook her head. "His lungs are weak, Marg. You'll have to be very careful."

"I know," Marguerite replied quietly.

"I wonder if she does know," Susan thought as she went on her snow-clogged way. There was no question in her mind that he was consumptive, as his mother had been. She had been doing all she could for him, but she feared he would be one she couldn't save—gentle Charlie, who was so good to everyone, especially to Marguerite.

By early February he was continuously confined to his bed, and there was no more Susan could do. Marguerite had to take leave from her teaching position to care for him.

He died quietly, as he had lived, just before the month was out.

"I thought maybe if he could make it till spring . . ." Marguerite said desolately.

"Why don't you come home and live with Mother and me?" Susan suggested. "It would be too lonely for you here."

They sent word of Charlie's death to his family in Dakota, and his brother, Henry, came. "We wanted the family represented at his funeral," he said.

"Henry's different," Susan remarked to Rosalie. "Yet he reminds me of Charlie. Sort of a gayer edition!"

"He's more worldly," Rosalie said.

Susan smiled. It took Ro, who had had less "worldly" exposure than the rest of them, to see straight through to the point. "Yes, you're right," she agreed.

With the funeral over, Henry gone, and Marguerite back in the home where she and Susan had grown up, things settled down into a certain routine. Marguerite went back to teaching, and Susan went on with her doctoring.

"It's like the old days," Susan said one evening when she and Marguerite and their mother sat down to supper.

"Only different," Marguerite said.

"Yes," Susan agreed, thinking of how it had been when Nicomi, her grandmother, and Iron Eye and Rosalie had been at that table. "Things don't stay the same, do they, Mother?"

Her mother shook her head.

"We have to learn to accept change. That was one of the things Father tried to teach us long ago."

Spring was late that year, but when it finally came, it was so beautiful that Susan at times thought she couldn't bear it. Sometimes when she was riding home from a call in early evening, she would dismount and let Pie graze while she gazed down on the greening willows that fringed the river like a band of chartreuse lace. If it weren't too late, she would venture into the woods to look for violets and Dutchman's-breeches and the shy lady's-slipper.

"What a wonderful place to live," she thought. And more and more she could see that her work was bearing fruit. "I'm not accomplishing miracles," she told Rosalie one evening, "but I am beginning to see some of the results of better hygiene and health habits. And we're losing fewer babies and fewer cases to infection."

"You don't need to convince me," Rosalie said. "I can see it on every hand. How pleased Father would be."

# The Story of Susan La Flesche Picotte

## Meet the Author

**Marion Marsh Brown** was born in Brownville, Nebraska. She grew up on a farm where she said she *"never lacked for interesting things to do."* She enjoyed riding horses, picking berries, climbing trees, swinging in a hammock, playing with the animals, and building tunnels through the haystack. Of all those things, reading was her favorite.

*"I had to find out if I could write things too,"* she said. *"When I was ten, I saw my first story in print. It was on the children's page of the Sunday newspaper. I still remember the prize I received for it—a book called* I Wonder Why. *That was a good book for me to have, for I wondered 'Why?' about a lot of things then, and still do today, and I believe this is an essential trait for an author to have."*

## Meet the Illustrator

**Diane Magnuson** has a degree in art and German and a master's degree in illustration. She has lived in many different places, but she began illustrating historical stories and Native American legends while living in the Northwest United States for 15 years. While they lived there, her husband was involved with Native American tribes, and his involvement in political issues brought many visitors and interesting discussions to their home.

Ms. Magnuson says of her work, *"Once the research and compositions are organized, I love to disappear into the painting, to become part of it and know the people in it."*

# Theme Connections

## Think About It

People didn't always want to accept the changes that Dr. Picotte suggested. Sometimes change is difficult for people. Here are some things for you to think about.

- What were some of Susan La Flesche Picotte's accomplishments? Which do you consider to be the greatest one?
- Susan La Flesche Picotte did more than treat illness. She tried to improve the health conditions in her community. What changes was she trying to make? Why were they important?
- What differences and similarities do you see between Dr. Picotte and a modern doctor?

Look at the Concept/Question Board to see if there are any questions that you can answer now. If the selection or your discussion raised new questions about medicine, post them on the Concept/Question Board.

## Record Ideas

Record any new information you remember and your reactions to this selection in your Writing Journal.

## Research Ideas

- Public health agencies do many different things to improve community health conditions. Explore what these are, and investigate questions that interest you.
- People are healthier and live longer today than they did a century ago. What has made this possible?

# Shadow of a Bull

from *Shadow of a Bull*
by Maia Wojciechowska
illustrated by Ramon Gonzalez Vicente

*Manolo Olivar is the son of Spain's most famous bullfighter. Although his father died after being gored by a bull, Manolo is expected to follow in his father's footsteps. Everyone expects him to be Spain's next great bullfighter. But, Manolo lacks* afición, *or desire. He knows he does not want to be a bullfighter, but he is unsure what he will become. One day while visiting a fighter who has been gored, Manolo realizes what he must do.*

On the way to the gored boy's house, Manolo listened to them tell about how bulls can hurt.

"The horn enters cleanly. If only it would exit that way. But either the man or the bull or both are moving at the time of the goring, and that's why the wounds are so bad."

"The horn tears into the body, ripping the muscles."

"And there is always the danger of infections. The horn is dirty, and before penicillin, it was almost always either amputation or death from infection."

"As far as the bullfighters are concerned, penicillin was the greatest invention of man."

"Poor devils! When they get gored in small towns there is never a doctor."

"And that's where they usually get gored."

"Even here in Arcangel, there is only one doctor who will touch a horn wound. Only one who knows anything about them, and he is getting old; when he is gone, maybe there will be no one."

"If you must get gored, be sure it's in Madrid."

"In Madrid they have a dozen doctors."

"I knew a doctor once who got rich on bullfighters. And then one day, he took his money and went to a printer and had millions of pamphlets printed. The pamphlet was called 'Stop the National Suicide'."

The men had never said anything before about pain, the amount of it a bullfighter had to endure. And Manolo had never thought before about pain. Now, listening to them, he thought that it would not be of dying that he would be afraid, but of the pain.

'El Magnifico,' lying on sheets that were as white as his face, looked to be about eighteen. The first thing Manolo noticed about him were his lips. They were pale, but he had been biting them. Drops of blood stood out in a row marking the places where the lips had been bitten. Without anyone having to tell him, Manolo knew that the boy was in great pain.

When they came into the room, 'El Magnifico' tried to hide his bloodied lips behind his hand. He did not say much, just that he was feeling all right. When he looked away from the men, he did not look out of the window, but at the wall where there was nothing but a stain. And when he turned back to them, his lips had fresh drops of blood on them.

"I was terrible," the boy said, trying to smile.

"You weren't there long enough," one of the men said, "to let us see how terrible."

"I would have been very bad," 'El Magnifico' said, fighting back tears.

"You might have been fine. It was a good little bull. You were too brave, and sometimes it's silly to be too brave. You don't let the people see how long your courage is, just how wide."

The boy's mother came into the room. She was a big woman with strong hands and a face that seemed carved from a rock.

"The doctor's coming," she said, not looking at the men but looking hard at her son. She waited for him to say something. He said nothing.

"Hasn't the doctor seen you?" one of the men asked.

The boy moaned and coughed to hide the sound of his pain.

"He was out of town," the mother said, looking now at them for the first time, her eyes accusing.

"The barber then, he took care of you in the infirmary?" the man wanted to know.

"Yes," the boy said, "he did the best he could."

"The barber's only a barber," the mother said angrily and left the room.

"He's in great pain. He doesn't show it, but he is in great pain," one of the men said softly to Manolo.

"It never hurts right after the goring. But when it starts hurting, it hurts for a long time," another added.

They heard footsteps outside. They were slow in reaching the door. The doctor was an old man. He shuffled when he moved from the door to the boy's bed. He looked tired. A shock of white hair fell listlessly over his wrinkled forehead as he bent over the boy.

"*Olá*. How goes it?" He smiled at the boy and passed his hand over the boy's forehead. He did not greet the men, nor did he seem to notice Manolo.

"The barber cleaned it and bound it," the boy said feebly, raising on his elbow and then falling back on the pillows.

The men began to move towards the door.

"Stay," the doctor said not looking at them, taking the light blanket off the boy's bed and reaching into his bag for a pair of scissors. "I want Olivar's son to see what a goring looks like. Come here," he commanded, and Manolo moved closer, his heart beating loudly. "Look!" The doctor had cut the bandage and the gauze and pushed them aside. A flamelike, jagged tear, a foot long and several inches deep ran straight from the boy's knee up his thigh. Manolo caught his breath at the sight of it. "Bend down and look here," the doctor said. "Those are puddles of clotted blood. There are about seven different reds beside, all meat. The muscles are purple. The wound is always narrower where the horn enters and wider where it exits. Not pretty, is it?"

Manolo moved away feeling sick; but the voice of the doctor brought him back, and with its sound, so sure and matter of fact, the feeling of sickness left him.

"I'll need your help," the doctor said, still looking at but not touching the wound. "It's a good, clean tear. The barber did his work well. He took the dirt out and cut off the dead flesh."

When he walked to the washbasin, his feet were not shuffling. He scrubbed his hands thoroughly. He put the surgical towel on the bedside table, took some instruments from the bag, put them on the towel, and then reached for a package of gauze pads and put those next to the instruments.

"Hand me those gloves," the doctor said to Manolo, pointing to a pair of rubber gloves in a plastic bag. "Let's see how good a nurse you'd make," he added. "Open the bag without touching the gloves and hold them out to me." Manolo did as he was told.

Manolo watched fascinated, as the doctor's hands moved surely into the wound, exploring the inside of it.

"The horn stayed away from the thigh bone," the doctor said. "He's a lucky boy. What I am doing now," he explained, speaking to Manolo, "is looking for foreign matter: dirt, pieces of horn, or dead flesh. But as I said before, the barber did a very good job of taking all those out of the wound. There is no danger of infection."

The admiration Manolo felt for the doctor was growing with each word, each gesture. No sound came from the pillow. With tenderness the doctor looked away from his work.

"He's fainted," he said with a smile. "Get the bottle of ammonia," he motioned towards the bag, "and a wad of cotton. Moisten the cotton and hold it under his nose."

Again Manolo did as he was told. When he opened the bottle, the strong odor of ammonia invaded his nostrils and spread through the entire room. He bent over the boy and passed the cotton directly under his nose. The boy coughed and jerked his head away.

"Good!" the doctor said watching, "he's not in shock. Just passed out from the pain. He will be fine. What he's got is one of those lucky gorings." His gloved hand pointed to the straight line of the torn flesh. "It's as good a goring as you could wish for, if you were wishing for a good goring. The bad ones are the ones that tear in and change angles. Those are the messy ones, the dangerous ones. But I don't want you to think this is nothing. It's the result of foolishness. Not the beast's, but the man's. The beast is led into the ring, the man walks in himself."

The doctor finished cleaning the wound and then stitched the flesh. Manolo was not asked again to help. He wished the doctor would once more request him to do something. As he watched the magic way the man's hands brought torn flesh together, he thought that what the doctor was doing and had done was the most noble thing a man could do. To bring health back to the sick, to cure the wounded, save the dying. This was what a man should do with his life; this, and not killing bulls.

"It will heal nicely. This one will. But then what?" The doctor walked to the wash basin and began washing the blood off the rubber gloves. "He," he pointed with his head to the boy, "will go on trying to prove that he can be good. And he isn't. But it's a point of honor with him. He will go on trying, and they will give him chances to try because he's fearless and the paying customers know that they will see a goring each time 'El Magnifico' is on the bill. But the tragedy is not that some people are bloodthirsty. The tragedy is that boys like him know of nothing else they want to do. I've grown old looking at wasted lives."

He walked over to Manolo and patted his head.

"The world is a big place," he said gently.

He seemed to want to add something, but he said nothing more. Silently, he put his instruments back in the bag and snapped it shut.

"Thank you for your help," the doctor said to Manolo, but his voice was tired now. The shuffle came back into his steps, and before he reached the door, he looked once again like a very old, very tired, man.

Walking back with the men, Manolo decided that if only he did not have to be a bullfighter he would be a doctor. He wanted to learn how to stop the pain and how to stop the fear of it. If only his father had been a doctor, a famous one, a bullfighters' doctor, then they would expect him to be one, too. And he would study hard. It would not be easy, but he would be learning to do something worthwhile.

He wondered if he were to tell the men, the six men, what he thought he would like to be, if they would listen to him. He looked at the men walking alongside him, talking once again about what they always talked about; and he knew that he would not tell them. He was who he was. A bullfighter's and not a doctor's son, and they expected him to be like his father. Maybe someday he could tell them.

# Shadow of a Bull

## Meet the Author

**Maia Wojciechowska** has lived an exciting, adventurous life. She was born in Warsaw, Poland, and came to the United States in 1942. Her jobs have included such things as detective, motorcycle racer, bullfighter, tennis player, and translator. In one year, she had 72 jobs!

Many of Ms. Wojciechowska's books are about the problem of trying to fit in with the rest of the world, but not fitting so well that you lose yourself. She said, "Shadow of a Bull *was mostly about pride and being locked in. . . . The word* pride *encompasses so much—honor and dignity and self-esteem. That sort of pride sometimes—most of the time—makes life harder than it needs to be. But without pride life is less.*"

## Meet the Illustrator

**Ramon Gonzalez Vicente** was born in Salamanca, Spain, where he also studied art. Later, he went to Barcelona, which is also in Spain, where he worked as an artistic director and illustrator for a publisher. Mr. Vicente has also illustrated for publishers in the United States, England, Germany, and other European countries. He has created illustrations for many books, but his favorite subject is children's literature.

# Theme Connections

## Think About It

For Manolo, the decision to become a doctor was a very difficult one. Here are some things for you to think about.

- Did reading this story convince you that you might like to be a doctor? Explain.
- Although most sports are not as dangerous as bullfighting, serious injuries are common in many sports. What, if anything, should be done about this? Support your answer.

Look at the Concept/Question Board to see if there are questions that you can answer now. If the selection or your discussion raised new questions about medicine, post them on the Concept/Question Board.

## Record Ideas

Did you learn anything from Manolo's situation that might help you in the future? What were your feelings about Manolo's situation? Record your thoughts in your Writing Journal.

## Research Ideas

- Becoming a doctor requires a great commitment. What education is involved? When must one start preparing? What special talents are needed?
- Sports medicine is a specialized field. Find out more about sports injuries and sports medicine. Investigate questions that interest you.

# Bibliography

## Bodyworks
**by Pete Sanders and Steve Myers.**
There are few marvels that equal the human body. Learn about your body and how each part functions to make a working whole.
Average

## Healing Warrior: A Story About Sister Elizabeth Kenny
**by Emily Crofford.** Sister Elizabeth Kenny became known all over the world after she developed a successful way to treat and rehabilitate polio patients.
Average

## The History News: Medicine
**by Phil Gates.** Extra! Extra! Read all about it! The development, discoveries, and disasters of medicine all appear in the newspaper headlines.
Average

## The Human Body
**by Steve Parker.** Have you ever wondered what your life would be like if you had no skin? Be the first in your class to know why blood is red, how the heart pumps, and other fascinating workings of the human body.
Easy

## Marie Curie and Her Daughter Irène

by **Rosalynd Pflaum.**   Marie and Irene are not your average mother and daughter team. Their scientific discoveries still impact medical treatments today.

Advanced

## North American Indian Medicine People

by **Karen Liptak.**   Learn the many different ways that Native American medicine people heal the sick.

Advanced

## Out of Darkness: The Story of Louis Braille

by **Russell Freedman.**   Discover how a 15-year-old boy invented a system using dots on paper that made it possible for blind people to read.

Average

## The Trouble with Tuck

by **Theodore Taylor.**   If you thought that seeing-eye companion dogs are only for people, think again! When a young girl's beloved Labrador retriever goes blind, she teaches the dog how to trust and follow a seeing-eye companion dog.

Easy

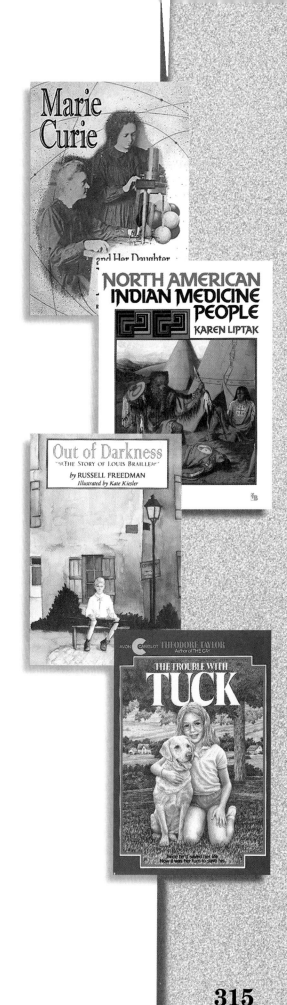

S ometimes life gets very hard. People live through natural disasters and wars and terrible accidents. How do they do it? What helps them to survive all of these things?

I'm still having diffi
finding fresh water
Luckily there have
been enough wild
berries to hold me
over. I don't kno
what to do for
now that the s
have run out. E
cloudy tonight
Maybe it wil
tomorrow.
I can't giv
after all, I've

# Island of the Blue Dolphins

from *Island of the Blue Dolphins*
by Scott O'Dell
*illustrated by Russ Walks*

*With the help of the white man's ship, Karana's
people have fled their island to escape the Aleuts,
their enemies. In their haste Karana is left behind on
the island. As she waits for a ship to return to rescue
her, Karana's hopes begin to fade.*

Summer is the best time on the Island of the Blue
Dolphins. The sun is warm then and the winds
blow milder out of the west, sometimes out of
the south.

It was during these days that the ship might return
and now I spent most of my time on the rock, looking
out from the high headland into the east, toward the
country where my people had gone, across the sea
that was never-ending.

Once while I watched I saw a small object which I
took to be the ship, but a stream of water rose from it
and I knew that it was a whale spouting. During those
summer days I saw nothing else.

The first storm of winter ended my hopes. If the white men's ship were coming for me it would have come during the time of good weather. Now I would have to wait until winter was gone, maybe longer.

The thought of being alone on the island while so many suns rose from the sea and went slowly back into the sea filled my heart with loneliness. I had not felt so lonely before because I was sure that the ship would return as Matasaip had said it would. Now my hopes were dead. Now I was really alone. I could not eat much, nor could I sleep without dreaming terrible dreams.

The storm blew out of the north, sending big waves against the island and winds so strong that I was unable to stay on the rock. I moved my bed to the foot of the rock and for protection kept a fire going throughout the night. I slept there five times. The first night the dogs came and stood outside the ring made by the fire. I killed three of them with arrows, but not the leader, and they did not come again.

On the sixth day, when the storm had ended, I went to the place where the canoes had been hidden, and let myself down over the cliff. This part of the shore was sheltered from the wind and I found the canoes just as they had been left. The dried food was still good, but the water was stale, so I went back to the spring and filled a fresh basket.

I had decided during the days of the storm, when I had given up hope of seeing the ship, that I would take one of the canoes and go to the country that lay toward the east. I remembered how Kimki, before he had gone, had asked the advice of his ancestors who had lived many ages in the past, who had come to the island from that country, and likewise the advice of Zuma, the medicine man who held power over the wind and the seas. But these things I could not do, for Zuma had been killed by the Aleuts, and in all my life I had never been able to speak with the dead, though many times I had tried.

Yet I cannot say that I was really afraid as I stood there on the shore. I knew that my ancestors had crossed the sea in their canoes, coming from that place which lay beyond. Kimki, too had crossed the sea. I was not nearly so skilled with a canoe as these men, but I must say that whatever might befall me on the endless waters did not trouble me. It meant far less than the thought of staying on the island alone, without a home or companions, pursued by wild dogs, where everything reminded me of those who were dead and those who had gone away.

Of the four canoes stored there against the cliff, I chose the smallest, which was still very heavy because it could carry six people. The task that faced me was to push it down the rocky shore and into the water, a distance four or five times its length.

This I did by first removing all the large rocks in front of the canoe. I then filled in all these holes with pebbles and along this path laid down long strips of kelp, making a slippery bed. The shore was steep and once I got the canoe to move with its own weight, it slid down the path and into the water.

The sun was in the west when I left the shore. The sea was calm behind the high cliffs. Using the two-bladed paddle I quickly skirted the south part of the island. As I reached the sandspit the wind struck. I was paddling from the back of the canoe because you can go faster kneeling there, but I could not handle it in the wind.

Kneeling in the middle of the canoe, I paddled hard and did not pause until I had gone through the tides that run fast around the sandspit. There were many small waves and I was soon wet, but as I came out from behind the spit the spray lessened and the waves grew long and rolling. Though it would have been easier to go the way they slanted, this would have taken me in the wrong direction. I therefore kept them on my left hand, as well as the island, which grew smaller and smaller, behind me.

At dusk I looked back. The Island of the Blue Dolphins had disappeared. This was the first time that I felt afraid.

There were only hills and valleys of water around me now. When I was in a valley I could see nothing and when the canoe rose out of it, only the ocean stretching away and away.

Night fell and I drank from the basket. The water cooled my throat.

The sea was black and there was no difference between it and the sky. The waves made no sound among themselves, only faint noises as they went under the canoe or struck against it. Sometimes the noises seemed angry and at other times like people laughing. I was not hungry because of my fear.

The first star made me feel less afraid. It came out low in the sky and it was in front of me, toward the east. Other stars began to appear all around, but it was this one I kept my gaze upon. It was in the figure that we call a serpent, a star which shone green and which I knew. Now and then it was hidden by mist, yet it always came out brightly again.

Without this star I would have been lost, for the waves never changed. They came always from the same direction and in a manner that kept pushing me away from the place I wanted to reach. For this reason the canoe made a path in the black water like a snake. But somehow I kept moving toward the star which shone in the east.

This star rose high and then I kept the North Star on my left hand, the one we call "the star that does not move." The wind grew quiet. Since it always died down when the night was half over, I knew how long I had been traveling and how far away the dawn was.

About this time I found that the canoe was leaking. Before dark I had emptied one of the baskets in which food was stored and used it to dip out the water that came over the sides. The water that now moved around my knees was not from the waves.

I stopped paddling and worked with the basket until the bottom of the canoe was almost dry. Then I searched around, feeling in the dark along the smooth planks, and found the place near the bow where the water was seeping through a crack as long as my hand and the width of a finger. Most of the time it was out of the sea, but it leaked whenever the canoe dipped forward in the waves.

The places between the planks were filled with black pitch which we gather along the shore. Lacking this, I tore a piece of fiber from my skirt and pressed it into the crack, which held back the water.

Dawn broke in a clear sky and as the sun came out of the waves I saw that it was far off on my left. During the night I had drifted south of the place I wished to go, so I changed my direction and paddled along the path made by the rising sun.

There was no wind on this morning and the long waves went quietly under the canoe. I therefore moved faster than during the night.

I was very tired, but more hopeful than I had been since I left the island. If the good weather did not change I would cover many leagues before dark. Another night and another day might bring me within sight of the shore toward which I was going.

Not long after dawn, while I was thinking of this strange place and what it would look like, the canoe began to leak again. This crack was between the same planks, but was a larger one and close to where I was kneeling.

The fiber I tore from my skirt and pushed into the crack held back most of the water which seeped in whenever the canoe rose and fell with the waves. Yet I could see that the planks were weak from one end to the other, probably from the canoe being stored so long in the sun, and that they might open along their whole length if the waves grew rougher.

It was suddenly clear to me that it was dangerous to go on. The voyage would take two more days, perhaps longer. By turning back to the island I would not have nearly so far to travel.

Still I could not make up my mind to do so. The sea was calm and I had come far. The thought of turning back after all this labor was more than I could bear. Even greater was the thought of the deserted island I would return to, of living there alone and forgotten. For how many suns and how many moons?

The canoe drifted idly on the calm sea while these thoughts went over and over in my mind, but when I saw the water seeping through the crack again, I picked up the paddle. There was no choice except to turn back toward the island.

I knew that only by the best of fortune would I ever reach it.

The wind did not blow until the sun was overhead. Before that time I covered a good distance, pausing only when it was necessary to dip water from the canoe. With the wind I went more slowly and had to stop more often because of the water spilling over the sides, but the leak did not grow worse.

This was my first good fortune. The next was when a swarm of dolphins appeared. They came swimming out of the west, but as they saw the canoe they turned around in a great circle and began to follow me. They swam up slowly and so close that I could see their eyes, which are large and the color of the ocean. Then they swam on ahead of the canoe, crossing back and forth in front of it, diving in and out, as if they were weaving a piece of cloth with their broad snouts.

Dolphins are animals of good omen. It made me happy to have them swimming around the canoe, and though my hands had begun to bleed from the chafing of the paddle, just watching them made me forget the pain. I was very lonely before they appeared, but now I felt that I had friends with me and did not feel the same.

The blue dolphins left me shortly before dusk. They left as quickly as they had come, going on into the west, but for a long time I could see the last of the sun shining on them. After night fell I could still see them in my thoughts and it was because of this that I kept on paddling when I wanted to lie down and sleep.

More than anything, it was the blue dolphins that took me back home.

Fog came with the night, yet from time to time I could see the star that stands high in the west, the red star called Magat which is part of the figure that looks like a crawfish and is known by that name. The crack in the planks grew wider so I had to stop often to fill it with fiber and to dip out the water.

The night was very long, longer than the night before. Twice I dozed kneeling there in the canoe, though I was more afraid than I had ever been. But the morning broke clear and in front of me lay the dim line of the island like a great fish sunning itself on the sea.

I reached it before the sun was high, the sandspit and its tides that bore me into the shore. My legs were stiff from kneeling and as the canoe struck the sand I fell when I rose to climb out. I crawled through the shallow water and up the beach. There I lay for a long time, hugging the sand in happiness.

I was too tired to think of the wild dogs. Soon I fell asleep.

# Island of the Blue Dolphins

## Meet the Author

**Scott O'Dell** was born in Los Angeles, California. His father was a railroad worker and so the family moved often, but they always lived by the ocean. One of their homes was on Rattlesnake Island, near Los Angeles, where they lived in a house on stilts. From the house they could watch sailing ships go by.

*Island of the Blue Dolphins* is based on a true story. The rest of it, according to Mr. O'Dell, *"came directly from the memory of the years I lived at Rattlesnake Island and San Pedro. From the days when with the other boys of my age I voyaged out on summer mornings in search of the world."*

# Theme Connections

## Think About It

- Imagine that you are alone on an island. How would you feel?
- What would you do first on the island? Would you look for food? Shelter? Help?

## Record Ideas

Did you like "Island of the Blue Dolphins"? Did you dislike it? Write your thoughts and feelings about the story in your Writing Journal.

## Write a Letter

Pretend you are Karana. You have found a bottle on the island. Write a short letter, which you will place in the sealed bottle and send across the water, asking for help. Your hope is that someone will read the letter and rescue you.

# Arctic Explorer:

## THE STORY OF MATTHEW HENSON

by Jeri Ferris

*Matthew Henson was the first African-American explorer to reach the North Pole. Before he made this famous expedition, he went on several trips to the arctic region with Robert Peary. During these trips, Henson learned the skills that would make him a great explorer. In this excerpt about Henson's first arctic journey, Peary has planned an expedition to North Greenland. He has little money and has asked Henson to help him without pay. Henson is eager to go. His job is to learn the survival techniques used by the Eskimos as they face the harsh, cold climate.*

Members of the 1891–1892 North Greenland Expedition (left to right): Cook, Henson, Astrup, Verhoeff, and Gibson. Josephine and Robert Peary are standing in back. John Verhoeff fell into a crevasse in Greenland in the spring of 1892 while exploring and was never seen again.

"It was in June 1891," Matt Henson wrote, "that I started on my first trip to the Arctic regions, as a member of what was known as the 'North Greenland Expedition.' "

America's newspapers predicted disaster. A small group of inexperienced men trying to survive in a frozen place that had killed better men than they? Impossible. Then reporters learned that a woman was going too—the new Mrs. Peary. "Now we know he's crazy!" said one newspaper about Peary.

Josephine Peary listed the expedition members in her diary: "Dr. Cook, Mr. Gibson, Mr. Astrup, Mr. Verhoeff, and Mr. Peary's faithful attendant in his surveying labors in Nicaragua, Matt Henson." The ship, *Kite*, was so small that the people and supplies barely fit. They were going to be gone for a year and a half, so they needed a lot of supplies. There were crates of food (enough for two and a half years, just to be safe) and cans of pemmican, the beef-fat-raisin mixture that the men and dogs would eat while crossing the ice cap. There were skis and snowshoes, guns and ammunition, sledges, woolen clothing, a stove, pots and pans, and camera equipment. And after the last one hundred tons of coal was piled on deck, Matt could hardly find a place to set down his hammer and nails while he put together the wood frame for their base camp house.

The *Kite* plunged on through the Atlantic, rolling and pitching and sending all the passengers except Henson and Peary to bed seasick. On June 21 Matt saw Greenland for the first time. Its steep, wild cliffs rose straight up from the icy water. As the *Kite* steamed north through Baffin Bay, Matt saw hundreds of icebergs——gleaming blue and white chunks of ice——from the size of small sailboats to that of enormous floating mountains. In the valleys of Greenland, Matt saw glaciers that looked like thick flowing cream, frozen into white walls. And on the very top of Greenland lay the five hundred thousand square miles of silent ice cap. Matt couldn't see it yet, but he knew it was there, waiting.

The *Kite* pushed farther north into heavy ice, which floated on the water like a field of white. There were splits and cracks in the ice, and through these cracks (called leads) the *Kite* forced its way. Sometimes there were no leads at all, and the captain would shout for more steam power. The *Kite* would dash forward and smash against the ice. Sometimes the ice would break, and the ship could continue. Sometimes it would not, and the ship would have to back up and try another way.

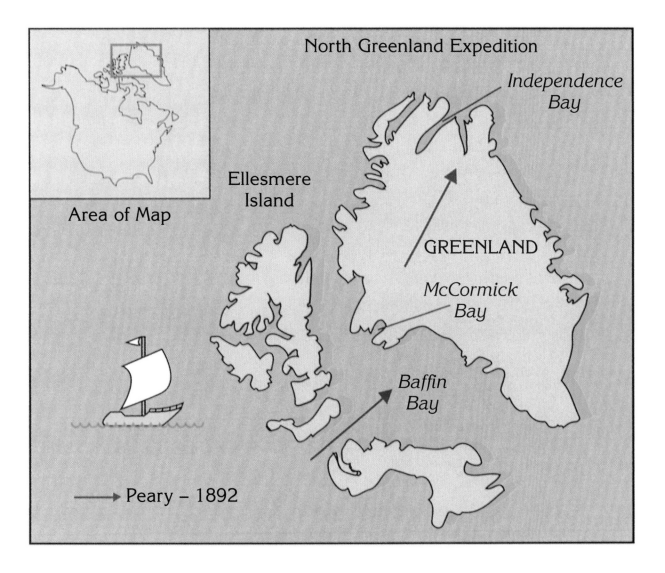

North Greenland Expedition

Area of Map

Ellesmere Island

*Independence Bay*

GREENLAND

*McCormick Bay*

*Baffin Bay*

→ Peary – 1892

When the *Kite* was as far north as it could go, it dropped anchor in McCormick Bay, Greenland, and the crew unloaded the supplies. At the end of July, the *Kite* sailed for home, leaving Matthew Henson, the Pearys, and the other four men to survive the arctic winter. (A ship could only get through the ice in the summer, and the long, dangerous trip over the ice cap could only be started in the spring with the return of 24-hour sunlight. So the men had to wait in the Arctic through the dark winter months.) Matt immediately began putting up their sturdy house, to make sure they would survive.

August 8 was Matt's 25th birthday. For the first time in his life, he had a birthday celebration. Mrs. Peary fixed mock turtle soup, stew of little auk (a bird the size of a robin) with green peas, eider duck, baked beans, corn, tomatoes, and apricot pie. Matt remembered the delight of that dinner long after the tin plates were put away. Seventeen years later he said of that day, "To have a party given in my honor touched me deeply."

While Matt finished the small wooden house, the other men went to find Eskimos to join their group. (The men would have to use sign language because none of them spoke Eskimo.) Peary needed Eskimo men to help hunt polar bears and seals and walruses and reindeer and caribou and foxes for furs and meat. He needed Eskimo women to chew the furs and sew them into pants and coats. The thickest wool coat from home would be useless in the Arctic; they had to have clothing made of the same fur that kept the arctic animals warm. In exchange for their work, Peary would give the Eskimos pots and pans, needles, tools, and other useful items.

On August 18 the men returned, and with them were four Eskimos: Ikwa, his wife, and their two children. The Eskimos walked slowly up to Matt and the Pearys. Then Ikwa stepped closer to Matt and looked at him carefully. His brown face lit up with excitement as he spoke rapidly to Matt in Eskimo.

Matt shook his head and tried to explain that he didn't understand, but Ikwa kept talking. Finally Ikwa took Matt's arm, pointed at the black man's skin, and said, "Inuit, Inuit!" Then Matt understood. "Inuit" must be what the Eskimos called themselves. Ikwa thought Matt was another Eskimo because he had brown skin, just as the Eskimos did. Matt looked down at the short fur-covered man, who smelled like seals and whale blubber. He looked into Ikwa's shining black eyes and smiled. From that moment on, the Eskimos called Matt "Miy Paluk," which meant "dear little Matthew," and they loved him as a brother.

In September Matt, Ikwa, Dr. Cook, and the Pearys took the whale boat and went to find more Eskimos. They didn't find a single Eskimo, but they did find some unfriendly walruses.

It began when the boat got mixed up with some walruses (250 walruses, Mrs. Peary said) that were peacefully fishing for clams. One after another the startled walruses poked their heads out of the water, spitting out clam shells and flashing their white tusks. Then an angry bull walrus roared, "Ook, ook, ook!" and headed straight for the boat. The water foamed and boiled as the rest of the herd charged right behind him, speeding along like torpedoes, all roaring their battle cry and tossing their enormous gray wrinkled heads. Matt and the others knew that just one tusk through the bottom of the boat would be the end of them. Ikwa shouted and pounded on the boat to frighten the walruses away, but the walruses weren't frightened. In fact, they were so angry that they tossed the boat up and down furiously. Bracing their feet, Matt and the others fired their guns while Mrs. Peary sat in the bottom of the boat and reloaded the guns as fast as she could. At last the walruses gave up. They dove to the bottom and disappeared, leaving a shaky group of explorers in a still-rocking boat.

Matt and an Eskimo friend return from a hunting expedition.

By the end of September, the dull red sun dipped lower each day and finally did not appear at all over the southern horizon. Every day was like a glorious sunset, with a golden, crimson glow on the mountain peaks. Then there was no sunset anymore, just one long night.

By the time the sun was gone, not to return until February, several Eskimo families were living at the camp in stone igloos (snow igloos were only used when the Eskimos traveled, following the animals whose meat and skins they needed).

That winter the men hunted by the full moon—by moonlight so bright that the blue-white ice sparkled. Peary planned for the spring trek. Astrup taught the men to ski. Gibson studied bird and animal life. Verhoeff studied rocks. Dr. Cook *wanted* to study the Eskimos by taking their pictures and measuring their bodies, but the Eskimos refused to let him near them. Finally Matt realized that they were afraid Dr. Cook would go home and make new people from the Eskimo pattern. So Matt got Ikwa to understand, and Dr. Cook got his pictures.

Meanwhile Matt studied with his Eskimo teachers. They taught him easy things, such as never to stand with his feet apart or his elbows sticking out, as this let the cold air close to his body. They taught him hard things, such as how to speak Eskimo. Matt learned, for example, that there is no Eskimo word for "hole." Instead there is a different word for "hole in igloo" or "hole in bear skin" or anything that has a hole.

Matt learned why the Eskimos smelled like walruses and seals and blubber—they *ate* walruses and seals and blubber. They also ate reindeer and polar bears and little auks. They ate the meat while it was still warm and raw and bloody; they ate it when it was frozen solid, by chipping off bite-size chunks; and sometimes they boiled it. They never ate carrots or beans or potatoes or apples or chocolate. In the Arctic the only food came from the bodies of the animals that lived there.

Matt learned how the Eskimos made the skin of a polar bear into clothing. Once the Eskimo man had killed the bear and removed its skin and scraped it as clean as he could, it was up to the Eskimo woman to finish. She had to chew the skin until all the fat was gone and it was completely soft. All day long the woman would fold the skin (with the fur folded inside), chew back and forth along the fold, make a new fold, and continue. It took two days to chew one skin. Then the woman would rest her jaws

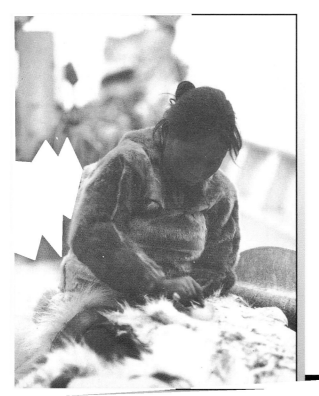

An Eskimo woman makes clothing out of an animal skin. Old Eskimo women had very short, flat teeth from chewing skins to soften them.

for one day before beginning on another skin. After the skin had dried, she would cut it up and sew it into a coat or pants. Her needle was made of bone, her thread was made from animal sinew, and her stitches had to be very, very tiny so not a whisper of wind could get through.

For Matt's winter outfit the women made stockings of arctic hare fur, tall boots of sealskin, polar bear fur pants, a shirt made of 150 auk skins (with the feathers next to Matt's skin), a reindeer fur jacket, and a white fox fur hood that went around his face. His mittens were made of bearskin with the fur inside.

But the piercing, freezing cold, colder than the inside of a freezer, took Matt's breath away, and the howling arctic wind drove needles of snow and ice

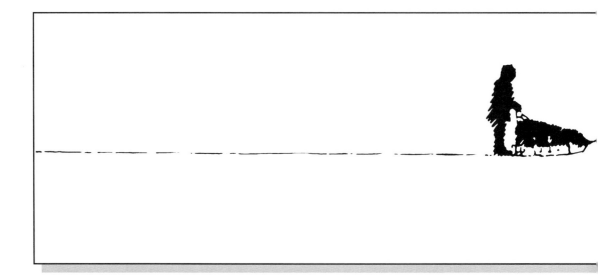

into his face. Even his new sealskin boots felt terrible, until he learned to stand still after he put them on in the morning. Then they would freeze instantly to the shape of his feet and wouldn't hurt as much.

Once Matt had his fur clothes, cold or not, he was ready to learn how to drive a sledge pulled by the 80- to 120-pound Eskimo dogs. But first, if a dog got loose, Matt had to catch him. He would drop a piece of frozen meat on the snow and dive on top of the dog as the animal snatched the meat. Then he would "grab the nearest thing grabbable—ear, leg, or bunch of hair," slip the harness over the dog's head, push his front legs through, and tie him to a rock. Finally, Matt said, he would lick his dog bites.

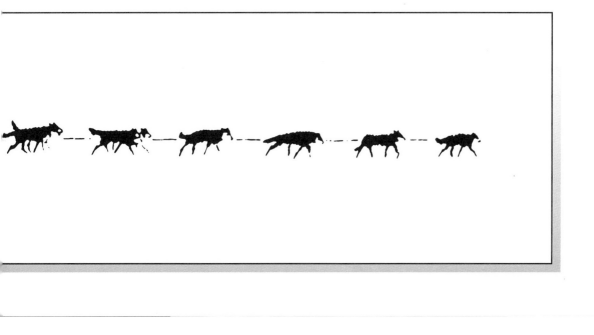

When the dogs were in their traces, they spread out like a fan in front of the sledge. The king dog, who was the strongest and fiercest, led the way in the center. Matt had watched the Eskimos drive the dogs and knew that they didn't use the 30-foot sealskin whip *on* the dogs but *over* the dogs. The trick was to make the whip curl out and crack like a gunshot right over the ear of the dog who needed it. Matt stepped up behind the sledge, shouted, "Huk, huk!" and tried to crack the whip. The dogs sat down. Matt tried again and again and again. After many tries and lots of help from his Eskimo teachers, Matt learned how to snap the whip over the dogs' ears and make them start off at a trot. Then he had to learn how to turn them (they didn't have reins, as horses do), how to make them stop, and how to make them jump over open water with the sledge flying behind.

Dogs in their traces fan out in front of a sledge. If they are starving, the dogs will eat their traces, which are made of sealskin.

There were five Eskimo families at the camp, each family with its own stone igloo. At first it was hard for Matt to go inside the igloos because of their peculiar smell (Eskimos did not take baths, and Matt said that an Eskimo mother cleans her baby just as a mother cat cleans her kittens), but he didn't want to be rude, so he got used to it. Opposite the entrance hole was the bed platform, built of stone and covered with furs. At the end of the bed platform was a small stone lamp, filled with whale blubber for fuel, with moss for the wick. This little lamp was the light and heat and cook stove for the igloo. The Eskimo woman melted snow in a small pan over the lamp and used the water for cooking meat and for drinking. (Eskimos did not build fires for heating or cooking.)

Matt learned how to build a snow igloo when he hunted with the Eskimos, far from the camp. Two Eskimos could cut 50 to 60 snow blocks (each block 6-by-18-by-24-inches) with their long snow knives and build a whole igloo in just one hour. One man would stand in the center and place the blocks in an 8-foot circle around himself. He would add more blocks, spiraling round and round, with the blocks closing in on the center as they rose higher, until the top snow blocks fit perfectly against each other and the roof was complete. Then they would carry in the furs and cooking lamp, and it was home. A chunk of frozen meat, perhaps part of a walrus, might be in the middle of the igloo, handy for snacks and also a good footstool. Snow igloos even had shelves. The Eskimos would stick their snowshoes into the wall and lay mittens on the snowshoe shelf to dry.

The dogs, who had thick silver gray or white hair with a layer of short fine fur underneath to keep them warm, lived outdoors in the snow. They would curl into balls, cover their noses with their tails, and sleep, warm as muffins (usually), even if it was –50°F.

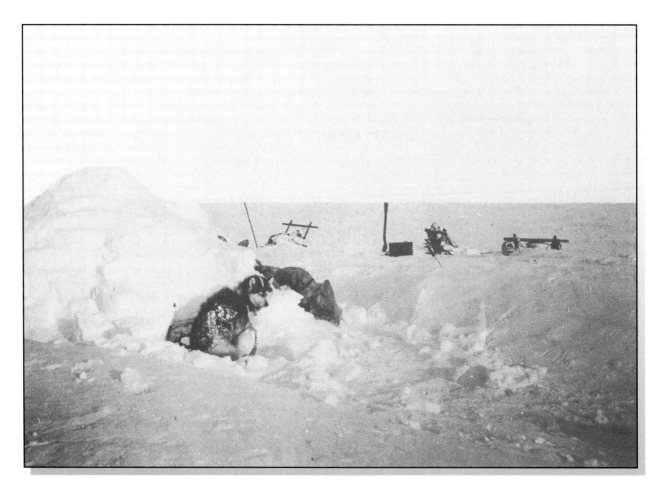

Dogs curl up outside Peary's igloo.

During the full moons Matt and the Eskimos hunted reindeer and arctic hares. The large pure white hares themselves could not be seen against the white snow, only their black shadows. They were like an army of frozen or leaping ghosts. And in the deep blackness of the arctic night, Matt saw hundreds of shooting stars, so thick and close they seemed to burst like rockets. While he watched the stars, the Eskimos explained that what Matt called the Big Dipper was really seven reindeer eating grass, and the constellation he called the Pleiades was really a team of dogs chasing a polar bear.

The Eskimos had no tables or chairs, no books or paper or writing, no money or bills to pay, no king or chief, no doctors or dentists, no schools or churches, no laws, and no wars. They needed shelter from the cold, strong dogs to pull their sledges, and animals they could hunt for furs and meat. Several families usually lived close together to help each other. If one man killed a walrus, he would share it with everyone. Perhaps in a few days another man would kill a bear or a reindeer; then that man would share it too.

Meanwhile in the wooden house, there was more to eat than raw meat, and there was a new cook. Mrs. Peary wrote in her diary for November 17, 1891, "Matt got supper tonight, and will from now until May 1 prepare all the meals under my supervision." For Christmas, at least, he didn't do all the cooking. Mrs. Peary prepared arctic hare pie with green peas, reindeer with cranberry sauce, corn and tomatoes, plum pudding, and apricot pie. Then, wrote Mrs. Peary, "Matt cleared everything away."

In February the sun returned. For days and days before it actually appeared, the sky was a magnificent dawn of pink, blue, crimson, and deep yellow, with rosy clouds. Then the sun appeared in the south at noon, but just for a moment the first day. Each day it rose a little higher. The crystal clear water in the bay was deep blue, and the air was thick with the sound of wings and songs as thousands of birds swooped and swarmed over the water and up the cliffs.

But Greenland's ice cap, which Matt intended to cross, was a frozen, lifeless desert of snow and howling wind and glaciers and deep crevasses. Even though Matt always covered the inside of his boots with soft dried moss for insulation, his heel froze when he helped haul boxes of pemmican and biscuits up to the ice cap in the beginning of May. (Freezing is very serious. The blood stops moving in the frozen part, and the skin and muscle can soon die.) Matt, who was the best at driving the dogs and at speaking the Eskimo language, had planned to be one of the first men to cross the ice cap, but Peary sent him back to the base camp. There were three reasons: one was the frozen heel; another was that someone had to protect Mrs. Peary at the camp; and the third was that Peary believed an explorer should have a college education in order to know what to do in an emergency.

During the short summer, while the others were gone, Matt went hunting so everyone would have plenty of fresh meat; he learned more of the Eskimo language; his foot healed; and he protected Mrs. Peary from danger.

In the end only Peary and Astrup actually crossed the ice cap. All the others turned back. The Eskimos, who feared Kokoyah, the evil spirit of the ice cap, refused to go at all. Peary did discover a large bay at the northeast corner of Greenland, which he named Independence Bay, but he did not find out if there was a way to get to the North Pole by land. He would have to try again. He asked Matt to come along again too.

# Arctic Explorer:

## THE STORY OF MATTHEW HENSON

## Meet the Author

**Jeri Ferris** grew up on a small Nebraska farm, with her own horse at home and a library nearby. She once said she had *"the ideal writer's childhood."*

Ms. Ferris taught for several years. When she realized how hard it was to find biographies of great and brave people, she began writing them herself. *"My goal is to make these determined men and women inescapably alive, to make their deeds inescapably real, and to plant the seeds of similar determination and self-confidence in the children who read about them. My goal is that children, no matter their ethnic and social backgrounds and despite the obstacles, will say to themselves, 'I, too, can make a difference.'"*

# Theme Connections

## Think About It

Sit with a small group of your classmates and talk about "Arctic Explorer: The Story of Matthew Henson."

- What problems did Matthew face when trying to survive?
- What did it take for Matthew to survive in this new world?

## Record Ideas

Like Matthew Henson, you have just arrived in the cold, harsh climate of the Arctic. What would your first thoughts be? Write those first thoughts in your Writing Journal.

## Interview with Matthew Henson

If you were given the opportunity to interview Matthew Henson about his expedition in North Greenland, what would you ask him? Write several questions that you would ask him about his expedition and the survival techniques he learned in the Arctic.

# Nachito's Teachings

from *Medicine Walk*
by Ardath Mayhar
illustrated by Sandy Rabinowitz

*While flying over the Arizona desert, Burr's father
has a heart attack. The plane crashes, leaving Burr forty
miles from safety and alone. Burr must now rely on his
will to survive and the teachings of Nachito, an Apache
who is the foreman of Burr's father's ranch, to
overcome the dangers of the desert.*

The morning was hot. The air was thin and dry,
and the sky was a faded blue that promised no
relief. I had spent my first night huddled into a
cranny in another of the dry washes that seemed to
runnel the whole area. I'd been as cold then as I was
hot now. There was a hogback ridge ahead. Again.
I seemed to do nothing but climb up or climb down.
I was one huge ache. A dry ache.

I was thirsty . . . more than thirsty, but I didn't touch
the bottle. I wasn't doing so well as those old Apache,
not by a long shot. I had taken a mouthful early and
maybe traveled a mile before I swallowed it. I hoped to
do a lot better next time. Just having water in my mouth
helped a lot. It held off the raspy-throated feeling; my
tongue didn't behave like used sandpaper. At noon I'd
take another mouthful and try to hold it half the
afternoon. If I could.

I was moving carefully, checking for loose rock and unexpected holes. A broken leg would mean the end, out here. Still, even that was getting to be automatic, and my mind kept wandering off, spinning strange notions.

Mom drifted out of a clump of rock up ahead. She was wearing the blue jumpsuit she liked best. In her hands was a glass of lemonade. "Hurry, Burr! It'll get warm before you drink it!" she was urging me. I could see her bronze hair moving in the breeze. Her bandana, stuck in her hip pocket, was fluttering, too.

351

I almost let go and ran to her, but I caught myself.
That wasn't here and now. That was the morning of
the awful day. I had run, then, grabbed the glass and
gulped down the liquid. She'd tousled my hair with
her strong fingers and said, "Want to go with me, old
chum? It's going to be an exciting show, and your Aunt
Martha would love for you to be there."

I had grinned at her over the rim of the glass. "Yeah.
I know how much she likes my comments on her
paintings. Thanks, Mom, but no thanks. I like pictures,
but I hate fine art. Or maybe I just don't like the kind of
people who go to things like that. I'd rather stay here
and go scavenging with Charlie."

She had laughed, that deep chuckle that always
made me feel good inside. "I don't really blame you. The
arty ones turn me off, too. But Martha would be hurt if I
didn't show up. Have fun, and don't get snakebit!"

I hadn't even kissed her goodbye. That still rankled,
deep down inside where nobody knew it but me. And
before she got to town a truck creamed her little
sports car.

I shook my head hard and came to, standing on the
rocky slope. I didn't need that kind of thing. I had to
keep my mind on what I was doing, not go wandering
around in a daze, daydreaming. That was a good way
to get killed, and I knew it all too well.

At noon I paused on top of a ridge. There was a stunted piñon growing there, and I thought of something Nachito had told me. I pulled a handful of the fragrant needles and tucked them into my pocket. One I put into my mouth and chewed. The acid taste made my mouth water, which was all to the good. A cheap drink, though not very satisfying. Still, it was enough to let me swallow a small pinch of raisins and half an apricot. I left the bottle untouched. It was a matter of pride, now.

I angled down the other side of the ridge. Its twin loomed ahead, and I groaned. All the relatives who had visited us had raved over the mountains in Arizona. It was sure and certain that they hadn't had to walk over them. Not only was it exhausting, but I was having trouble keeping directions straight in my head, what with all the going up and down and back and forth, finding passable places. I must have traveled twelve or fifteen miles since I set out, but I probably hadn't gone more than five miles east. If that.

I lucked into a game trail about halfway down the ridge. It meandered among the rocky ledges, but it was better than trying to find a way down the steep slope with no guide at all. I was stepping along, half in a dream again and fussing at myself about it, when I heard a buzzing rattle.

I froze. Where was it? I turned my eyeballs in their sockets, not moving anything else. Right to left. Back again. There! Up ahead, its dusty colors hiding it against the baked rock and dust of the trail, was a diamond-back. Its head was forward, forked tongue testing the air. Its tail was quivering furiously.

I hate snakes. I'm not exactly afraid of them; something in my inside just squirms when I see the way they move. But I was afraid of this one. To be bitten, out here alone, would be bad. Fatally bad.

Something popped into my mind. Charlie handled snakes. Live ones, rattlers and all. He had never been bitten. Nachito trained Charlie. I often overheard their conversations. What was it Nachito had told him? I could see the seamed, saddle-colored face, the narrow squinted eyes, as the old man oiled harness leather and talked, while we polished bits and stirrups.

"The snake, he is a part of the land. He is wise, in his own way, and he is dangerous, for he knows only his own way. A man knows more than a snake. He can cow a snake, if he doesn't smell of fear. A serpent knows one thing: a fearful man is dangerous to him. He will strike if he smells fear on you. But if you are not afraid . . . not a little bit . . . you can calm him. You can make him wonder, deep in that small, strange brain, what it is that you are and can do. And then you are the winner."

That had been something Nachito had worked out for himself, I thought, for none of the Apache hands seemed to know about it. But it sounded as if it might be true. Nachito usually knew what he was talking about.

I stared at the long, coiled shape. I made myself relax, muscle by muscle, without moving a peg. My nerves quit jumping and lay quiet. My breathing eased. My hands unclenched. The snake's head lowered to a point just above the first coil. The buzz changed its pitch.

The diamond-back wasn't a horrible-looking creature, once you thought about it. It was beautiful, in its own way. Strong and sleek, patterned in subdued colors just right for its world. And the poison; it was no worse than my own ability to pick up a stick and smash the creature flat.

I looked into the serpent's eyes. It lowered its head even more. I didn't blink, but set my will against that of the snake. I urged it with all my might to go on about its business among the rocks. The rattle rasped irritably.

Time crawled past. The sun moved slowly down toward the top of the ridge high above, though I didn't spare much thought for it. And at last the snake began uncoiling. It curled its head about as if looking for a direction. I willed harder than ever, sweat pouring off me—from the sun, now, not from fear. And the rattler slid away among the rocks.

My knees felt weak. My heart was pounding, but not with fear. I'd been working harder, those past minutes, than ever before in my life. And I'd won! A feeling of triumph swept over me. Nachito had been right! And I'd been able to use his words to make myself unafraid. If I could do this much, maybe I just might make it!

My head was light with relief when I went on. The trail eased down, into the cooler bowl of shadow that was the eastern slope of the ridge, safe now from the sun. I picked up my pace as the going grew easier.

I smelled water!

Between the ridge I'd just come down and the toes of the neighboring mesa ran a narrow valley. At its bottom there was a wide streambed with a trickle of water snaking down its middle. Cottonwoods were growing along the banks, and scrub and a few piñons lined its course.

I badly wanted to run the rest of the way. But I'd been walking over this kind of terrain for a while now. I knew the sort of trap it could set for a foot that wasn't very careful. I held myself back by main force, but I did fumble for the water bottle and drain it into my mouth.

Something inside me perked up to attention. "That was a foolish thing," it said to me, almost in a real voice. "What if the water down there is alky-water? What if it's polluted so you can't drink it? What'll you do then? And now you've spoiled your control. You'll have to start all over again."

It wasn't exactly me talking, way down there inside myself. It was partly Nachito's teachings, partly my listening to the tales the Apache hands told and to Charlie's family stories. This wasn't my own country. My kind had never had to face it, raw, the way the Apache had. But the Apache were human beings, no more, no less. What they could learn to do, surely I could—if I had the time left before a rattler or the sun or thirst got me. But I knew how lucky I was to have shared even a little of Charlie's training. It gave me a handle on things that I'd never have been able to work out for myself.

# Nachito's Teachings

## Meet the Author

**Ardath Mayhar** grew up in Texas on her family's dairy farm, which she took over when she was only 17. Her days were spent with *"the cows, the cruddy milking machines, the manure, the hay, the weather."* In the evenings, she studied languages and wrote poetry.

At the age of forty-three, Ms. Mayhar *"reformed."* She gave up the dairy farm and the poetry and took up yoga and novels. She said, *"I honestly believe that being upside down [yoga] stimulated my bursting forth into fantasy novels, short stories, and even a regular newspaper column."*

Ms. Mayhar writes something every day. If she gets bogged down in a story, she writes letters. When she travels, she misses writing at her typewriter.

## Meet the Illustrator

**Sandy Rabinowitz** was surrounded by art while growing up. Both her parents taught art, and the classes were often held in their home. As an adult, her first published work was a story of her father's she retold and illustrated, called *The Red Horse and the Bluebird.*

She is married to another artist and writer, Paul, and has three children. In addition, she cares for an assortment of animals including a horse, a pony, a basset hound, three cats and a bunny.

# Theme Connections

## Think About It

- How does Burr apply the teachings of Nachito to his predicament?
- What moments of triumph did Burr experience while in the desert?

## Record Ideas

What would you have felt like if you were Burr alone in the desert fighting to survive? Write about your thoughts and feelings in your Writing Journal.

## Write a Paragraph

Burr was stranded in a harsh, unfamiliar environment and was able to survive by using Nachito's teachings. Write a paragraph about how you think Burr will be a different person after his experience. What did he learn?

# McBroom and the Big Wind

Sid Fleischman
*illustrated by Walter Lorraine*

I can't deny it——it does get a mite windy out here on the prairie. Why, just last year a blow came ripping across our farm and carried off a pail of sweet milk. The next day it came back for the cow.

But that wasn't the howlin', scowlin', almighty *big* wind I aim to tell you about. That was just a common little prairie breeze. No account, really. Hardly worth bragging about.

It was the *big* wind that broke my leg. I don't expect you to believe that——yet. I'd best start with some smaller weather and work up to that bonebreaker.

I remember distinctly the first prairie wind that came scampering along after we bought our wonderful one-acre farm. My, that land is rich. Best topsoil in the country. There isn't a thing that won't grow in our rich topsoil, and fast as lightning.

The morning I'm talking about our oldest boys were helping me to shingle the roof. I had bought a keg of nails, but it turned out those nails were a whit short. We buried them in our wonderful topsoil and watered them down. In five or ten minutes those nails grew a full half-inch.

So there we were, up on the roof, hammering down shingles. There wasn't a cloud in the sky at first. The younger boys were shooting marbles all over the farm and the girls were jumping rope.

When I had pounded down the last shingle I said to myself, "Josh McBroom, that's a mighty stout roof. It'll last a hundred years."

Just then I felt a small draft on the back of my neck. A moment later one of the girls——it was Polly, as I recall——shouted up to me. "Pa," she said, "do jackrabbits have wings?"

I laughed. "No, Polly."

"Then how come there's a flock of jackrabbits flying over the house?"

I looked up. Mercy! Rabbits were flapping their ears across the sky in a perfect V formation, northbound. I knew then we were in for a slight blow.

"Run, everybody!" I shouted to the young'uns. I didn't want the wind picking them up by the ears. "Will*jill*hester*chester*peter*polly*tim*tom*mary*larry*and-little*clarinda*——in the house! Scamper!"

The clothesline was already beginning to whip around like a jump rope. My dear wife, Melissa, who had been baking a heap of biscuits, threw open the door. In we dashed and not a moment too soon. The wind was snapping at our heels like a pack of wolves. It aimed to barge right in and make itself at home! A prairie wind has no manners at all.

We slammed the door in its teeth. Now, the wind didn't take that politely. It rammed and battered at the door while all of us pushed and shoved to hold the door shut. My, it was a battle! How the house creaked and trembled!

"Push, my lambs!" I yelled. "Shove!"

At times the door planks bent like barrel staves. But we held that roaring wind out. When it saw there was no getting past us, the zephyr sneaked around the house to the back door. However, our oldest boy, Will, was too smart for it. He piled Mama's heap of fresh biscuits against the back door. My dear wife, Melissa, is a wonderful cook, but her biscuits *are* terribly heavy. They made a splendid door stop.

But what worried me most was our wondrous rich topsoil. That thieving wind was apt to make off with it, leaving us with a trifling hole in the ground.

"Shove, my lambs!" I said. "Push!"

The battle raged on for an hour. Finally the wind gave up butting its fool head against the door. With a great angry sigh it turned and whisked itself away, scattering fence pickets as it went.

We all took a deep breath and I opened the door a crack. Hardly a leaf now stirred on the ground. A bird began to twitter. I rushed outside to our poor one-acre farm.

Mercy! What I saw left me popeyed. "Melissa!" I shouted with glee. "Will*jill*hester*chester*peter*polly*-tim*tommarylarry*andlittle*clarinda*! Come here, my lambs! Look!"

We all gazed in wonder. Our topsoil was still there——every bit. Bless those youngsters! The boys had left their marbles all over the field, and the marbles had grown as large as boulders. There they sat, huge agates and sparkling glassies, holding down our precious topsoil.

But that rambunctious wind didn't leave empty-handed. It ripped off our new shingle roof. Pulled out the nails, too. We found out later the wind had shingled every gopher hole in the next county.

Now that was a strong draft. But it wasn't a *big* wind. Nothing like the kind that broke my leg. Still, that prairie gust was an education to me.

"Young'uns," I said, after we'd rolled those giant marbles down the hill. "The next uninvited breeze that comes along, we'll be ready for it. There are two sides to every flapjack. It appears to me the wind can be downright useful on our farm if we let it know who's boss."

The next gusty day that came along, we put it to work for us. I made a wind plow. I rigged a bedsheet and tackle to our old farm plow. Soon as a breeze sprung up I'd go tacking to and fro over the farm, plowing as I went. Our son Chester once plowed the entire farm in under three minutes.

On Thanksgiving morning Mama told the girls to pluck a large turkey for dinner. They didn't much like that chore, but a prairie gust arrived just in time. The girls stuck the turkey out the window. The wind plucked that turkey clean, pinfeathers and all.

Oh, we got downright glad to see a blow come along. The young'uns were always wanting to go out and play in the wind, but Mama was afraid they'd be carried off. So I made them wind shoes——made 'em out of heavy iron skillets. Out in the breeze those shoes felt light as feathers. The girls would jump rope with the clothesline. The wind spun the rope, of course.

Many a time I saw the youngsters put on their wind shoes and go clumping outside with a big tin funnel and all the empty bottles and jugs they could round up. They'd cork the containers jam full of prairie wind.

Then, come summer, when there wasn't a breath of air, they'd uncork a bottle or two of fresh winter wind and enjoy the cool breeze.

Of course, we had to windproof the farm every fall. We'd plant the field in buttercups. My, they were slippery——all that butter, I guess. The wind would slip and slide over the farm without being able to get a purchase on the topsoil. By then the boys and I had reshingled the roof. We used screws instead of nails.

Mercy! Then came the *big* wind!

It started out gently enough. There were a few jackrabbits and some crows flying backward through the air. Nothing out of the ordinary.

Of course the girls went outside to jump the clothesline and the boys got busy laying up bottles of wind for summer. Mama had just baked a batch of fresh biscuits. My, they did smell good! I ate a dozen or so hot out of the oven. And that turned out to be a terrible mistake.

Outside, the wind was picking up ground speed and scattering fence posts as it went.

"Will*jill*hester*chester*peter*polly*tim*tom*mary*larry*and-little*clarinda*!" I shouted. "Inside, my lambs! That wind is getting ornery!"

The young'uns came trooping in and pulled off their wind shoes. And not a moment too soon. The clothesline began to whip around so fast it seemed to disappear. Then we saw a hen house come flying through the air, with the hens still in it.

The sky was turning dark and mean. The wind came out of the far north, howling and shrieking and shaking the house. In the cupboard, cups chattered in their saucers.

Soon we noticed big balls of fur rolling along the prairie like tumbleweeds. Turned out they were timber wolves from up north. And then an old hollow log came spinning across the farm and split against my chopping stump. Out rolled a black bear, and was he in a temper! He had been trying to hibernate and didn't take kindly to being awakened. He gave out a roar and looked around for somebody to chase. He saw us at the windows and decided we would do.

The mere sight of him scared the young'uns and they huddled together, holding hands, near the fireplace.

I got down my shotgun and opened a window. That was a *mistake*! Two things happened at once. The bear was coming on and in my haste I forgot to calculate the direction of the wind. It came shrieking along the side of the house and when I poked the gunbarrel out the window, well, the wind bent it like an angle iron. That buckshot flew due south. I found out later it brought down a brace of ducks over Mexico.

But worse than that, when I threw open the window such a draft came in that our young'uns *were sucked up through the chimney*! Holding hands, they were carried away like a string of sausages.

Mama near fainted away. "My dear Melissa," I exclaimed. "Don't you worry! I'll get our young'uns back!"

I fetched a rope and rushed outside. I could see the young'uns up in the sky and blowing south.

I could also see the bear and he could see me. He gave a growl with a mouthful of teeth like rusty nails. He rose up on his hind legs and came toward me with his eyes glowing red as fire.

I didn't fancy tangling with that monster. I dodged around behind the clothesline. I kept one eye on the bear and the other on the young'uns. They were now flying over the county seat and looked hardly bigger than mayflies.

The bear charged toward me. The wind was spinning the clothesline so fast he couldn't see it. And he charged smack into it. My, didn't he begin to jump! He jumped red-hot pepper, only faster. He had got himself trapped inside the rope and couldn't jump out.

Of course, I didn't lose a moment. I began flapping my arms like a bird. That was such an enormous *big* wind I figured I could fly after the young'uns. The wind tugged and pulled at me, but it couldn't lift me an inch off the ground.

Tarnation! I had eaten too many biscuits. They were heavy as lead and weighed me down.

The young'uns were almost out of sight. I rushed to the barn for the wind plow. Once out in the breeze, the bedsheet filled with wind. Off I shot like a cannonball, plowing a deep furrow as I went.

Didn't I streak along, though! I was making better time than the young'uns. I kept my hands on the plow handles and steered around barns and farmhouses. I saw haystacks explode in the wind. If that wind got any stronger it wouldn't surprise me to see the sun blown off course. It would set in the south at high noon.

I plowed right along and gained rapidly on the young'uns. They were still holding hands and just clearing the tree tops. Before long I was within hailing distance.

"Be brave, my lambs!" I shouted. "Hold tight!"

I spurted after them until their shadows lay across my path. But the bedsheet was so swelled out with wind that I couldn't stop the plow. Before I could let go of the handles and jump off I had sailed far *ahead* of the young'uns.

I heaved the rope into the air. "Will*jill*hester*chester*-peter*polly*tim*tom*mary *larry*andlittle*clarinda*!" I shouted as they came flying overhead. "Hang on!"

Hester missed the rope, and Jill missed the rope, and so did Peter. But Will caught it. I had to dig my heels in the earth to hold them. And then I started back. The young'uns were too light for the wind. They hung in the air. I had to drag them home on the rope like balloons on a string.

Of course it took most of the day to shoulder my way back through the wind. It was a mighty struggle, I tell you! It was near suppertime when we saw our farmhouse ahead, and that black bear was still jumping rope!

I dragged the young'uns into the house. The rascals! They had had a jolly time flying through the air, and wanted to do it again! Mama put them to bed with their wind shoes on.

The wind blew all night, and the next morning that bear was still jumping rope. His tongue was hanging out and he had lost so much weight he was skin and bones.

Finally, about midmorning, the wind got tired of blowing one way, so it blew the other. We got to feeling sorry for that bear and cut him loose. He was so tuckered out he didn't even growl. He just pointed himself toward the tall timber to find another hollow log to crawl into. But he had lost the fine art of walking. We watched him jump, jump, jump north until he was out of sight.

That was the howlin', scowlin' all mighty *big* wind that broke my leg. It had not only pulled up fence posts, but the *holes* as well. It dropped one of those holes right outside the barn door and I stepped in it.

That's the bottom truth. Everyone on the prairie knows Josh McBroom would rather break his leg than tell a fib.

# McBroom and the Big Wind

## Meet the Author

**Sid Fleischman** worked as a reporter after he graduated from college. He also wrote novels, suspense stories, and screenplays. Years later, he wrote his first children's book—it was for his own children.

Mr. Fleischman's interest in tall tales grew out of a keen interest in folklore. His McBroom books are filled with exaggeration and humor, characteristics common to tall tales.

Mr. Fleischman writes at a big table cluttered with library books, pens, pencils, letters, notes, and projects. He has been a full-time freelance writer since 1952.

## Meet the Illustrator

**Walter Lorraine** was born in Worcester, Massachusetts, on February 3, 1929. He studied art at the Rhode Island School of Design. Later he was a book designer for a large publishing company and worked with children's book illustrators. Eventually, he started illustrating books himself. Mr. Lorraine says, *"Good illustrators have something to say. Whatever their techniques or styles, they always make a particular individual statement. Whether to convey fact or fiction, they are essentially storytellers who use pictures instead of words."*

# Theme Connections

## Think About It

- Why would a one-acre farm on the plains be a harsh environment?
- What suggestions does this tall tale offer for surviving a harsh environment?

## Record Ideas

 McBroom's humorous plans for using the wind may spark many interesting ideas for your writing. Write about these ideas in your Writing Journal.

## Write a Tall Tale

Select a region of the country and a problem that might exist there because of the region's climate or environment. Write a short tall tale about that region with a hero like McBroom who survives the environment.

# The Grasshopper

David McCord
*illustrated by Nelle Davis*

Down
a
deep
well
a
grasshopper
fell.

By kicking about
He thought to get out.
   He might have known better,
   For that got him wetter.

To kick round and round
Is the way to get drowned,
   And drowning is what
   I should tell you he got.

But
the
well
had
a
rope
that
dangled
some
hope.
And sure as molasses
On one of his passes
   He found the rope handy
   And up he went, *and he*

it
up
and
it
up
and
it
up
and
it
up
went

And hopped away proper
As any grasshopper.

379

# The Big Wave

from *The Big Wave*
by Pearl S. Buck
*illustrated by Yoriko Ito*

*Jiya and his family live in a small Japanese fishing village. When a distant volcano erupts, it causes a tidal wave. As the giant wave approaches the village, Jiya's father forces him to climb to safety on a nearby mountain. He climbs to the terraced farm of his friend Kino's family. The rest of Jiya's family stays behind. From the mountaintop, Jiya watches as the wave hits.*

Upon the beach where the village stood not a house remained, no wreckage of wood or fallen stone wall, no little street of shops, no docks, not a single boat. The beach was as clean of houses as if no human beings had ever lived there. All that had been was now no more.

Jiya gave a wild cry and Kino felt him slip to the ground. He was unconscious. What he had seen was too much for him. What he knew, he could not bear. His family and his home were gone.

Kino began to cry and Kino's father did not stop him. He stooped and gathered Jiya into his arms and carried him into the house, and Kino's mother ran out of the kitchen and put down a mattress and Kino's father laid Jiya upon it.

"It is better that he is unconscious," he said gently. "Let him remain so until his own will wakes him. I will sit by him."

"I will rub his hands and feet," Kino's mother said sadly.

Kino could say nothing. He was still crying and his father let him cry for a while. Then he said to his wife:

"Heat a little rice soup for Kino and put some ginger in it. He feels cold."

Now Kino did not know until his father spoke that he did feel cold. He was shivering and he could not stop crying. Setsu came in. She had not seen the big wave, for her mother had closed the windows and drawn the curtains against the sea. But now she saw Jiya lying white-pale and still.

"Is Jiya dead?" she asked.

"No, Jiya is living," her father replied.

"Why doesn't he open his eyes?" she asked again.

"Soon he will open his eyes," the father replied.

"If Jiya is not dead, why does Kino cry?" Setsu asked.

"You are asking too many questions," her father told her. "Go back to the kitchen and help your mother."

So Setsu went back again, sucking her forefinger, and staring at Jiya and Kino as she went, and soon the mother came in with the hot rice soup and Kino drank it. He felt warm now and he could stop crying. But he was still frightened and sad.

"What will we say to Jiya when he wakes?" he asked his father.

"We will not talk," his father replied. "We will give him warm food and let him rest. We will help him to feel he still has a home."

"Here?" Kino asked.

"Yes," his father replied. "I have always wanted another son, and Jiya will be that son. As soon as he knows that this is his home, then we must help him to understand what has happened."

So they waited for Jiya to wake.

"I don't think Jiya can ever be happy again," Kino said sorrowfully.

"Yes, he will be happy someday," his father said, "for life is always stronger than death. Jiya will feel when he wakes that he can never be happy again. He will cry and cry and we must let him cry. But he cannot always cry. After a few days he will stop crying all the time. He will cry only part of the time. He will sit sad and quiet. We must allow him to be sad and we must not make him speak. But we will do our work and live as always we do. Then one day he will be hungry and he will eat something that our mother cooks, something special, and he will begin to feel better. He will not cry any more in the daytime but only at night. We must let him cry at night. But all the time his body will be renewing itself. His blood flowing in his veins, his growing bones, his mind beginning to think again, will make him live."

"He cannot forget his father and mother and his brother!" Kino exclaimed.

"He cannot and he should not forget them," Kino's father said. "Just as he lived with them alive, he will live with them dead. Someday he will accept their death as part of his life. He will weep no more. He will carry them in his memory and his thoughts. His flesh and blood are part of them. So long as he is alive, they, too, will live in him. The big wave came, but it went away. The sun shines again, birds sing, and earth flowers. Look out over the sea now!"

Kino looked out the open door, and he saw the ocean sparkling and smooth. The sky was blue again, a few clouds on the horizon were the only sign of what had passed——except for the empty beach.

"How cruel it seems for the sky to be so clear and the ocean so calm!" Kino said.

But his father shook his head. "No, it is wonderful that after the storm the ocean grows calm, and the sky is blue once more. It was not the ocean or the sky that made the evil storm."

お父さんじゃは大丈夫

"Who made it?" Kino asked. He let tears roll down his cheeks, because there was so much he could not understand. But only his father saw them and his father understood.

"Ah, no one knows who makes evil storms," his father replied. "We only know that they come. When they come we must live through them as bravely as we can, and after they are gone, we must feel again how wonderful is life. Every day of life is more valuable now than it was before the storm."

"But Jiya's family——his father and mother and brother, and all the other good fisherfolk, who are lost——" Kino whispered. He could not forget the dead.

"Now we must think of Jiya," his father reminded him. "He will open his eyes at any minute and we must be there, you to be his brother, and I to be his father. Call your mother, too, and little Setsu."

Now they heard something. Jiya's eyes were still closed, but he was sobbing in his sleep. Kino ran to fetch his mother and Setsu and they gathered about his bed, kneeling on the floor so as to be near Jiya when he opened his eyes.

In a few minutes, while they all watched, Jiya's eyelids fluttered on his pale cheeks, and then he opened his eyes. He did not know where he was. He looked from one face to the other, as though they were strangers. Then he looked up into the beams of the ceiling and around the white walls of the room. He looked at the blue-flowered quilt that covered him.

None of them said anything. They continued to kneel about him, waiting. But Setsu could not keep quiet. She clapped her hands and laughed. "Oh, Jiya has come back!" she cried. "Jiya, did you have a good dream?"

The sound of her voice made him fully awake. "My father—my mother—" he whispered.

Kino's mother took his hand. "I will be your mother now, dear Jiya," she said.

"I will be your father," Kino's father said.

"I am your brother now, Jiya," Kino faltered.

"Oh, Jiya will live with us," Setsu said joyfully.

Then Jiya understood. He got up from the bed and walked to the door that stood open to the sky and the sea. He looked down the hillside to the beach where the fishing village had stood. There was only beach, and all that remained of the twenty and more houses were a few foundation posts and some big stones. The gentle

385

little waves of the ocean were playfully carrying the light timber that had made the houses, and throwing it on the sands and snatching it away again.

The family had followed Jiya and now they stood about him. Kino did not know what to say, for his heart ached for his friend-brother. Kino's mother was wiping her eyes, and even little Setsu looked sad. She took Jiya's hand and stroked it.

"Jiya, I will give you my pet duck," she said.

But Jiya could not speak. He kept on looking at the ocean.

"Jiya, your rice broth is growing cold," Kino's father said.

"We ought all to eat something," Kino's mother said. "I have a fine chicken for dinner."

"I'm hungry!" Setsu cried.

"Come, my son," Kino's father said to Jiya.

They persuaded him gently, gathering around him, and they entered the house again. In the pleasant cosy room they all sat down about the table.

Jiya sat with the others. He was awake, he could hear the voices of Kino's family, and he knew that Kino sat beside him. But inside he still felt asleep. He was very tired, so tired that he did not want to speak. He knew that he would never see his father and mother any more, or his brother, or the neighbors and friends of the village. He tried not to think about them or to imagine their quiet bodies, floating under the swelling waves.

"Eat, Jiya," Kino whispered. "The chicken is good."

Jiya's bowl was before him, untouched. He was not hungry. But when Kino begged him he took up his porcelain spoon and drank a little of the soup. It was hot and good, and he smelled its fragrance in his nostrils. He drank more and then he took up his chopsticks and ate some of the meat and rice. His mind was still unable to think, but his body was young and strong and glad of the food.

When they had all finished, Kino said, "Shall we go up the hillside, Jiya?"

But Jiya shook his head. "I want to go to sleep again," he said.

Kino's father understood. "Sleep is good for you," he said. And he led Jiya to his bed, and when Jiya had laid himself down he covered him with the quilt and shut the sliding panels.

"Jiya is not ready yet to live," he told Kino. "We must wait."

The body began to heal first, and Kino's father, watching Jiya tenderly, knew that the body would heal the mind and the soul. "Life is stronger than death," he told Kino again and again.

さあじや食べ
鶏肉 おいしい

387

But each day Jiya was still tired. He did not want to think or to remember—he only wanted to sleep. He woke to eat and then to sleep. And when Kino's mother saw this she led him to the bedroom, and Jiya sank each time into the soft mattress spread on the floor in the quiet, clean room. He fell asleep almost at once and Kino's mother covered him and went away.

All through these days Kino did not feel like playing. He worked hard beside his father in the fields. They did not talk much, and neither of them wanted to look at the sea. It was enough to look at the earth, dark and rich beneath their feet.

One evening, Kino climbed the hill behind the farm and looked toward the volcano. The heavy cloud of smoke had long ago gone away, and the sky was always clear now. He felt happier to know that the volcano was no longer angry, and he went down again to the house. On the threshold his father was smoking his usual evening pipe. In the house his mother was giving Setsu her evening bath.

"Is Jiya asleep already?" Kino asked his father.

"Yes, and it is a good thing for him," his father replied. "Sleep will strengthen him, and when he wakes he will be able to think and remember."

"But should he remember such sorrow?" Kino asked.

"Yes," his father replied. "Only when he dares to remember his parents will he be happy again."

They sat together, father and son, and Kino asked still another question. "Father, are we not very unfortunate people to live in Japan?"

"Why do you think so?" his father asked in reply.

"Because the volcano is behind our house and the ocean is in front, and when they work together for evil, to make the earthquake and the big wave, then we are helpless. Always many of us are lost."

"To live in the midst of danger is to know how good life is," his father replied.

"But if we are lost in the danger?" Kino asked anxiously.

"To live in the presence of death makes us brave and strong," Kino's father replied. "That is why our people never fear death. We see it too often and we do not fear it. To die a little later or a little sooner does not matter. But to live bravely, to love life, to see how beautiful the trees are and the mountains, yes, and even the sea, to enjoy work because it produces food for life——in these things we Japanese are a fortunate people. We love life because we live in danger. We do not fear death because we understand that life and death are necessary to each other."

# The Big Wave

## Meet the Author

**Pearl S. Buck** was three months old when her parents took her to China, where she grew up. She wrote her first story at age nine. It was published in an English-language newspaper there. Afterward the newspaper printed many of her stories and even paid her for them. She decided then that one day she would be a real writer.

Growing up in China with American parents, Buck saw how people from different backgrounds separated themselves from each other. Because she had both Chinese and American friends, she often felt as though she lived in two worlds. And she realized early that the worlds were not the same. She made it her life's work to try and bring the cultures together and to speak out against every kind of bigotry.

## Meet the Illustrator

**Yoriko Ito** grew up in Japan. When she was a little girl, she knew she wanted to paint. It wasn't until after she came to San Francisco at age 21 that she knew she wanted to study art. However, she says she became a children's book illustrator by accident. She showed her portfolio to some authors at a librarians' conference, and an author introduced her to a publisher. *"I was really lucky,"* says Ms. Ito.

Now Ms. Ito works at the Dreamworks film company. She painted backgrounds for movie animation for *The Prince of Egypt* and *El Dorado*. Ms. Ito advises young artists, *"You have to do your best always. If you believe in something, don't doubt your ability. . . . Remember, you can't please everybody. Trust yourself."*

# Theme Connections

## Think About It

- What did Jiya face after the tidal wave?
- What steps did Jiya have to go through before he could be happy again?

## Record Ideas

In your Writing Journal, record your feelings if you were Kino and you were trying to convince Jiya, your best friend, to keep on living.

## Role-play

Choose a partner. Pretend one of you is Jiya. The other is Kino. Kino must try to convince Jiya to keep on living. Jiya does not want to survive. Act out this scene.

# Solitude

A. A. Milne
*illustrated by Ernest H. Shepard*

I have a house where I go
   When there's too many people,
I have a house where I go
   Where no one can be;
I have a house where I go,
Where nobody ever says "No";
Where no one says anything——so
   There is no one but me.

# Anne Frank:

# The Diary of a Young Girl

*Anne Frank*
*translated from the Dutch*
*by B. M. Mooyaart-Doubleday*
*illustrated by Susan Keeter*

D uring World War II, many Jewish families in Germany and elsewhere in Europe hid to avoid being sent to concentration camps. Anne Frank and her family moved to Holland to escape the Nazis. When the Nazis came to Holland, the Franks hid for two years in a secret annex in Mr. Frank's office building. During this time, Anne kept a diary of her daily thoughts, feelings, and activities. Her father found these diaries after her death in a concentration camp in 1945 and had them published. These are a few of her first diary entries.

I hope I shall be able to confide in you completely, as I have never been able to do in anyone before, and I hope that you will be a great support and comfort to me.
*Anne Frank, 12 June 1942.*

*Wednesday, 8 July, 1942*

Dear Kitty,

Years seem to have passed between Sunday and now. So much has happened, it is just as if the whole world had turned upside down. But I am still alive, Kitty, and that is the main thing, Daddy says.

Yes, I'm still alive, indeed, but don't ask where or how. You wouldn't understand a word, so I will begin by telling you what happened on Sunday afternoon.

At three o'clock (Harry had just gone, but was coming back later) someone rang the front doorbell. I was lying lazily reading a book on the veranda in the sunshine, so I didn't hear it. A bit later, Margot appeared at the kitchen door looking very excited. "The S.S. have sent a call-up notice for Daddy," she whispered. "Mummy has gone to see Mr. Van Daan already." (Van Daan is a friend who works with Daddy in the business.) It was a great shock to me, a call-up; everyone knows what that means. I picture concentration camps and lonely cells——should we allow him to be doomed to this? "Of course he won't go," declared Margot, while we waited together. "Mummy has gone to the Van Daans to discuss whether we should move into our hiding place tomorrow. The Van Daans are going with us, so we shall be seven in all." Silence. We couldn't talk any more, thinking about Daddy, who, little knowing what was going on, was visiting some old people in the Joodse Invalide; waiting for Mummy, the heat and suspense, all made us very overawed and silent.

Suddenly the bell rang again. "That is Harry," I said. "Don't open the door." Margot held me back, but it was not necessary as we heard Mummy and Mr. Van Daan downstairs, talking to Harry, then they came in and closed the door behind them. Each time the bell went, Margot or I had to creep softly down to see if it was Daddy, not opening the door to anyone else.

Margot and I were sent out of the room. Van Daan wanted to talk to Mummy alone. When we were alone together in our bedroom, Margot told me that the call-up was not for Daddy, but for her. I was more frightened than ever and began to cry. Margot is sixteen; would they really take girls of that age away alone? But thank goodness she won't go, Mummy said so herself; that must be what Daddy meant when he talked about us going into hiding.

Into hiding——where would we go, in a town or the country, in a house or a cottage, when, how, where . . . ?

These were questions I was not allowed to ask, but I couldn't get them out of my mind. Margot and I began to pack some of our most vital belongings into a school satchel. The first thing I put in was this diary, then hair curlers, handkerchiefs, schoolbooks, a comb, old letters; I put in the craziest things with the idea that we were going into hiding. But I'm not sorry, memories mean more to me than dresses.

At five o'clock Daddy finally arrived, and we phoned Mr. Koophuis to ask if he could come around in the evening. Van Daan went and fetched Miep. Miep has been in the business with Daddy since 1933 and has become a close friend, likewise her brand-new husband, Henk. Miep came and took some shoes, dresses, coats, underwear, and stockings away in her bag, promising to return in the evening. Then silence fell on the house; not one of us felt like eating anything, it was still hot and everything was very strange. We let our large upstairs room to a certain Mr. Goudsmit, a divorced man in his thirties, who appeared to have nothing to do on this particular evening; we simply could not get rid of him without being rude; he hung about until ten o'clock. At eleven o'clock Miep and Henk Van Santen arrived. Once again, shoes, stockings, books, and underclothes disappeared into Miep's bag and Henk's deep pockets, and at eleven-thirty they too disappeared. I was dog-tired and although I knew that it would be my last night in my own bed, I fell asleep immediately and didn't wake up until Mummy called me at five-thirty the next morning. Luckily it was not so hot as Sunday; warm rain fell steadily all day. We put on heaps of clothes as if we were going to the North Pole, the sole reason being to take clothes with us. No Jew in our situation would have dreamed of going out with a suitcase full of clothing. I had on two vests, three pairs of pants, a dress, on top of that a skirt, jacket, summer coat, two pairs of stockings, lace-up shoes, woolly cap, scarf, and still more; I was nearly stifled before we started, but no one inquired about that.

Margot filled her satchel with schoolbooks, fetched her bicycle, and rode off behind Miep into the unknown, as far as I was concerned. You see I still didn't know where our secret hiding place was to be. At seven-thirty the door closed behind us. Moortje, my little cat, was the only creature to whom I said farewell. She would have a good home with the neighbors. This was all written in a letter addressed to Mr. Goudsmit.

There was one pound of meat in the kitchen for the cat, breakfast things lying on the table, stripped beds, all giving the impression that we had left helter-skelter. But we didn't care about impressions, we only wanted to get away, only escape and arrive safely, nothing else. Continued tomorrow.

Yours, Anne

*Thursday, 9 July, 1942*

Dear Kitty,

So we walked in the pouring rain, Daddy, Mummy, and I, each with a school satchel and shopping bag filled to the brim with all kinds of things thrown together anyhow.

We got sympathetic looks from people on their way to work. You could see by their faces how sorry they were they couldn't offer us a lift; the gaudy yellow star spoke for itself.

Only when we were on the road did Mummy and Daddy begin to tell me bits and pieces about the plan. For months as many of our goods and chattels and necessities of life as possible had been sent away and they were sufficiently ready for us to have gone into hiding of our own accord on July 16. The plan had had to be speeded up ten days because of the call-up, so our quarters would not be so well organized, but we had to make the best of it. The hiding place itself would be in the building where Daddy has his office. It will be hard for outsiders to understand, but I shall explain that later on. Daddy didn't have many people working for him: Mr. Kraler, Koophuis, Miep, and Elli Vossen, a twenty-three-year-old typist who all knew of our arrival. Mr. Vossen, Elli's father, and two boys worked in the warehouse; they had not been told.

I will describe the building: there is a large warehouse on the ground floor which is used as a store. The front door to the house is next to the warehouse door, and inside the front door is a second doorway which leads to a staircase. There is another door at the top of the stairs, with a frosted glass window in it, which has "Office" written in black letters across it. That is the large main office, very big, very light, and very full. Elli, Miep, and Mr. Koophuis work there in the daytime. A small dark room containing the safe, a wardrobe, and a large cupboard leads to a small somewhat dark second office. Mr. Kraler and Mr. Van Daan used to sit here, now it is only Mr. Kraler. One can reach Kraler's office from the passage, but only via a glass door which can be opened from the inside, but not easily from the outside.

From Kraler's office a long passage goes past the coal store, up four steps and leads to the showroom of the whole building: the private office. Dark, dignified furniture, linoleum and carpets on the floor, radio, smart lamp, everything first-class. Next door there is a roomy kitchen with a hot-water faucet and a gas stove. Next door the W.C. [water closet]. That is the first floor.

A wooden staircase leads from the downstairs passage to the next floor. There is a small landing at the top. There is a door at each end of the landing, the left one leading to a storeroom at the front of the house and to the attics. One of those really steep Dutch staircases runs from the side to the other door opening on to the street.

The right-hand door leads to our "Secret Annexe." No one would ever guess that there would be so many rooms hidden behind that plain gray door. There's a little step in front of the door and then you are inside.

There is a steep staircase immediately opposite the entrance. On the left a tiny passage brings you into a room which was to become the Frank family's bed-sitting-room, next door a smaller room, study and bedroom for the two young ladies of the family. On the right a little room without windows containing the washbasin and a small W.C. compartment, with another door leading to Margot's and my room. If you go up the next flight of stairs and open the door, you are simply amazed that there could be such a big light room in such an old house by the canal. There is a gas stove in this room (thanks to the fact that it was used as a laboratory) and a sink. This is now the kitchen for the Van Daan couple, besides being general living room, dining room, and scullery.

A tiny little corridor room will become Peter Van Daan's apartment. Then, just as on the lower landing, there is a large attic. So there you are, I've introduced you to the whole of our beautiful "Secret Annexe."

Yours, Anne

*Friday, 10 July, 1942*
Dear Kitty,

I expect I have thoroughly bored you with my long-winded descriptions of our dwelling. But still I think you should know where we've landed.

But to continue my story——you see, I've not finished yet——when we arrived at the Prinsengracht, Miep took us quickly upstairs and into the "Secret Annexe." She closed the door behind us and we were alone. Margot was already waiting for us, having come much faster on her bicycle. Our living room and all the other rooms were chock-full of rubbish, indescribably so. All the cardboard boxes which had been sent to the office in the previous months lay piled on the floor and the beds. The little room was filled to the ceiling with bedclothes. We had to start clearing up immediately, if we wished to sleep in decent beds that night. Mummy and Margot were not in a fit state to take part; they were tired and lay down on their beds, they were miserable, and lots more besides. But the two "clearers-up" of the family——Daddy and myself——wanted to start at once.

The whole day long we unpacked boxes, filled cupboards, hammered and tidied, until we were dead beat. We sank into clean beds that night. We hadn't had a bit of anything warm the whole day, but we didn't care; Mummy and Margot were too tired and keyed up to eat, and Daddy and I were too busy.

On Tuesday morning we went on where we left off the day before. Elli and Miep collected our rations for us, Daddy improved the poor blackout, we scrubbed the kitchen floor, and were on the go the whole day long again. I hardly had time to think about the great change in my life until Wednesday. Then I had a chance, for the first time since our arrival, to tell you all about it, and at the same time to realize myself what had actually happened to me and what was still going to happen.

Yours, Anne

# Anne Frank:
## *The Diary of a Young Girl*

## Meet the Author

**Anne Frank** was four when her family fled to Amsterdam, Holland, to escape the Nazis. The Nazis eventually came to Holland, so the Franks went into hiding. They moved into the attic of her father's warehouse, a place they called the "Secret Annexe." For two years, they did not leave the attic. Anne wrote in her diary about everything that happened there.

Anne's parents had given her the small, clothbound book for her thirteenth birthday. She wrote inside, *"I want to write, but more than that, I want to bring out all kinds of things that lie buried deep in my heart. . . . I want this diary itself to be my friend, and I shall call my friend Kitty."*

In 1944 the Franks were discovered and taken to concentration camps. Of the eight people in the Secret Annex, only Anne's father survived. When he returned to Amsterdam, Miep and Elli gave him the diary they had found in the Annex.

## Meet the Illustrator

**Susan Keeter** has art degrees from Syracuse University. Ms. Keeter's mother and stepfather ran an art school in their home so Ms. Keeter had access to art materials and instruction throughout her childhood.

This story particularly affected Ms. Keeter because her mother was born the same year as Anne Frank. She says, *"I look at my mother, her friends, her work, the beauty she creates and wonder what Anne Frank would have accomplished—how she would have changed the world—if she had been allowed to live a full life."*

# Theme Connections

## Think About It

What would you miss most if you had to go into hiding, as Anne did, in order to survive? Divide into small groups. Talk about what you would miss most if you went into hiding.

- What people would you miss?
- What activities would you miss?
- Would you miss any special foods?

## Record Ideas

In your Writing Journal, write a list of the people and things you would miss most if you went into hiding in order to survive.

## Write a Diary Entry

Anne Frank wrote her innermost thoughts and feelings in her diary. Write a diary entry and record your thoughts and feelings.

# FINE Art

*Minamoto no Yorinobu Swimming across a bay to attack the rebellious Tadatsune.* 1879. **Tsukioka Yoshitoshi.** Woodblock print. Robert Schaap Collection, Vincent van Gogh Museum, Rijsmuseum, Amsterdam.

*Choctaw Removal.* 1966. **Valjean McCarthy-Hessing.** Watercolor on paper. Museum purchase, The Philbrook Museum of Art, Tulsa, Oklahoma.

*Buchenwald Concentration Camp Survivors.* 1945. **Margaret Bourke-White.** Photograph. Photo: Margaret Bourke-White, Life Magazine ©Time Inc.

*The Old Plantation.* c.1790–1800. **Artist unknown.** Watercolor on laid paper. Abby Aldrich Rockefeller Folk Art Center. Photo: ©Colonial Williamsburg Foundation.

# Music
## & Slavery

Wiley Blevins
*illustrated by Ashley Bryan*

*Mother was let off some days at noon to get ready for spinning that evening. She had to portion out the cotton they was gonna spin and see that each got a fair share. When mother was going round counting the cards each had spun she would sing this song:*

> *Keep your eye on the sun.*
> *See how she run.*
> *Don't let her catch you with your work undone.*
> *I'm a trouble, I'm a trouble.*
> *Trouble don't last always.*

*That made the women all speed up so they could finish before dark catch 'em, 'cause it be mighty hard handlin' that cotton thread by firelight.*

*Bob Ellis*
*slave in Virginia*

The life of many slaves in the United States was often full of fear and misery. Long hours were often spent picking cotton in the hot summer sun. At night, the slaves ate what little food their owners had given them and frequently slept on dirt floors. The slaves lived in run-down, overcrowded cabins and owned only the few clothes and possessions their masters had given them. They lived in fear of being beaten if they did not work hard enough or disobeyed their owners. They were not paid, and they were not allowed to leave their homes without special permission.

These terrible living conditions and lack of freedoms made many slaves want to escape. For most, however, there was no real hope of escape. Each day was a struggle to survive. One way the slaves dealt with these hardships was through music. It was a way to express both their sadness and their hope.

The slaves brought with them from Africa a strong tradition of music. Song and dance were an important part of their daily lives. They sang as they worked. They sang to celebrate. They sang when they were sad. They continued this tradition in the new world.

Slaves also brought instruments with them. The drum was the most important instrument used by them in Africa. However, many slave owners believed drums were being used to send secret messages. Therefore, drums were forbidden on most plantations. Instead, slaves kept the strong rhythms of their songs by clapping their hands, stomping their feet, swaying their bodies, and using other instruments such as the banjo. The banjo, developed by the slaves, became a commonly used instrument and is still in use today.

Many of the songs the slaves sang were developed as they worked in the fields. Singing helped take their minds off the difficulties of their work. These songs often changed over time. Many songs required a leader who would sing one line of the song while the others sang the response. These "call and response" chants were unique to slave music. Some songs that survived have become well-known spirituals, or religious songs. These songs, including "Swing Low Sweet Chariot" and "Go Down Moses," are based on stories in the Bible in which people were kept as slaves. Slaves were punished, often severely beaten, if they spoke against slavery. Through the spirituals, they could sing about the brutality of slavery without fear of being punished. Many of these songs are still sung today and are a tribute to the rich musical heritage of the slaves.

# MANY THOUSAND GONE

*illustrated by Ashley Bryan*

No more auc-tion block for me,    No    more,    No    more,

No more auc-tion block for me,    Ma - ny   thou-sand   gone.

No more peck of corn for me,
No more,
No more,
No more peck of corn for me,
Many thousand gone.

No more hundred lash for me,
No more,
No more,
No more hundred lash for me,
Many thousand gone.

# Walk Together Children

*illustrated by Ashley Bryan*

O,   Walk to-geth-er child-ren,   Don't you get wea-ry,
Sing to-geth-er child-ren,   Don't you get wea-ry,

Walk   to-geth-er child-ren,   Don't you get   wea-ry,
Sing   to-geth-er child-ren,   Don't you get   wea-ry,

Walk   to-geth-er child-ren,   Don't you get wea-ry, There's a
Sing   to-geth-er child-ren,   Don't you get wea-ry, There's a

great   camp meet-ing   in   the   Prom-ised Land.

Going to mourn and ne-ver tire, — Mourn and ne-ver

tire, — Mourn and ne-ver tire, — There's a

**D.S.**

great camp meet-ing in the Prom-ised Land. O,

# Music & Slavery

## Meet the Author

**Wiley Blevins** grew up in West Virginia. During his childhood, he heard stories about his grandfather's life on a Virginia plantation. The stories were often about the music and celebrations of the slaves. Mr. Blevins always wondered, *"How could slaves spend so much time singing and celebrating?"*

Mr. Blevins began to study slavery and music further. He says, *"It became clear to me how the music of slaves was a way for them to cope with their brutal living conditions. It was one of their survival mechanisms."*

## Meet the Illustrator

**Ashley Bryan** started writing and illustrating his own books in kindergarten. He bound them and gave them away as gifts for his friends and family. By the time he was in fourth grade, he had already created hundreds of books.

Mr. Bryan now lives in Isleford, Maine, on an island off the coast. He carries a sketchbook to draw people he meets and interesting places he sees as he travels. When he's not traveling, he paints at home during the day and works on his books at night.

# Theme Connections

## Think About It

Think about what music makes you happy and forget your problems. Remember the slaves in this selection used music as a way to cope with their difficult lives. Tell a partner what songs make you happy.

## Record Ideas

In your Writing Journal, write down the songs that comfort you when you are upset.

## Write a Song

The slaves used music to make their lives more bearable. Write the lyrics for a song that would make you happy. Share your song with your classmates.

# Bibliography

### Akiak: A Tale from the Iditarod

**by Robert J. Blake.** Akiak is a 10-year-old lead sled dog who has raced the Iditarod dogsled race seven times. Now, in her last chance to win, she is injured and must be left behind. But no one has reckoned with Akiak's courage and determination.

### Dashing Through the Snow: The Story of the Jr. Iditarod

**by Sherry Shahan.** Learn about becoming a dogsled driver, or musher, in the Junior Iditarod, a junior dogsled race fashioned after the difficult 1,151-mile race for adult mushers.

### Earthquake Terror

**by Peg Kehret.** What would you do if you were stranded on an island during an earthquake and your sister depended on you for her survival?

### Homesteading: Settling America's Heartland

**by Dorothy Hinshaw Patent.** Can you imagine how hard it must have been to settle on the American prairies a century ago? Could you have risen to the challenge?

## North American Indian Survival Skills

**by Karen Liptak.** How did the Native Americans survive without modern technology? Read and find out their amazing secrets.

## The Outdoor Adventure Handbook

**by Hugh McManners.** Whether you are camping in your backyard or in the wilderness, this book tells you everything you need to know about camping with a few survival hints thrown in.

## Pilgrim Voices: Our First Year in the New World

**edited by Peter and Connie Roop.** Reading from original Pilgrim diaries, you will find out what it was like to sail across the Atlantic, meet Native Americans, and survive a difficult first year in Plymouth.

## Zlata's Diary: A Child's Life in Sarajevo

**by Zlata Filipovic.** The Eastern European city Sarajevo is more than just a headline or a news story. It was home to eleven-year-old Zlata until war closed the schools, cut off the electricity and water, and forced people to seek refuge in foreign countries.

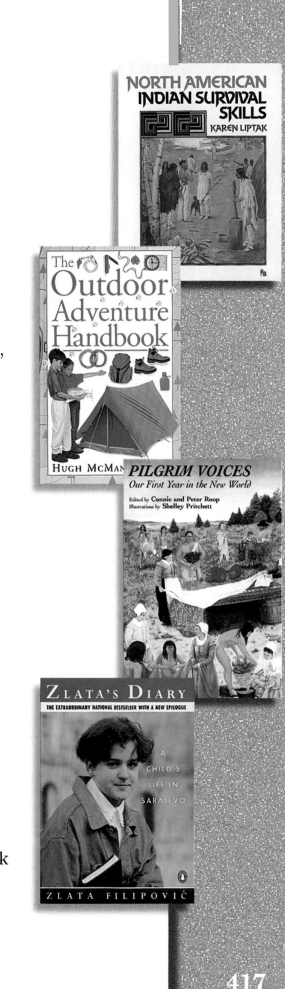

# Communication

**H**ow do you let other people know what you want? Do you have a baby sister or brother? How does the baby tell others what he or she wants? Can you tell what your pet dog or cat or bird wants? How? It's all communication, and it takes as many forms as there are people and animals that need to communicate.

# Whales: Songs from the Deep

from *Animal Communication*
by Jacci Cole

A young humpback whale approaches a diver on the ocean surface.

Out on the open sea, researcher William Schevill sat quietly in his boat, listening, his tape recorder running. Under the ocean's surface, in an underwater canyon of the Bahamas, a lone humpback whale played. The whale made a sound, then waited for it to echo off the canyon walls. It made the same sound again, one note higher, and waited for the echo. It did this again and again, making the notes higher and higher until it reached its own top note. Then it tried new sounds, making gurgles and roars, waiting for the echo before making another

Humpback whales feed.

sound. The humpback played this elaborate game until a distant group of whales called, and the lone humpback swam to join them.

What had this humpback been doing, Schevill wondered. Was it playing a game, enjoying the sound of its own voice? Was it testing the limits of its voice like professional singers do? Could this have been a form of communication? When the other whales called out, how did the humpback know their cries meant "Come join us" instead of "Leave, we don't want you here"?

The ancient philosopher Aristotle wrote about whales, claiming they could "speak." But until recently these writings were ignored and passed off as legend. Now we have submarines that move below the surface of the ocean. We can hear firsthand the noises of marine life. We can hear today the voices of whales. But even now we don't know what they are saying.

Whale watcher Victor B. Scheffer tells us that "no man can say that he has probed deeply into the natural history of the whale. Moving through a dim, dark, cool, water world of its own, the whale is timeless and ancient; part of our common heritage and yet remote, awful, prowling the ocean floor a half-mile down, under the guidance of powers and senses we are only beginning to grasp."

This is true mainly because whales are difficult to study. They spend most of their time under water. When they do surface, they offer us only glimpses of themselves—a flipping tail here, a waterspout there.

Studying whales is also difficult because they are being overhunted, many species to the brink of extinction. Four different kinds of whales (the blue, humpback, fin, and sperm whales) are being killed faster than they can reproduce.

However, we do know some things about whales. We know they are social creatures, enjoying the company of other whales of their kind. They travel, eat, and play in large groups. The mothers are very loving and protective of their calves. But for the most part whales remain a mystery.

One researcher, Jacques Y. Cousteau, states, "The only creatures on earth that have bigger—and maybe better—brains than humans are the Cetacea, the whales and dolphins. Perhaps they could one day tell us something important, but it is unlikely that we will hear it, because we are coldly, efficiently, and economically killing them off."

Do the whales have something they could tell us? Do they have a language they use to communicate with each other? Because of the limitations of their environment, the shadowy water, whales appear to communicate mostly by touch and sound. Mother whales and their calves nuzzle and rub alongside each other as they swim. When young whales swim off to explore underwater canyons they and their mothers continually send out clicks and chirps, apparently to keep track of each other's locations.

French oceanographer Jacques Cousteau and his crew prepare to dive during an expedition.

Whale groups spread over large areas of the ocean when they travel. Many scientists believe that with a variety of sounds whales constantly communicate information about food or any possible danger lurking in the area.

Though whales' means of communication may seem limited to us, some scientists believe whales possess a high intellect "Their system of communication seems to have reached a rather high stage of development," researcher Edwin Colbert states. "The brain is highly developed in these mammals, and recent experiments indicate that whales are remarkably intelligent."

Scientists believe dolphins' intelligence and their talent for complex communication go hand in hand. Is this true for their cousins the whales? Or is it instinct that motivates whales? Do whales have highly developed brains that are similar to ours?

Only recently have scientists found that the whale's brain is as unique and complex as ours. Portions of the human brain are "silent." These silent areas are devoted to developing our thinking, our imagination, our ability to think of the future, and our sense of ethics. (Other parts of the brain relate to our actions. They send messages that allow us to hit a baseball, pick up a pencil and write, and do all kinds of other activities.) If we didn't have the silent areas, we would not have our ability to make decisions about what is right or wrong. These areas help us to be understanding and compassionate and to get along with people.

Studies by Drs. Paul Yakolov, Sam Jacobs, and Peter Morgane show that the "silent" areas are larger in whales' brains. The sperm whale has the largest brain of any species on our planet. Its brain has six times the mass (bulk) of a human brain. The doctors' studies reveal that this additional mass holds the silent area. Does this silent area give whales compassion and imagination? Does it help them communicate their feelings and ideas with each other? Do whales dream of the future?

Most researchers admit that the relationship between the size of the whale's brain and its intelligence is yet to be determined. Dr. John Lilly, however, strongly believes that whales' ability to think and communicate, "within their particular evolution and in their particular environment, may be comparable and even superior to our own."

A humpback whale cruises with its calf at the surface of the Pacific Ocean.

## Instinct or Intelligence?

On the other hand, scientist and writer Loren Eiseley believed that instinct rather than intelligence guides a whale: "Animals are molded by natural forces they do not comprehend. To their minds, there is no past and no future."

Lilly strongly disagrees. Who are we, he asks, to determine the standards for intelligence among large-brained mammals of the sea? "May there not be domains only a few men have penetrated in which whales may be superior?" he asks. "May not their philosophies and traditions be more complex? They probably have very advanced ethics and laws developed over millennia and passed on. . . . Their memories are probably much greater than ours."

Lilly also argues against Loren Eiseley's point that animals can only live for the present, that it is only their instinct for survival that governs their actions. Lilly contends that "like those among us with no written language (the Masai, for example), they probably have long histories which they recount to their young, who must memorize them in detail."

Could this be true? Do whales live, as Lilly says, in societies where complex histories and traditions are passed on? What should we think of this idea?

Whale watcher Victor B. Scheffer contends that we shouldn't concern ourselves with the similarities and differences between us and whales. He says, "Like humans, some whales live in families, play in the moonlight, talk to one another, and care for one another in time of trouble. We humans can feel a bond there. But is it not enough simply to respect whales as whales? Instead of wondering whether they can reason, or worry, or think ahead as we humans can, perhaps we should be content to admire them for their unique minds and bodies."

## Song of the Humpback

The song of the humpback has captured the intense interest of many biologists. Why do they sing these songs, and do they sing them all the time? Do the songs carry messages to other whales, or are they just for fun?

Jacques Cousteau says both the male and female humpback sing. He states that they sing their song "day and night during their long migration to and from the warm southern waters."

Dr. Roger Payne disagrees. For several months during 1971, Payne and his colleague, Scott McVay, recorded humpbacks off the coast of Bermuda. They found that all the humpbacks in one area sing the same underwater song. However, they also found that the whales sing only in their winter breeding ground and not while traveling.

Later, Payne's wife Katy, also a whale watcher and researcher, found that not only are humpback whales "singers" but also "composers, constantly tinkering with their song so that it changes completely in only a few years." As individual whales make minor changes in the song, others learn those changes and pass them on. The Paynes theorized that the changes take place as the breeding season progresses and not between seasons.

But they had some questions. Why do some whales change the songs? And why do the whales sing only at their breeding grounds?

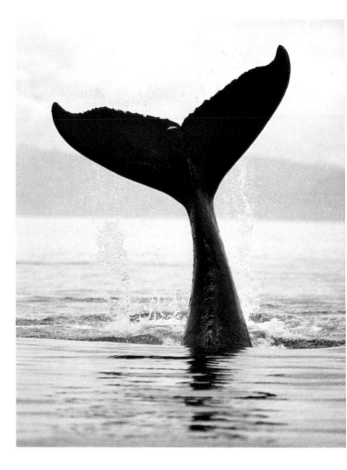

A humpback whale tail splashes out of the water's surface in Alaska.

Ten years after the Paynes' first observations, a strange coincidence occurred that not only shed light on these mysteries but also changed their minds about some of their previous ideas.

While listening to a recording of humpback songs from Baja California, Roger and Katy Payne recognized patterns and variations that they had heard in songs of humpback whales in Hawaii. They thought someone must have mislabeled the tape. They telephoned the friend who had sent them the tape and were stunned by her reply. No, the tape was not mislabeled. The tape was recorded near the Revillagigedo Islands off the coast of Baja California.

The Paynes couldn't believe what they were hearing! If the tape proved the songs of the whales near Hawaii were the same as those of the Baja California whales, then their theory that whales don't sing during migration would be completely discredited. Whales must sing while migrating or other whales couldn't hear the songs and learn them. This possibility also contradicted scientists' belief that whales never met at all during migration.

If whales do sing when they migrate, that would help explain why the songs changed so much every year. If whales from the far corners of the world compared notes, of course the songs would change!

## An Ocean Chorus

Scientists have long assumed, says Roger Payne, that "humpback whales that winter in different locations follow separate patterns of migration." In other words, they travel different routes. The humpbacks of Hawaii migrated in the spring to some area of the Aleutian Islands off the coast of

Alaska; the whales from Baja California went to a more easterly point around southern Alaska. Supposedly, the two groups would never meet. Their songs would be different.

But the evidence on the tape suggests that some humpbacks changed their migration routes. Why they changed and how often they changed, the Paynes did not know. They wondered if changes in the migration routes affected the changes in the songs. When their paths crossed, did the whales from one group teach their particular song to the whales from the other groups?

## A Special Language

Whale researcher Peter Tyack was also looking for answers. No one knew yet whether or not the different sound that whales make contain particular messages or have meanings for other whales. But Tyack feels they must mean something.

He has studied humpbacks and the social sounds that they make while they eat and play. These sounds vary in tone and in loudness, and they range from mews to groans and clicks to grunts. These particular sounds differ from those the whales use for singing. Tyack hoped to find out what the noises mean. He believes they are used for communication.

In an experiment, Tyack replayed recordings of humpback songs underwater. Nearby whales just moved away. When he replayed a tape of social sounds, some whales seemed to be interested and moved toward the speaker floating beneath the boat. One whale, in fact, became very friendly and nearly overturned the tiny vessel!

Why were the whales interested only in the social sounds and not the songs? Tyack thinks his studies show that the humpbacks sing their songs for specific reasons. "Singing," he observes, "appears to be related to courtship. Singers often interrupt their song and dash off to join other whales, usually including females." He states that the singers are males. This view differs from the Paynes' theory that all humpbacks sing. The singing males, Tyack adds, all surface for breath during the same theme of the song. The songs are long, patterned sequences and they are repeated over and over.

Researcher Jim Darling agrees with Tyack that only the male humpbacks sing for mating purposes, but he doesn't believe they sing to the females. He thinks the males sing to keep other males away and to establish leadership in their herds. These dominance displays are very similar to those of rams, who in their mating season charge each other with their horns. He says the ram who can prove he has the strongest horns usually becomes the dominant male. Darling believes it may be the male humpback with the longer or more intricate song that becomes the dominant male in the group.

Whale watchers view a humpback whale.

## Puzzling Changes

It is the changes in the humpback song that really have Jim Darling puzzled. "Could it be that 'grows' is a better word than 'changes'?" he asks. He suggests that males of different levels of leadership would have obviously different songs. "The two necessary characteristics of the new display would be that it could be sensed by other males over some distance and that it could change or grow to reflect the dominance position of the male," he states.

He admits there are still more questions than answers. "There are many obvious questions. Are the songs only a signal from male to male, or do they mean something to females also? Is the humpback's song genetically determined [inherited] or can he choose what he sings?"

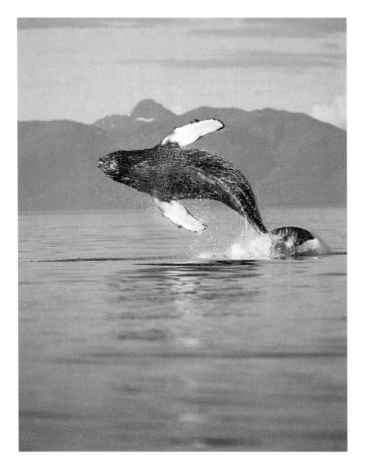

A humpback whale leaps from the water off of southeast Alaska.

## Other Songs?

Still more questions need to be answered. Do other whales have songs like the humpbacks? To find some answers, Roger Payne went south to Argentina to learn about right whales. Right whales, he found, are very social, have close-knit families, and make a variety of chirps, moans, gurgles, whinnies, and other sounds, but no songs. Scott McVay went north to Alaska to record bowhead whales. He was equally disappointed that he heard no songs from the bowheads. Are humpbacks, then, the only "singing" whales?

Author Barbara Brooks thinks perhaps they are. She observes that whales rely on what they hear——on "sonar, a variety of cries and sounds, and acute hearing for communication across vast ocean distances. But unique (apparently) even among whales are the clearly organized 'sonic repertoires' of the humpback whale, which, like bird songs, include themes that occur in repeated sequences."

Perhaps the biggest question is why the humpbacks sing at all. If other whales don't sing messages to each other, what does this say about humpbacks? Has their ability to communicate with each other evolved to a higher form than that of other whales? Will future research answer these questions or will the humpback remain a mystery? It will be an exciting challenge for future researchers to seek out these giants of the sea and discover their hidden secrets.

# Whales: Songs from the Deep

## Meet the Ocean Explorer

**Jacques Yves Cousteau** always had a love of the sea. The beauty of the underwater world fascinated him even as a child. In order to understand the sea more fully, Mr. Cousteau and a French engineer, Émile Gagnan, invented the Aqua-lung. The Aqua-lung is a breathing apparatus that allows a diver to stay underwater for a long period of time.

Throughout his long career as an ocean explorer, Mr. Cousteau photographed and filmed sharks, whales, dolphins, and other underwater sea life. He commanded the ship *Calypso*, which was used for sea investigations. He also conducted numerous experiments, wrote books, and produced television shows in order to share his love of the sea with the rest of the world.

# Theme Connections

## Think About It

- What are the ways the humpback whales communicate with each other?
- Why do they communicate with each other?
- What evidence was given in the selection that supports the belief that the humpback whales communicate with each other through their songs?
- What evidence was given in the selection that supports the belief that the humpback whales do not communicate with each other through their songs?
- Do you believe that whales use their songs to communicate?

## Record Ideas

What have you learned about how animals can communicate from this selection? Record your thoughts in your Writing Journal.

## Share an Experience

Think of a time you have seen an animal trying to communicate. This animal may be your pet, a friend's pet, an animal at the zoo, or one you have seen on television. Share with a classmate how you think the animal was communicating and what it was trying to communicate. Listen to your classmate's experience as well.

# Whalesong

by Judith Nicholls

I am
ocean voyager,
sky-leaper,
maker of waves;
I harm no man.

I know
only the slow tune
of turning tide,
the heave and sigh
of full seas meeting land
at dusk and dawn,
the sad whale song.
I harm no man.

# Wordless Speech

from *My Friends the Wild Chimpanzees*
excerpt printed in *The Importance of Jane Goodall* by Paula Bryant Pratt
🍁 by Jane Goodall 🍁

"The apes have a large vocabulary of calls, each signifying an emotion such as fear, pain, or pleasure. When a group arrives at a food-laden tree and gives excited 'food barks,' other chimps within earshot often call in response and hurry to the feast. If one chimp gives a low, uneasy 'hoo' when he sights an alarming object, others always peer in the same direction. When a youngster screams in fright or pain his mother invariably hurries to him.

The chimpanzees have also evolved a complex nonverbal communication based on touch, posture, and gesture, in many respects almost identical to the nonverbal communication used by man. Gesture and facial expression play a major part among humans. For instance, an arm placed gently around another's shoulder may convey a message of sympathy more eloquently than words. . . .

Chimpanzees rely to a very great extent on communication by touch during their interactions. Physical contact seems to play a particularly vital role in the apes' emotional life, especially during infancy, when the mother's touch provides the youngster with its chief source of security. . . .

Chimpanzees, like people, exchange greetings when they meet. . . . When this occurs, an observer can usually determine the relationship of one chimp to the other. They may meet as two friends and show pleasure in their reunion, or one may make submissive gestures, acknowledging the other's higher rank. . . .

Many of the apes' forms of greeting startlingly resemble our own. They often kiss. . . . Hand-holding, as a gesture of greeting, is not common . . . but it does occur. . . .

The similarity of many chimpanzee gestures and postures to those of man is to Hugo and me one of the most exciting aspects of our study."

# Wordless Speech

## Meet the Author

**Jane Goodall** was born in London, England. Soon after graduating high school, Ms. Goodall traveled to Kenya, where she met Louis Leakey, a famous naturalist and paleontologist, or scientist who studies fossils. Leakey offered her a job studying wild chimpanzees in Tanzania. She began by watching the chimps from a distance through binoculars. Slowly, she moved closer and closer, until they were used to her. The more she learned about them, the more she knew there was to learn. Her six-month assignment turned into a life-long passion. She has stayed in Tanzania for more than 30 years.

Ms. Goodall says, *"I want to make [people] aware that animals have their own needs, emotions, and feelings—they matter. I want to give kids a passion, an understanding and awareness of the wonder of animals."*

# Theme Connections

## Think About It

Why did Jane Goodall name this selection "Wordless Speech"? Here are some questions to help you decide:

- How do chimpanzees communicate nonverbally?
- How do chimpanzees communicate verbally?
- How is the communication of chimpanzees similar to human communication? How is it different?

## Record Ideas

Answer these questions in your Writing Journal:

- Do you think chimpanzee forms of communication should be called "wordless speech"? Why or why not?
- What did the selection teach you about communication?

## Act out a Nonverbal Story

In groups, act out a story about some familiar event such as a birthday party or a sports competition, using only nonverbal ways of communicating. Remember, this means you can use sounds, facial expressions, and movement, but not words.

# Koko's Kitten

from *Koko's Kitten*
by Dr. Francine Patterson
*photographs by Ronald H. Cohn*

Koko's full name is Hanabi-Ko, which is Japanese for Fireworks Child. She was born on the Fourth of July. Every year, I have a party for Koko with cake, sparkling apple cider, and lots of presents.

Koko knows what birthdays are. When asked what she does on her birthday, Koko answered, "Eat, drink, (get) old."

Three days before Koko's party, I said, "I'm going shopping today. What do you want for your birthday?"

"Cereal there. Good there drink," Koko signed.

"But what presents do you want?" I asked.

"Cat," answered Koko.

Later, she repeated, "Cat, cat, cat."

I wasn't surprised that Koko asked for a cat. I have been reading to Koko for many years and two of her favorite stories have been "Puss in Boots" and "The Three Little Kittens."

Koko gets very involved in the stories I read her. When reading the story of the three little kittens who lose their mittens, Koko sees that their mother is angry and that the kittens are crying.

"Mad," Koko signs.

Koko loves picture books. Gorilla books are her favorites. Cat books are next. She likes to go off on her own with a book to study the pictures and sign to herself.

On her birthday, I gave Koko the usual assortment of presents—apple juice, some special fruits and nuts, and a baby doll. I didn't want to give Koko a stuffed toy because I knew she'd eventually destroy it.

The only durable toy cat I could find was in a mail order catalogue and I ordered it right away. It was made of cement and covered with vinyl and black velvet. I chose it because it looked real and it was sturdy—gorilla-proof. The toy cat didn't arrive in time for Koko's birthday, so I decided to save it for Christmas.

In December, I made a list for Koko. I drew about twenty pictures—fruits, vegetables, nuts, dolls, combs, and blankets. Every year, Koko gets a stocking and lots of presents. She loves Christmas.

"What do you want for Christmas?" I asked as I showed Koko the pictures.

Koko carefully studied the booklet. Then she pointed to a doll, nuts—and a cat.

Koko signs "cat"

I bought Koko some nuts and a new doll. I wrapped the toy cat and put it with the rest of her presents.

On Christmas morning, Koko ate her cereal and opened her stocking. It was filled with nuts. Koko threw the nuts aside and went to her next present.

Koko unwrapped a doll.

"That stink," Koko signed.

Then came the velvet cat.

"That red," she signed.

Koko often uses the word red to express anger. Koko was very upset. She started running back and forth, banging on her walls. She was doing display charges past me. They were angry, angry charges.

It is natural for gorillas to display when frightened or in great danger. They run sideways, pound their chests, then go down on all fours, and run back and forth.

But this was Christmas, usually a happy day for Koko, and she was with people she loved.

Later in the day, Barbara, a friend who had known Koko since she was a baby gorilla, arrived.

"That looks like a black cat," Barbara said to Koko. "Would you show it to me?"

Koko signs "mad"

Koko did not answer. She pulled a blanket over her head.

"Could I see it?" Barbara asked.

Koko pulled a rag over the toy cat, then tossed it in the air. "Cat that," Koko signed.

"Please let me see it," said Barbara.

Koko gave her a toy dinosaur instead.

I finally understood Koko's strange behavior. She was unhappy with her Christmas present. I had made a mistake. Koko did not want a cement and velvet toy cat. Koko wanted a real cat. Koko wanted a pet.

Things don't always happen quickly where we live. Every day is full of its own activities. So it was almost six months later when Karen, one of my assistants, arrived with three kittens. The kittens had been abandoned by their mother and raised by a dog, a Cairn terrier.

Karen showed the kittens to Koko.

"Love that," Koko signed.

As we showed Koko the kittens, she gave each one her blow test. When Koko meets a new animal or person, she blows in their face. I think she is trying to get a better scent. When she blows at a person, she expects them to blow back. Maybe she expected the kittens to blow back, too.

The first kitten was smoky gray and white. Koko's blow test took him by surprise. The second kitten was a tailless gray tabby. He was also startled by the blow test. The third kitten, a brown tabby, did not react at all.

After the blow test, Koko seemed to have made some judgments about the kittens.

"Which one do you want?" we asked.

"That," signed Koko, pointing to the tailless tabby.

Koko chooses the tabby

I am not sure why Koko picked the gray tabby as her favorite. I never asked her. Perhaps it was because he didn't have a tail—a gorilla has no tail.

That night, all three kittens went home with Karen. Two days later, the kittens came back for another visit. Koko was happy to see them.

"Visit love tiger cat," Koko signed.

First she picked up the smoky gray and white one. Then Koko took the tailless tabby and carried him on her thigh. After a while, she pushed him up onto the back of her neck.

"Baby," Koko signed.

She cradled the tabby in her legs and examined its paws. Koko squeezed, and the tabby's claws came out.

"Cat do scratch," Koko signed. "Koko love."

"What will you name the kitty?" I asked.

"All Ball," Koko signed.

"Yes," I said. "Like a ball, he has no tail."

Ball stayed overnight as a visiting kitten. By the end of the week, Ball was a permanent member of our household.

Koko had her kitten at last.

For the first few weeks, Ball lived in my house. Every evening at six o'clock, I would take Ball to Koko's trailer for an evening visit. I carried the kitten in my pocket as I prepared Koko for bed. Koko soon grew accustomed to this routine.

"What happens at night?" I asked.

"All Ball," signed Koko.

"Right," I said. "Ball visits you at night."

When he was older, Ball snuck into Koko's trailer by himself. It worried me in the beginning. I did not know how Koko would treat the kitten unsupervised. As it turned out, Koko was always gentle. Ball was never afraid of her.

Kittens should not be separated from their mothers until they are at least six weeks old. Poor Ball was abandoned by his mother at birth, which might have accounted for some of his faults.

Ball was an unusual cat. He was very aggressive. He would go up to people and bite them for no reason. He would bite Koko, too.

"Cat bite. Obnoxious," Koko signed, but she never struck back.

Koko did not like to be scratched or bitten, but she loved Ball in spite of his naughty behavior.

"Tell me a story about Ball," I said.

Koko signs "love"

"Koko love Ball," she signed.

Koko treated Ball as if he were her baby.

The very first time she picked him up, she tried to tuck him in her thigh. That's where mother gorillas put their infants. Older babies are carried on their mothers' backs. Koko tried this with Ball, too.

Koko was a good gorilla mother. She combed and petted Ball to keep him clean. She also examined his eyes, ears, and mouth to make sure he was healthy. It was Koko who discovered Ball's ear mites.

Ball was often a topic of conversation during Koko's lessons.

"Love visit," Koko signed when Ball and I arrived for a morning lesson.

"Ball," I said.

"Trouble," signed Koko. "Love."

Koko seemed to enjoy conversations about her kitten. This dialogue took place between Koko and a research assistant named Janet.

"I'll give you some grapes if you tell me about Ball, the cat," Janet said.

"Soft," Koko signed.

"What kind of animal is he?" Janet asked.

"Cat, cat, cat," Koko answered.

"Do you love Ball?"

"Soft, good cat cat," Koko signed.

In addition to sign language, art is another way I test Koko's perceptions. Ball lay with a green toy on an orange towel. I gave Koko a canvas and some paints and asked her to draw Ball. Koko had ten colors to choose from. First she picked black for Ball's body. Next she picked orange for the towel and green for the toy.

"What about Ball's eyes?" I asked.

Koko picked tan.

Koko loves to play games. Her favorites are "chase," "blow-it," and "tickle."

Koko likes to be tickled, and she thinks that others will like it, too.

"Tickle," Koko signed to Ball when they were lying on the floor together.

Ball was not a good tickler, nor did he like to be tickled. So Koko and I pretended. I tickled Koko while carrying the kitten in my hand. Koko thought this was very funny.

"Chase, blow-it. Enjoy," Koko signed to Ball.

In blow-it, Koko blows as hard as she can into the face of her playmate. It's not hard to understand why this game was not one of Ball's favorites.

Chase is similar to tag. Players run back and forth and chase each other. This is a popular game among gorillas in the wild. But Ball never quite caught on to chase.

"Ball" sitting on Koko's back

Koko did not realize that kittens don't necessarily enjoy gorilla games. Koko did understand that kittens like warmth, affection, and attention. And Koko supplied plenty.

On a foggy December morning, one of the assistants told me that Ball had been hit by a car. He had died instantly.

I was shocked and unprepared. I didn't realize how attached I had grown to Ball, and I had no idea how the news would affect Koko. The kitten meant so much to her. He was Koko's baby.

I went to Koko at once. I told her that Ball had been hit by a car; she would not see him again.

Koko did not respond. I thought she didn't understand, so I left the trailer.

Ten minutes later, I heard Koko cry. It was her distress call—a loud, long series of high-pitched hoots.

I cried, too.

Three days later, Koko and I had a conversation about Ball.

"Do you want to talk about your kitty?" I asked.

"Cry," Koko signed.

"Can you tell me more about it?" I asked.

"Blind," she signed.

"We don't see him anymore, do we? What happened to your kitty?" I asked.

"Sleep cat," Koko signed.

A few weeks later, Koko saw a picture of a gray tabby who looked very much like Ball. She pointed to the picture and signed, "Cry, sad, frown."

It was an unhappy time.

News of All Ball's death traveled quickly. We received thousands of letters. People of all ages wrote to us and expressed their sympathy. Some sent cards, others sent photographs, and many children created pictures. They all had one message: that Koko should have a new kitten.

As we approached Christmas, I wanted to get Koko a new kitten. I had no idea how difficult that would turn out to be.

On December 20, Barbara asked Koko, "What would you like for Christmas?"

"Cat cat tiger cat," was Koko's reply.

We heard of a Manx who was soon expecting a litter. We waited weeks until we discovered that the cat was just getting fat. Christmas came and went.

In January I showed Koko a picture of three kittens. One had a long tail, one had a short tail, and one was tailless.

"When you get another kitty, what kind would you like?" I asked.

"That," Koko signed as she pointed to the tailless cat.

"We'll get you a kitty like that," I said. "Is that okay?"

"Good. Nice," Koko answered.

"How do you feel about kitties?" I asked.

"Cat gorilla have visit," she signed. "Koko love."

Koko was ready for a new kitten if only I could find one.

More time went by. I called the Humane Society. They had no kittens at all—let alone a rare, tailless Manx. I called many other places and was disappointed again and again. I was told that not many kittens were born during that time of year.

The worst part of this period was my feeling that I was letting Koko down. I'd watch as someone would ask Koko, "Where's your cat?" And she would look around almost as if she were doing a double take, as if she were looking for Ball.

Then our luck changed. We received a letter from a breeder of Manx cats who wanted to help. He didn't have any kittens then, but he called other Manx breeders nearby until he located a litter of Manx kittens in Southern California. They were just about ready to leave their mother.

We set the date for March 17. The day before, I told Koko she was getting a new kitty—a red kitty. Red is Koko's favorite color. She was very excited.

Then, another delay.

The breeder called. "I'm sorry," he said. "The kitten is not coming today."

Koko was upset. I was disappointed.

"Trouble," she signed.

"We are having trouble getting you a new kitty. We have been trying very hard," I explained.

Finally, on March 24, a red, tiger-striped Manx was brought to our home. Seeing the kitten, Koko purred with pleasure. It was a wonderful moment. She placed him on her chest and petted him.

"Let me hold the kitty," I said.

But Koko would not let go. She kissed and cradled her kitten.

"Baby," she signed.

Koko was happy. Her new kitten had come to stay.

"Lipstick" playing with Koko

# Koko's Kitten

## Meet the Author

**Dr. Francine Patterson** (known as Penny to her friends) has been teaching Koko since the gorilla was one year old. She taught Koko sign language, and the gorilla communicates with humans.

Dr. Patterson has written articles for numerous periodicals including *National Geographic* and *Science*. She has also contributed to several books. She has written two children's books about Koko: *Koko's Kitten* and *Koko's Story*.

## Meet the Photographer

**Ronald H. Cohn** grew up in Chicago, Illinois, within walking distance of the Museum of Science and Industry. He spent all his weekends there. *"That really did it for me,"* he says. *"I had some curiosities, and they were satisfied there. My visits there gave me a very broad interest in all kinds of science."*

Mr. Cohn has been working with Dr. Patterson and Koko from the beginning of the project. *"Koko is like my daughter,"* he says. *"I see her every day."*

Mr. Cohn has this advice for students: *"If you are interested in something, read about it. Try to fulfill your curiosities and find a way to do what you want to do."*

# Theme Connections

## Think About It

- What types of things can Koko communicate to Dr. Patterson?
- Why do you think Dr. Patterson taught Koko American Sign Language?
- What did Dr. Patterson learn about Koko's ability to communicate?

## Record Ideas

In your Writing Journal, write what you have learned about communication from the reading and class discussions. Also, record any questions about communication that you have that have not been answered yet.

## Make a Chart

In a group, write "Verbal Communication" on a piece of chart paper and write below it all the different forms of verbal communication you can think of. Beside that column, write "Non-Verbal Communication" and write below it all the different forms of non-verbal communication you can think of. For example:

| Verbal Communication | Non-Verbal Communication |
| --- | --- |
| | |
| | |
| | |
| | |
| | |

# Breaking into Print

## Before and After the Invention of the Printing Press

Stephen Krensky
*illustrated by Bonnie Christensen*

In a long room with seven tables and seven windows, a French monk sat hunched over a parchment page. He dipped a goose quill in some ink and began to write. The quill made a scratching sound, like a cat clawing at a closed door.

The monk worked six hours almost every day for many months. He hoped to finish before the first snow fell.

The monk was making a book.

The monastery was a small part of a great empire, an empire with far more soldiers than books. Its emperor, Charlemagne, both read and spoke Latin, but he could write little more than his name.

His scribes, however, created a new script that made writing easier to understand.

Parchment was made from a specially prepared animal skin, usually from sheep or goats. The best parchment, called vellum, was made from calfskin. Monks worked only in natural light. The risk of fire from candles posed too great a danger to their precious manuscripts.

Across the countryside, reading and writing counted for little. Few roads were free of robbers or wolves. In the villages, warring peasants lived and died without ever seeing a book.

In time, the villages knew longer periods of peace. The peasants began to eat better and made goods to trade on market day. Successful merchants learned to read and write so that they could keep records of their business. Sometimes their children were taught as well.

Under Charlemagne's rule (800–814 A.D.) Latin was firmly established as the language of the court and education. Charlemagne's scribes also pioneered leaving spaces between words and starting phrases with capital letters.

In the Middle Ages, people believed in superstitions and magic to explain things such as thunderstorms and diseases. Rome had a population of about 500,000 in 300 A.D. After the fall of its empire, no European city had more than 20,000 people for hundreds of years.

More books were now needed, more than the monks could manage alone. In the new book-making guilds, many hands worked together.

Many such books were made with a new material called paper. It was much cheaper than parchment and especially useful for wood or metal block printing.

Block printing was first developed in Asia in the eighth century. No press was used for the printing process. After the blocks were etched and inked, paper was rubbed on them to make a print.

In faraway China, printers had been using paper for centuries. And around 1050, the Chinese printer Pi Sheng had invented movable type using baked clay tablets. Yet few Chinese printers were excited about the invention. Their alphabet has thousands of characters. Only in a dream could printers create so much type. And even if they managed this feat, organizing the type would turn the dream into a nightmare.

The Koreans made further progress. They were actually printing books with movable type around 1400. But their written language is as complicated as Chinese, which discouraged them from making too much of the process.

In the German town of Mainz, one young man knew nothing of Chinese or Korean printing methods. But he was interested in the idea and process of printing. His name was Johannes Gensfleisch, but he followed the old custom of taking his mother's name: Gutenberg.

As a young goldsmith and gem cutter, Gutenberg had learned how to cut steel punches and cast metal in molds. He knew which metals were hard and which were soft, which melted easily and which could take great heat without melting. Over the next few years, Gutenberg tinkered with the printing process.

Although he had a simpler alphabet than the Chinese or Koreans, he still faced many obstacles. There was no room for sloppy or careless design. Printed letters had to fit as closely together as handwritten ones. Printed words had to fall in a straight line. Printed lines had to leave even spaces above and below.

Gutenberg also had to find the proper metal to cast letters and the right ink to use. If the metal was too hard, it would break too easily. If the metal was too soft, it would lose its shape too quickly. As for the ink, it could not be too thick or too thin or likely to fade over time.

Gutenberg cast 290 different letters, numbers, punctuation marks, and other symbols in preparation to printing his first book.

Gutenberg was very practical. He did not believe in reinventing things that already worked fine. So he adapted a winepress for printing. He made it taller, so that the work could be done at waist height, and he created a rolling tray for sliding the paper in and out.

Gutenberg spent almost twenty years building and tinkering. He invented adjustable molds to make letters in different widths. He found the right alloy for casting his letters. He built the upper and lower type cases for storing capital and small letters. He even created the long, grooved composing stick for quickly assembling lines of print.

Gutenberg's great project was a two-column Bible.

It reflected everything he knew of the art of printing.

Gutenberg began working on the Bible project in 1452. It took more than three years to complete. The Gutenberg Bible, published in 1456, was printed in a run of 200 copies. Though it was started with two presses, six presses were eventually used together. As many as 50 copies were printed on vellum, requiring up to 5,000 animal skins.

Soon, other printers were building on Gutenberg's work. They added more than one ink to a page. They added illustrations to the text.

They began printing more than religious works and public notices. They began printing philosophy and poetry and stories of the imagination.

In almost no time at all, printing grew beyond the reach of one man or firm. New printers were setting up shop as fast as they could learn the craft. A generation earlier, printers had produced a single book in a few months. Now they were printing thousands of books a year.

New schools sprang up to teach people how to read. And since books were no longer rare or costly, students as well

Lower costs played a great part in the success of printing. By 1463, ten printed Bibles sold for the price of one manuscript copy. By the year 1500, there were more than 1,000 printers in Europe, and they had printed millions of books.

as teachers could own them. This freed the students from memorizing so much and gave them more time to think.

There were geography books for Christopher Columbus and science books for Nicolaus Copernicus. And there were art and science and engineering and many other books for Leonardo da Vinci, who studied almost everything.

Reading and writing were no longer just for studious monks or highborn lords and ladies. Books were no longer chained up in private libraries or boldly sold for a king's ransom.

The printing press took learning and knowledge from just a privileged few and shared them with everyone else. And that change, more than any other act, set the stage for the modern world to come.

Despite the success of printed books, some wealthy people looked down on them as plain and coarse. Although many schools were for rich students, some poor students were educated for free.

# Breaking into Print

*Before and After the Invention of the Printing Press*

## Meet the Author

**Stephen Krensky** was always interested in fiction and illustrating, but he never thought of becoming a writer. He didn't write down his stories. He made them up in his head at night, using characters from stories he had read.

In college, Mr. Krensky became interested in writing and illustrating stories for children. Since then he has written more than 40 books on subjects including dinosaurs, summer camp, ancient military leader Alexander the Great, Native American children, and teachers.

*"People often ask me how I can write something that twelve-year-olds or nine-year-olds or six-year-olds will want to read. I'm not sure, but I do know that the part of me that was once twelve and nine and six is not neatly boxed and tucked away in some dusty corner of my mind."*

## Meet the Illustrator

**Bonnie Christensen** studied at the Center for Book Arts and Parsons School of Design.

Her first book was an alphabet book she was going to print by hand on a press more than 170 years old. But an editor saw samples of her work and bought the book for her publishing company to print.

*"I love books,"* Ms. Christensen says, *"both for children and adults, antique and new, short and long, with or without illustrations, and so I've come to love the book arts, which include printing, papermaking, book-binding and wood engraving."*

# Theme Connections

## Think About It

The selection states that because of the printing press, students didn't have to memorize everything and could have time to think. Working in a small group, discuss how you think the printing press helped people like Leonardo da Vinci do his work.

## Record Ideas

 Use your Writing Journal to write down the ideas your group discussed. You may choose to simply list your ideas or to present them in chart form.

## Make a List

- Make a list of all the types of different books you read and how they make your life better. Work with a partner to come up with as many types of books as possible.

# FINE Art

***Symbols.*** 1984. **Ida Kohlmeyer.** Oil, graphite, and pastel on canvas.
$69 \frac{1}{2} \times 69$ in. The National Museum of Women in the Arts,
Washington, D.C., gift of Wallace and Wilhelmina Holladay.

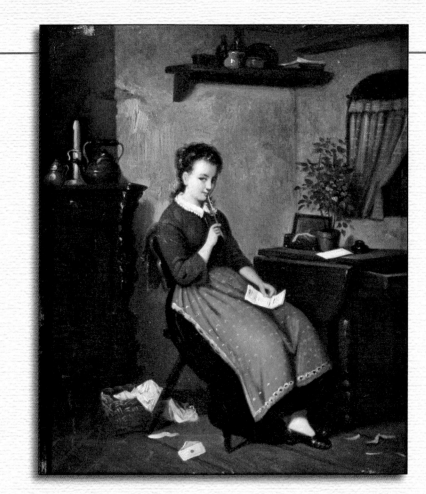

***Young Girl Writing a Love Letter.***
**Johan G. Meyer Von Bremen.**
Josef Mensing Gallery, Hamm-Rhynern,
Germany. Photo: SuperStock.

***The News Room.***
**Jane Wooster
Scott.** Collection
of Vernon Scott IV.
Photo: SuperStock.

# Louis Braille
## The Boy Who Invented Books for the Blind

from *Louis Braille: The Boy Who Invented Books for the Blind*

by Margaret Davidson
illustrated by Bob Dorsey

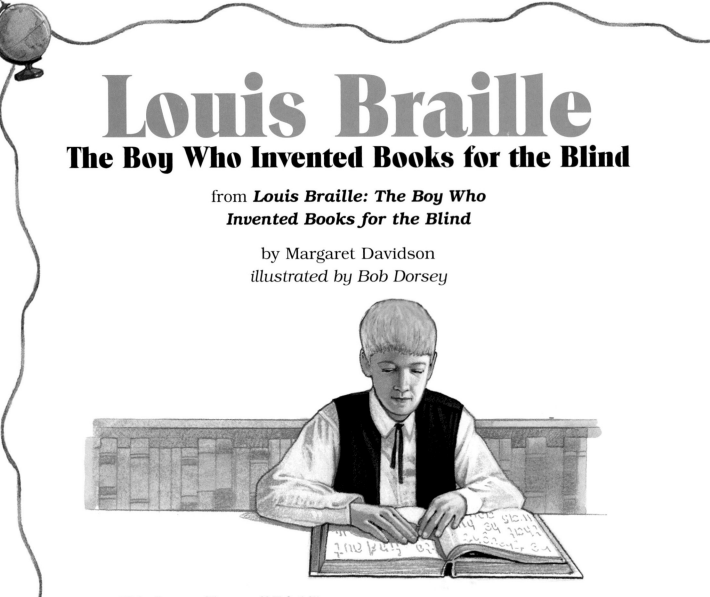

### "It's Just a Show-off Trick!"

So the busy months passed. And Louis grew happier and happier with his life at school. Only one thing was wrong——but it was the most important thing of all.

Louis was taking reading lessons. But it wasn't anything like what he had dreamed of for so long. In 1820 there was only one way for the blind to read. It was called *raised-print*. Each letter of the alphabet was raised from the page. It stood up from the paper background so it could be felt with the fingers. This sounded easy. But it wasn't.

Some of the letters were simple to feel. But others were almost impossible to tell apart. The *Q*'s felt like *O*'s. The *O*'s felt like *C*'s. The *I*'s turned out to be *T*'s and the *R*'s were really *B*'s.

But Louis was determined. Again and again his fingers traced the raised letters until he could tell them apart—most of the time. Then letter by letter he began to feel out words.

But it was so slow! Louis was one of the brightest boys in the school. But often even he forgot the beginning of a sentence before he got to the end of it. Then he had to go back the whole way and start over again.

It would take months to read a single book this way! "This isn't really reading," Louis cried one day. "It's just a show-off trick!"

"It's the best we can do," a teacher answered. "People have tried to find a better way for years."

Louis knew this was true. He knew that people had tried so many things—raised letters, lowered letters, letters of stone and letters of string, letters of wax and letters of wood. One man had even made an alphabet of pins. Louis tried to imagine how it would feel to read a page of pins. Ouch!

Besides, Louis soon learned that in the entire school library there were just fourteen books. Just fourteen! And there were good reasons for this. The raised-print books were very expensive to make. Each one had to be made by hand. They were also big and hard to store. Each letter had to be at least three inches from top to bottom—or blind fingers could not feel it. So only a few words could fit on a page.

No. Louis knew now that there would never be many books for the blind. Not the raised-print way. Then there must be another, better way! There just had to be! Soon that was all Louis could think——or talk——about. And his friends got good and tired of it.

"Do shut up, Louis," they begged.

"But it's so important!" Louis tried to explain. "Don't you see? Without books we can never really learn! But just think what we could grow up to be if only we could read. Doctors or lawyers or scientists. Or writers even! *Anything* almost."

"All right," one of the boys snapped. "We want to read too. Find us a way, if you're so smart."

"I can't," Louis cried. "I'm blind!"

Then one day in the spring of 1821 Captain Charles Barbier came to the Institute. Captain Barbier had worked out a way for his soldiers to send messages to each other in the dark. He called it nightwriting. The Captain thought it might work for the blind too.

Nightwriting used raised dots. A word was broken down into sounds. Each sound was given a different pattern of raised dots. The dots were pushed——or punched——into heavy sheets of paper with a long pointed tool called a *stylus*. When the paper was turned over, raised dots could be felt on the other side.

Dots! At first the blind boys were very excited. There were so many things right about dots! They were so small——just feel how many fit under a single fingertip. And they were so easy to feel!

But before long the boys knew that many things were wrong with Captain Barbier's nightwriting, too. There were so many things it would not do. There was no way to make capital letters or write numbers. There was no way to make periods or commas or exclamation points. It took up far too much room. But most of all it was so hard to learn and hard to feel.

Nightwriting might work well enough for soldiers to send simple notes like "advance" or "enemy is behind you." But it was no way to read or write many words. It was no way to make many books for the blind.

So nightwriting was a failure. Did that mean dots were a failure too? Louis didn't think so. As the days passed it was all he could think of. He even dreamed of dots at night.

And before long Louis made up his mind. He was going to do it himself. He was going to work out a way for the blind to *really* read and write with dots! Quickly and easily. At least he was going to try with all his heart and mind.

Louis set right to work. He was almost never without his tools now. Wherever he went he took heavy sheets of paper, a board to rest them on, and his stylus—the long, thin tool for punching dots. (The stylus was shaped almost exactly like an *awl*—the tool that had made Louis blind.)

Captain Barbier soon heard that someone was trying to make his nightwriting better. He hurried to the Institute to see who it was.

Louis was excited when he learned he was going to meet Captain Barbier, the man who had invented nightwriting. It was Captain Barbier who had worked with dots in the first place! Would the Captain like his ideas? Louis hoped so!

But things went wrong from the start. Captain Barbier's eyebrows rose with surprise as Louis tapped into the room. He had been expecting a man. Not a twelve-year-old boy! Louis couldn't see the look on Captain Barbier's face. But he could hear the chill in his voice.

"I hear you think you have worked out some improvements on my system," the Captain said.

"Yes . . . yes, sir," Louis answered.

"Well?"

"Sir . . . ?" said Louis, confused.

"Explain, explain!"

Louis tried. But the more he talked, the more he could tell that Captain Barbier wasn't really listening.

But Louis kept trying. "S . . . sir. One thing that must be worked out. We must find a way for words to . . . to be spelled the same way again and again."

"Why?" said the Captain. His voice was cold as ice.

"So . . . so we can have books——many books."

"Why?" the Captain asked again. Captain Barbier was like many other people in Louis's day. He felt sorry for blind people. He would never be cruel to them. But he did not think they were as smart as other people——people who could see. He thought blind people should be satisfied with simple things——like being able to read short notes and signs and directions. He certainly didn't think they needed many books!

"Is that all?" said the Captain.

"Yes . . ." Louis was almost whispering now.

"Very interesting," Captain Barbier snapped. "I will think about it." But Louis knew he would not. Captain Barbier was a proud man——too proud. He was used to giving orders and having them obeyed. He might have been able to accept these ideas from another man. But from a boy? A half-grown child? No, he didn't like it. He didn't like it at all!

Captain Barbier said a few more stiff words. Then with a bang of the door he was gone.

Louis sighed. He knew he would get no help from the Captain. He would have to work alone.

Louis tried not to waste a single minute. Even when he
was home on vacation, he worked on his dots. Often his
mother would pack him a lunch of bread and cheese and
fruit, and he would wander out to sit on some sunny
hillside. Other times he sat by the side of the road, bent
over his paper and board. "There is Louis, making his
pinpricks," the neighbors said with a smile as they
passed. What was he doing? Was it some kind of a game
the blind boy was playing to keep himself busy? Louis
didn't try to explain. He just went on punching patterns
of dots.

At home in Coupvray Louis had plenty of free time to
work on his experiments. At school it was not nearly so
easy. There were so many other things to do. Louis had to
go to class. He had to spend an hour or two in one of the
workshops every day. He had to practice his music and
do his homework. He had to eat meals with the rest of the
boys—or someone would come looking for him.

But Louis still found time to work on his ideas. He worked in bits and pieces. He worked before breakfast. And between classes. He worked after dinner. And late at night.

That was the best time of all. The boys were all asleep, and everything was quiet. Hour after hour Louis bent over his board, experimenting with different patterns of dots.

Sometimes he got so tired he fell asleep sitting up. Sometimes he became so excited he forgot what time it was and worked until he heard the milk wagons rattling by under his window. Louis would raise his head with surprise then. For he knew it was early morning. He had worked the whole night through again! Then Louis would crawl into bed to nap for an hour or two—before he had to get up yawning for breakfast and his first class.

Louis's friends became more and more worried about him.

"You never sleep!"

"Half the time you forget to eat!"

"And for what?" a third boy snapped. "A wild goose chase! That's what!"

"Maybe you're right," Louis always answered them softly. And he kept on working.

Three years went by——three years of hard work and trying and not quite succeeding.

Sometimes Louis got so tired he could hardly lift his hand. And sometimes he became very, very discouraged.

Again and again Louis had simplified Captain Barbier's patterns of dots. But still they were not simple enough. No, reading with dots was still too hard.

Were the boys right? Was this a wild goose chase? Men had been working on this problem for hundreds of years——smart men, important men, older men. And one after another *they* had failed. Who did he think he was? What right did he have to think he could do better than they? "Sometimes I think I'll kill myself if I don't succeed," Louis said to Gabriel.

Then Louis had a new and very different idea. It seemed so simple——after he'd had it. Captain Barbier's nightwriting had been based on *sounds*. But there were so many sounds in the French language. Sometimes it took almost a hundred dots to write out a simple word. This was far, far too many to feel easily with the fingertips. But what if he used dots in a different way? What if the patterns of dots didn't stand for sounds at all? What if they stood for the letters of the alphabet instead? There were only twenty-six of them, after all!

Louis was filled with excitement. He was sure he was right! Now he worked even harder. And everything began to fall into place.

First Louis took a pencil and marked six dots on a heavy piece of paper. He called this six-dot pattern a *cell*. It looked like this:

He numbered each dot in the cell:

Then he took his stylus and raised dot number one—
that would stand for *A*:

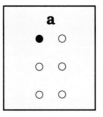

He raised dots number one and two—and that would
stand for *B*:

Raised dots number one and four would be *C*:

Louis made letter after letter. And when he was finished Louis Braille's alphabet of dots looked like this:

| a | b | c | d | e | f | g |
|---|---|---|---|---|---|---|
| h | i | j | k | l | m | n |
| o | p | q | r | s | t | u |
| v | w | x | y | z | | |

Louis ran his fingers over his alphabet. It was so simple! So simple! Fifteen-year-old Louis Braille felt like shouting or crying or laughing out loud. All the letters of the alphabet had been made out of the same six dots—used over and over again in different patterns! He knew it wouldn't look like much of anything to people who could see. But it wasn't supposed to! It was meant to be felt! Quickly. Easily. And it worked!

# Louis Braille
## The Boy Who Invented Books for the Blind

## Meet the Author

**Margaret Davidson** has written several biographies for children. Some of her books have been written under the names Mickie Compere and Mickie Davidson.

Ms. Davidson says about writing books, *"I've been asked [how I came to write books], and the only valid answer I've been able to scare up is that I loved to read when I was a child. It was a whole world to me."*

When she's not writing, Ms. Davidson enjoys art, reading, and visiting museums.

## Meet the Illustrator

**Bob Dorsey** has been a professional illustrator for 17 years, working with a wide range of media and a variety of subjects. Some of his favorite projects include portraits, wildlife, children, and sports. Mr. Dorsey is well known for the many portraits that he has done for the National Baseball Hall of Fame in Cooperstown, New York. His paintings have been exhibited throughout the United States.

# Theme Connections

## Think About It

Biographies are stories about the lives of important people. Join with a small group of your classmates and discuss why Louis Braille was an important person. Here are some things to talk about:

- What did Louis Braille do that was important? Why was it important?
- Why did Louis Braille do what he did?
- How did the work of Louis Braille make a difference to people?

## Record Ideas

Record in your Writing Journal the ideas that you thought about and talked about with your classmates. Write a brief paragraph in your Writing Journal about the importance of Louis Braille.

## Write a Biographical Sketch

Select a classmate and write a biographical sketch of him or her about four or five sentences in length. Talk to your partner about what kind of information he or she would like in the biographical sketch. Draw a portrait of the classmate to include with the biographical sketch.

# Connections

Diane Siebert
*illustrated by Aaron Meshon*

Extending high above the ground,
They stretch forever, wrapped around
The voices sent to rendezvous
With other voices passing through.

And as they travel far away,
The wind-blown conversations sway
As rows and rows of resting birds
Perch happily on miles of words.

481

# One TV Blasting and a Pig Outdoors

from *One TV Blasting and a Pig Outdoors*
by Deborah Abbott and Henry Kisor
*illustrated by Daniel Powers*

"BEEP, BEEP, BEEP," announces my alarm clock. My favorite music blares from my radio.

"Conan, honey, time to rise and shine!" my mom calls.

Stanley, our dog, jumps off my bed and peers out the window. A deep, throaty growl erupts as he spots his Labrador friend, Cody, on his morning walk with his master.

I wait until I hear my brother, Colin, turn off the shower; then I head for the bathroom.

After a quick breakfast, I dash out the door. "Don't forget your lunch," Dad reminds me.

Halfway to school, my best friend, Adam, yells from behind me, "Wait up, Conan! I can't walk that fast this early."

In school, the clanging of lockers echoes through the halls. I skip into my classroom just as the bell rings. As I slip behind my desk, the public address system blares, "Good morning, students. Our special assembly celebrating Martin Luther King, Jr.'s, birthday begins at 9:00 sharp. Teachers, please bring your students to the auditorium at 8:55."

As we enter the auditorium, the school band is playing. The program begins with everyone reciting the Pledge of Allegiance. Then we listen to a recording of the "I Have a Dream" speech by Martin Luther King, Jr. We finish by singing "We Shall Overcome."

This is what my morning is like: full of sound, of noise and chatter. What would it be like never to hear any of the ordinary sounds we take for granted? What would it be like to live in a world of silence? No alarm clock. No radio. No songs or pianos or guitars. No shouted reminders from my parents. No sounds from my dog. No hails from unseen friends. No announcements from the school PA system. No famous voices from our past.

It would be a very different world.

It is my dad's world.

My dad is deaf.

My father hasn't heard a sound since he was three years old, when a disease called meningitis destroyed his hearing.

My dad talks. But he sounds different from other people. His voice is breathy and monotonous, almost like a foghorn heard through the mist and wind from far away at sea. He sounds that way because he can't hear himself talk.

"It's like drawing a picture with your eyes shut," he says. "You can't watch where the pencil goes. The picture isn't as skillfully drawn as it would be if you could see it while you drew it."

But you can understand what Dad says, especially if you stop to listen.

Sometimes I can't hear him over the noise of other things, such as a passing truck. Because he can't hear the truck, he doesn't know he must raise his voice so I can hear him. I have to say, "Dad, a loud truck went by. What did you say?"

My dad reads lips. He can understand what most people are saying if they speak slowly enough and look right at him. If they turn their backs to him, he is lost.

Sometimes he has trouble understanding strangers. When that happens, he will ask someone he can understand to tell him what the other person has said. If there is nobody around, Dad will simply ask the other person to repeat and repeat until Dad gets it right.

If he still can't understand, Dad will pull out pencil and paper and ask the other person to write down the message. This does not happen very often, though. And it almost never happens with people Dad knows, because he's used to their ways of speaking.

Lipreading is not easy because so many sounds look alike. Did someone say "hat" or "cat"? The other words in a sentence often help Dad tell the difference. If the person says, "Put the hat on your head," Dad will know nobody's talking about a cat.

Sometimes Dad makes huge mistakes, and they can be funny. One day when Colin was little, he ran into the living room from the kitchen and said to Dad, "What's that big loud noise?"

Dad got up from the couch and peered out the window with a puzzled expression. "What pig outdoors?" he asked.

"What's that big loud noise?" and "What's that pig outdoors?" look almost exactly alike when you say them. Try saying these questions in front of a mirror without making a sound, and you'll see.

Colin and I learned to lipread, too, because we are around Dad so much and just picked it up by watching his lips as he spoke. We tease Mom by talking to each other at the dinner table without using our voices. Dad knows what we say, but Mom can't understand. (Lipreading is a knack. Some people pick it up easily, and some don't.) Sometimes she thinks we are planning to play a trick on her. But we aren't talking about her at all!

I also have fun lipreading across the room at school, if my target isn't too far away. I mouth the words silently and then lipread what my friend says back to me. The teachers don't like it any more than Mom does.

Many deaf people use sign language, but Dad doesn't know how to sign. When he was growing up, there weren't any other deaf children in the little town where he lived. He had to learn to speak so that he could have friends and go to school. To do this, he took speech lessons.

He still does. He has to practice his speech so people can understand him. He makes up these crazy sentences with all the sounds he needs to practice. For example, he sometimes needs to make his "e" sounds a little sharper. We'll find him sitting at the dining room table saying over and over, "Evil babies eat eels by the seashore."

My father says he's like a baseball pitcher who needs to throw every day to keep his skills sharp. "If I don't practice," he says, "I'll have trouble getting my words in the 'strike zone' where people can understand them easily."

My dad is a newspaper editor and columnist, and he writes books, too. He makes speeches and appears on television and radio shows. He says the speech lessons really pay off. They are hard work, but worth the effort.

Sometimes someone asks why he doesn't learn sign language. He says it's because he has to take speech lessons in order to do his job well, and right now he doesn't have time to do both. He might learn someday, though.

Many people believe deaf children should learn sign language first, then learn to speak. Other people feel that it is more important for deaf children to learn to speak first. Deaf people themselves disagree about this.

Dad says he thinks the choice is a difficult one. He is glad his parents chose the path of speech and lipreading for him, but he will support whatever choice the parents of deaf children make. "It's like religion," he says. "People disagree about the best way to worship. But we don't judge people by the church they choose, do we?"

One problem, Dad says, is that deaf people are not all the same. Some are born without hearing. Others lose their hearing in early childhood, as he did. Still others become deaf as adults, many as they grow old. There are different kinds of deafness, too. Some people, like Dad, are profoundly deaf, which means without usable hearing. Some are severely deaf, others are slightly deaf. Some people can hear low sounds but not high ones. Some can hear better with hearing aids, some cannot. Some grow up with sign language while others grow up with spoken language. Many learn both speech and sign language.

People use different words to describe their hearing loss, or lack of hearing. Many people use "hearing-impaired" as an overall term for any kind of hearing loss.

Others who speak sign language are very proud of it and do not think that their ears are "impaired" at all. They call themselves Deaf people, with a capital *D*.

Still others prefer the term "hard-of-hearing." Many of these people can hear with hearing aids.

"I can't hear at all," says Dad. "I am deaf."

"We're all different," he adds, "and our needs are different. Making the right choices to take care of our needs is more important than the labels we use to describe ourselves."

Dad often tells us stories about what it was like to be deaf when he was little.

Right after he lost his hearing, he had a very hard time. Meningitis, an infection of the membranes that cover the brain, not only made him deaf, but paralyzed him temporarily and caused him to lose his sense of balance.

The high fever of meningitis apparently affected his brain's ability to tell his arms and legs what to do, but the paralysis wore off after a few weeks. His balance organs, which are part of the ears, were damaged by the fever, too. To this day, Dad cannot walk in a straight line with his eyes shut. He needs to have a horizon to focus upon. His eyes have taken over for his ears in more ways than one.

Soon my father also forgot how to talk, because he couldn't hear himself or anyone else. He didn't understand that he had to move his lips and make sounds with his voice box so that other people could hear the words he was thinking.

He quickly learned to lipread simple things like "ball" and "throw." But anything more complicated was impossible for him to understand.

One day Dad wanted some chewing gum. (He liked it so much he remembered how to say the word "gum"!) His mother didn't have any, and neither did the store. This was during World War II, and there was a shortage of chewing gum. My grandmother had to drive him to the store to show him the empty chewing-gum shelves.

How did Dad learn to speak? He already could talk when he became deaf, and although for a while he forgot how, the memory of speaking never quite left him. His mother and father——my Nana and Granddad——found a special teacher of the deaf. This teacher believed in teaching deaf children to speak by first teaching them how to read. She believed parents should be the teachers, and she taught them how to teach their children.

Every day Nana sat down with Dad at a little table to teach him how to read. At some point, Dad says, he made the connection between word and thing. He does not remember how it happened, but he says it must have been very much like the famous moment in which Helen Keller, the deaf and blind philosopher and writer, learned that the word "water" meant the cold fluid that was being poured over her hand from the backyard pump. The dam of silence burst, and the magic of language washed over young Helen.

"For me, the floodgates of memory must have opened at that moment, too," Dad once said. "I must suddenly have remembered what it was like to talk."

I once asked my father whether it was a printed word or a spoken word that allowed him to make the connection. "I just don't know," he replied. "It happened so long ago, when I was very young. I think learning that a word printed on paper stood for an object, like an apple, reminded me that a certain sound made with the mouth also stood for the same thing."

In the beginning, Dad had to learn all over again how individual sounds were made. "Ap-puh," he would say when he saw the piece of fruit. He had a hard time remembering the "l" sound, and Nana had to show him, with the help of a mirror, how to place the tip of his tongue behind his teeth to say "apple."

When Dad's friends, who could hear, saw that Dad was learning to read, they asked Nana to teach them, too. Some days Dad's house looked like a preschool, with all his little friends learning as Nana gave reading lessons to everyone.

Soon Nana brought home books from the library. Every evening Nana or Granddad would sit down with Dad, but they did not read to him, like most parents. He read to them. For him, it was both reading practice and speech practice. But he says he didn't think of it as practice. A new book each evening meant a new adventure, and that was how he grew to love reading.

When Dad was very young, he started reading "The Night before Christmas" to Nana, Granddad, and his brother, my Uncle Buck, every Christmas Eve. He kept on reading that wonderful poem each year, and he was still reading by the tree in Nana and Granddad's living room on Christmas Eve when he was twenty-one years old.

Now, every Christmas Eve we still hear, in Dad's familiar, funny voice, "' 'Twas the night before Christmas / And all through the house / Not a creature was stirring / Not even a mouse . . .'" I bet he'll still be reciting it when *he* is a granddad.

My father says he grew to love reading not just because every story carried him into a new world, but also because it helped him learn things he missed because he couldn't hear. For example, he might not understand a teacher explaining how an automobile engine works, because that's a complicated process, and if he missed one part, he'd miss the whole thing. But a book could provide him with a complete explanation.

There weren't any schools for the deaf in the small town where Dad grew up. But because Dad was reading already, the principal of the regular school said he could try kindergarten there. If he learned, he could stay in the school.

Dad learned, and he continued attending regular schools. If he couldn't understand the teacher, he would ask for extra reading, and that always helped him fill the gaps in his learning.

He was shy about his speech, which he knew sounded odd.

"I had more ways of ducking out of giving an oral report than a zebra has stripes," Dad told me with a laugh. "I would always mysteriously come down with the flu on the morning I was to speak before a class."

He managed to graduate from high school without giving a single speech. Not until he was much older and had become well known in his community did he discover that people were interested in what he had to say, not how he said it. Only then did he lose his fear of speaking in public. "I grew up," Dad says simply, "and now I give speeches all the time."

When he was still young, other kids liked and respected Dad because he was a good reader and a good athlete, and that made them want to get to know him. He often helped his hearing friends with their reading, and he was always one of the first picked for teams.

He became a good swimmer and in high school was on the swimming team that won the state championship. How did he know when to start? Sometimes, but not often, he could feel the crack of the starter's pistol. "And I just kept my eye on the hand of the swimmer next to me," he said. "When I saw it move, off I'd go."

"Being good at something helped make up for speaking funny," he once told me. "It made people respect me." And when people got to know Dad, they and he had very little trouble talking to one another. He could read their lips easily, and they could understand his speech without difficulty.

There were a few misunderstandings, but sometimes they made everyone laugh, even Dad. One day, walking home from school with a friend, my father sneezed loudly. The friend turned to Dad and said something. "What?" said Dad. The friend said the word again. "What?" Dad asked again.

After repeating the word two more times, Dad's friend took a piece of chalk out of his pocket and wrote on the sidewalk:

KAYZOONHITE

Dad took one look and bent double from laughing. He took the chalk from his friend and wrote underneath the word:

GESUNDHEIT

"No wonder I couldn't understand!" Dad told his friend. "You couldn't spell it right!"

Then it was his friend's turn to laugh.

# One TV Blasting and a Pig Outdoors

## Meet the Authors

**Deborah Abbott's** love of books began with her mother, who was also a children's writer. About writing Ms. Abbott says, *"I think about a story for a long time before I write. I always write something and then put it away for a while. Later I look at it again and edit it. There is something uniquely satisfying about finding just the right words so that the sentences read just the way you want them."*

**Henry Kisor** is the book editor for the *Chicago Sun-Times* newspaper and has also written several books. He wrote this book with his wife, Deborah Abbott.

Mr. Kisor says *"As a child I loved reading newspapers and magazines. From all this reading I think I developed a sense of story, whether fiction or nonfiction, and learned that there is joy in the telling."*

## Meet the Illustrator

**Daniel Powers** always loved drawing and painting, but he never went to art school until recently. He completed his degree in illustration at Marywood University in Pennsylvania in 1996. Mr. Powers lives in the high desert country of New Mexico, and he enjoys hiking there with his wife and two dogs.

# Theme Connections

## Think About It

Although this selection is realistic fiction and not an informational essay, it provides a lot of information about ways to help deaf people hear. In groups discuss:

- What would it be like to have hearing loss or to be deaf?
- What would it be like to have people treat you differently because of your hearing loss or your different way of speaking?

## Record Ideas

Work with a classmate and list in your Writing Journal the problems Conan's father encountered and how he overcame each one.

## Share a Story

Plan a short story about a day in your life if you were deaf or hard of hearing. Find a partner and read each other's stories. See which parts of your story were similar to or different from your partner's.

# Bibliography

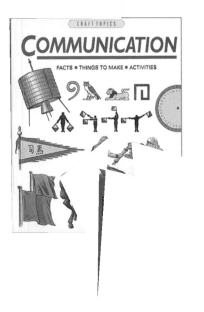

### Communication

**by Ting Morris.** What do early cave paintings and modern technology have in common? Communication!

### Communications: Sending the Message

**by Thomas Streissguth.** Meet the inventors and scientists who are responsible for the biggest breakthroughs in communication technology.

### Handtalk School

**by Mary Beth Miller and George Ancona.** Join these children at a school for the deaf while they prepare their Thanksgiving play and learn the basics of American Sign Language at the same time.

### How Animals Communicate

**by Bobbie Kalman.** Fireflies blink, cranes dance, and whales sing. Learn about the mysteries of animal communication.

## Julie's Wolf Pack

**by Jean Craighead George.**   Kapu the gray wolf must lead his pack through the harsh arctic wilderness. How do the wolves communicate?

## The Printer's Apprentice

**by Stephen Krensky.**   Freedom of the press was incorporated into the Bill of Rights for a reason. See what journalism was like before that document was written.

## The Story of Communications

**by Anita Ganeri.**   From the earliest signs, symbols, and languages, to current breakthrough technology, this book provides a world of information about the history and the future of communications.

## The Unbreakable Code

**by Sara Hoagland Hunter.**   A boy's grandfather tells his own story of being a "Navaho Code-talker" during World War II.

# Trail of Freedom

First were the Native Americans. Different tribes and societies occupied parts of North America. Then the Europeans came and began to set up colonies. That was more than 150 years before the United States came into being. What was life like during those years? It wasn't all log cabins and teepees and battles over territory. A complex society grew up that led to the America we know today. So it's *your* history— even if your ancestors didn't come over on the *Mayflower*!

Baltimore

Philadelphia

Amsterdam

Plimoth

IROQUOIS · LONGHOUSE

TIP · PEKOE*

& Sedition in BOSTON

PHILADELPHIA · PENNSYLVANIA

FREEDMAN BLACKSMITH in ye COLONIES

COLONIAL TRAD

# Early America

by Trevor Matheney

W hen the colonists arrived in America, they were beginning a new life in what to them was a "new world." They weren't completely aware of the long and varied history of the place they called the Americas.

There is evidence that long before Columbus in 1492 or John Cabot in 1497 ever set foot in the Americas, nomadic groups had traveled from Asia and spread out through what is now the United States and South America. These people formed tribes such as the Hopewell and Powhatan and great civilizations such as the Aztec and Inca. In addition, artifacts that have been found suggest visits by the Japanese, Chinese, and Phoenicians.

By the early 1500s many Spanish, English, French, and Portuguese explorers, fishermen, and traders were traveling to the Americas and returning with tales of giant forests, huge stretches of land, and plenty of clear blue waters.

This was particularly interesting to European men. For the most part in Europe at that time, only the oldest son could inherit the land of his father. Thus, for many younger sons the only way to have

Hopewell Culture (300 B.C.–A.D. 500), Ohio: Raven or crow with a pearl eye cut from a sheet of copper

land of their own was to leave Europe. The idea of settling in the New World of the Americas became very attractive.

Other people wanted to escape some of the problems they faced in Europe. In many places in Europe, people were not allowed religious freedom. Some of these people felt they would be able to worship as they pleased in the New World.

Spain and England were the first countries to build settlements in the Americas. These settlements were called colonies. The first Spanish settlement was established at St. Augustine, Florida, in 1565.

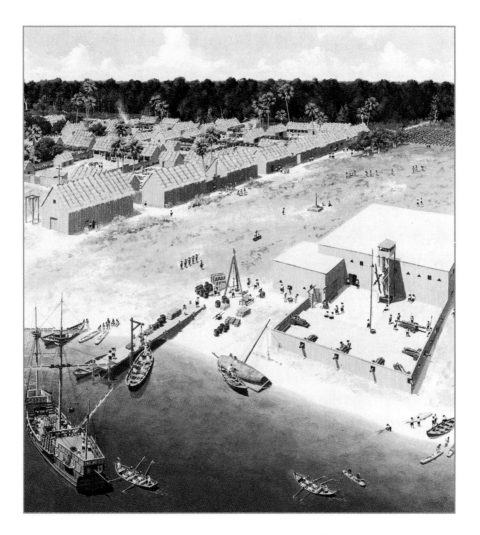

Spanish settlement at St. Augustine, Florida

Sir Walter Raleigh's expedition to Roanoke Island, 1585

In 1585, the English began a colony on Roanoke Island off the coast of what is now North Carolina. This colony failed. However, another attempt to colonize Roanoke Island was made in 1587. It was here that Virginia Dare, the first English child born in America, was born. In 1590, when supply ships returned from England to the Roanoke Colony, everyone had disappeared. No one knows what happened to these early colonists. Because of this, the Roanoke Colony has become known as the Lost Colony.

The Jamestown Colony, founded in 1607, and the Plymouth Colony, founded in 1620, were the first two English colonies that survived. The Jamestown Colony grew into what was called the Virginia Colony. The Plymouth Colony was located in what is now Massachusetts and is where the Pilgrims first settled.

The colonists had to face the hardships of living in a new, unfamiliar land. Many died of disease or starvation. Most of the early colonists were farmers, growing corn, beans, and other food and raising their own animals. They made their own clothes, built their own homes, and worked long, hard days. Few colonial children went to school. Often parents used the Bible to teach their children to read. A few colleges were eventually started for men only. The first college in the colonies was Harvard, founded in 1636 in Massachusetts.

The Native Americans helped these early colonists survive their first years in the New World. However, some Native American groups were upset at having their lands taken by these new people who often brought with them unfriendly ways and diseases deadly to the Native Americans. As more and more colonists arrived, they began taking land from these groups. Several wars were fought between the colonists and the Native Americans. In 1675, a Native American leader named King Philip led the Wampanoag and Narragansett tribes in a war against the colonists in Massachusetts and Rhode Island. These were the same tribes who had helped the colonists survive their first years in the New World. Now, they were angry. Both tribes were nearly destroyed in this war. Clashes between the colonists and the Native Americans continued throughout the colonial period.

Native Americans helping English: Dutch fur trader

Although the colonies were governed by England, not all colonists were English. Many were from Germany, France, the Netherlands, Sweden, Ireland, and Scotland. Others were brought from Africa as indentured servants and later, slaves. By 1700 there were about 250,000 colonists living in the thirteen English colonies in America.

The colonies were different in many ways. For example, in Massachusetts, many of the colonists came as families looking for land to settle. The Rhode Island and Pennsylvania colonies were settled by religious groups in search of freedom to worship as they pleased. The New York Colony became a very culturally and ethnically diverse colony. People from all countries began to settle there.

Many early colonists were unmarried men under the age of twenty-five. In the Maryland Colony, most colonists were single men who arrived as indentured servants. They would work for a period of time, up to seven years, before being given their freedom. In exchange, they received food and shelter, and often learned a trade. Over half of these Maryland colonists died of starvation and disease within a few years of arriving in the colonies.

As the number of indentured servants decreased, there was a shortage of workers in the colonies. To fill this shortage, the colonists turned to slavery. In some colonies, over one-fourth of the population consisted of African slaves. However, not all colonial Africans were slaves. Some had come to America as indentured servants and when their indenture was served they were free to work as they saw fit.

England was not the only country to own land in America. Spain owned what is now Florida, and France owned much of the land west of the thirteen English colonies. This prevented the English colonists from spreading out. Because of this, the population in the English colonies became more concentrated. Cities and towns grew out of the early settlements.

The colonists began to feel they lived in a country so different from England that English law and the English government no longer served them well. These ideas would lead to the Revolutionary War, in which the thirteen English colonies would become the United States of America.

# Early America

## Meet the Author

**Trevor Matheney** is a pen name of Wiley Blevins, who wrote "Music and Slavery" from Unit 4. Mr. Blevins grew up in the South and eventually became a teacher. He has taught both in the United States and in Ecuador. Currently Mr. Blevins lives in New York City, where he is a writer and an editor.

# Theme Connections

## Think About It

Even though people wanted very much to come to America, many difficulties faced the early settlers. Here are some things for you to think about.

- Suppose the only way you could get to America was as an indentured servant. Would you have done it? Explain.
- At first, Native Americans helped the colonists survive. Later, they were at war with them. How do you explain what went wrong? What are your feelings about that?

Look at the Concept/Question Board to see if there are questions that you can answer now. If the selection or your discussion raised new questions about colonial life, post them on the Concept/Question Board. Maybe the next selection will help answer the questions.

## Record Ideas

 Have any of your ideas about the colonists changed after reading this selection? Record your thoughts, ideas, and feelings in your Writing Journal.

## Research Ideas

- Explore what life was like for colonial children. Did they have schools? Did they have to work?
- Find out more about the people who first settled in your area. What Native American groups lived in this area? Who were the first settlers? What did they do for a living?
- The Native Americans helped the colonists at first but later fought them. List the events that led to warfare between the two groups. Come up with a plan that might have prevented the fighting.

# The Voyage Of The Mayflower

Patricia M. Whalen
*illustrated by James Watling*

Pelted by rain under a black sky, the ninety-foot *Mayflower* rolled and pitched on mountainous waves. Its masts were bare because during a storm, a sailing ship must lower all its sails and drift with the wind to avoid capsizing or breaking apart.

Below the main deck, the passengers huddled in the dark. They could hear the wind howling and the waves thudding against the vessel's wooden sides and washing over the deck. Seawater dripped down on them through the canvas covering the deck gratings and seeped through the seams in the planking. The passengers were soaked and shivering; several were seasick besides. As frightened adults tried to comfort terrified children, they prayed for safety in the storm and an end to the long, terrible voyage.

Suddenly, above the din of the storm, they heard the noise of splitting timber. One of the beams supporting the deck had cracked! The ship was in danger of sinking. Then someone remembered a great iron screw brought from Holland. Carefully, the ship's carpenter positioned it beneath the beam and braced it. It would hold; the passengers and crew could reach land safely.

Crossing the Atlantic in 1620 was extremely risky. A wooden ship could leak or break apart in a storm. Since the sails could be raised only in fair weather, it was impossible to predict how long a voyage would last. To avoid the stormy autumn months, ships usually made the crossing in spring or summer. They almost never sailed alone.

Aware of these dangers, the Pilgrims had planned to cross the ocean in two ships in the summer of 1620. The English Separatists from Holland (who called themselves Saints) borrowed money from London businessmen and purchased a small ship, the *Speedwell*. For the Separatists' safety, and to help them establish a profitable colony, the businessmen recruited additional volunteers in London. The businessmen rented the *Mayflower*, a ship three times the size of the *Speedwell*, for these recruits, whom the Separatists called Strangers. The Saints and Strangers met for the first time in Southampton, England, a few days before the ships sailed on August 5.

The tiny *Speedwell* had been refitted with taller masts and larger sails so it could keep up with the *Mayflower*. These changes, however, caused the ship to leak badly at sea. On August 12, the ships put into Dartmouth. After the *Speedwell* was examined and repaired, they set off again on August 23. Two days later, the *Speedwell* began to leak again, and the vessels headed for Plymouth, England. There the ships' masters, carpenters, and principal passengers agreed that the *Speedwell* could not make the crossing.

Over the next few days, the sixty-seven Strangers on the *Mayflower* made room for thirty-five of the Saints from the *Speedwell*, along with their belongings and provisions. On September 6, the *Mayflower* set out from Plymouth alone. The one hundred two passengers, including thirty-four children, would not see land for sixty-six days.

The *Mayflower*, like all ships of the time, was built to carry cargo, not passengers. A few families crowded into the "great cabbin" in the stern. Most of the passengers, however, traveled in bunks or tiny "cabbins" below the main deck and above the hold, where cargo was stored. In this "'tween decks" area, they had only five feet of head room. Each person's living space was smaller than the mattress of a modern twin bed.

The Pilgrims suffered other discomforts. Many were seasick, particularly at the beginning of the voyage. In storms, they were constantly wet and cold. They could not bathe or wash and dry their clothes and bedding. For toilet purposes, they used buckets.

In fair weather, the adults and children who had recovered from seasickness could leave their dim, foul-smelling quarters for the wind and spray of the main deck. The adults took deep breaths of the cold, tangy air and stretched cramped muscles. The younger children, forbidden to run around, played quiet games. Damaris Hopkins, age three, and Mary and Remember Allerton, ages four and six, "tended the baby" (played with dolls). Six- and nine-year-old brothers Wrestling and Love Brewster played "I Spy" and "Hunt the Slipper" with six- and seven-year-old Jasper and Richard More. Finger games such as cat's cradle and paper, scissors, stone were popular with eight-year-old Humility Cooper, Ellen More, John Cooke, John Billington, and Bartholomew Allerton. Elizabeth Tilley, age fourteen, and Mary Chilton and Constance Hopkins, both fifteen, helped prepare the meals.

For cooking, the passengers built charcoal fires in metal braziers set in sandboxes. There was so little space, however, that only a few people could cook at once. When storms made lighting fires dangerous, everyone ate cold meals.

After morning prayers, they ate a simple breakfast of cheese and ship's biscuit (hard, dry biscuit). If cooking was allowed, they might have porridge. Their midday meal might consist of ship's biscuit and cheese or, in fair weather, cooked "pease pottage," boiled salt fish, pork, or beef and any freshly caught bonito or porpoise. Before retiring, they had a light supper. Everyone, even the children, drank beer with their meals because it was preferred to water.

Not until December 11, more than a month after first sighting land, did the Pilgrims decide where they would build their colony. One day, before an exploring party left the *Mayflower,* the passengers and crew had another narrow escape. In his family's "cabbin," fourteen-year-old Francis Billington tried making "squibs" (small fireworks) by lighting short pieces of rope. He then fired a couple of muskets and a fowling piece near an open, half-full barrel of gunpowder. No one knows why his mischief did not blow up the ship.

The *Mayflower* remained anchored offshore during the winter while the Pilgrims built their new homes. On April 5, 1621, the ship set sail for England. With the prevailing winds and currents, it made the return trip in only thirty-one days.

# The Voyage Of The Mayflower

## Meet the Illustrator

**James Watling** was educated at the Barron School of Art and Leeds College of Art. He began teaching in 1954, first in secondary schools, then at McGill University in Montreal after he moved to Canada from England. He retired as an Associate Professor in Art Education in 1995. Some of Mr. Watling's interests include gardening, woodworking, nature and wildlife. He has been illustrating since the 1960s and continues this today.

# Theme Connections

## Think About It

The journey from England to the east coast of America was plagued by problems and dangers. This was only the beginning of a difficult life for the Pilgrims. Form small groups to talk about what you have learned about colonial life. Here are some things to think about.

- Was it wise to bring children on the *Mayflower?* Explain. What else could the Pilgrims have done?
- Why did it take the Pilgrims so long to decide where to build their colony? What things did they have to look for?

Look at the Concept/Question Board to see if there are questions that you can answer now. If the selection or your discussion raised new questions about colonial life, post them on the Concept/Question Board.

## Record Ideas

 Did you learn new things from this selection? What important information do you want to remember? Record this information in your Writing Journal.

## Research Ideas

- Explore what it was like in Europe at the time the Pilgrims made their journey to America. Why did people want to leave Europe and face the risks of coming to America?
- Find out more about the *Mayflower*. How was it built? Could it have been bigger, safer, or more comfortable?
- Research to find recipes for the foods, or similar foods, that the Pilgrims had on the *Mayflower*. Try out some of these recipes and share the results.

# The Early Houses

from *The Pilgrims of Plymouth*
by Barbara Beck

Early home of the Pilgrims

518

The first homes built by the Pilgrims had only one room, with an overhead loft for sleeping. Felling trees and sawing them into planks was no easy task, especially since these houses were built in cold weather and the lumber had to be hauled a quarter of a mile to the settlement. The roofs were thatched with rushes, and the chimneys were made of sticks of wood daubed with clay. The tiny windows were covered with oilpaper and were heavily draped with cloth to keep out the cold.

Each house had a large fireplace, in front of which everyone gathered for warmth, food, and light. Cranes were used to hold large brass and iron cooking pots and kettles over the wood fire. A huge table, a stool or two, some plain wooden chairs, a chest, and beds took up most of the space in the tiny house. At bedtime, the children went up the ladder to the sleeping loft.

Naturally there was a lot of clutter. The table might hold a freshly killed duck, some herbs from the garden, a basket of wild berries, the Bible and perhaps another book, a loaf of bread fresh from an outdoor oven, bowls, and a gun in need of repair. The walls had many pegs on which clothing was hung. Stored in other parts of the room might be a barrel of beer, a musket, a fowling piece for shooting wild birds, a keg of gunpowder, a bag of feathers for stuffing a mattress or pillow, a whisk broom, a small chest for clothing and linens, woodcutting tools, and many other things.

Early home of the Pilgrims——interior showing fireplace

It was not long before the colonists found their quarters too cramped, and by 1640 many new and larger homes had been constructed. These houses were built around central brick chimneys and had wooden roofs; thatched roofs were no longer used because of the risk of fire. In addition to a kitchen, the new houses had a parlor, which was often used as a bedroom. Upstairs were two more bedrooms with fireplaces.

In some families the most prized belonging was a huge homemade fourposter bed. A big bag stuffed with feathers often served as a mattress. Less well-to-do folk stuffed their mattresses with bits of cloth, while the really poor people slept on corn husks. Mattress springs were made of cords laced across the bed; they were always getting loose and sagging. Underneath the bed was a truckle, or trundle, bed——a small bed that was stored under the bigger bed in the daytime and pulled out at night. Cribs, cradles, and cots were put anywhere there was room. There were plenty of blankets for warmth.

The wide pine-board floors were scoured with beach sand to keep them clean. By the 1640s, most of the oil-paper windows had been replaced by diamond-paned casements that still did not let in much light. Both outside and inside, the walls were made of cedar. Unpainted cedar clapboards were often put up only on the front of a house for the benefit of passersby. The Pilgrim houses were not log cabins. The log cabin was introduced to America in the 1640s by Delaware Bay settlers from Sweden.

Many houses also had attached lean-tos. These supplied space for additional bedrooms or perhaps for a study.

# The Early Houses

## Meet the Author

**Barbara Beck** was born on March 25, 1927, in Boston, Massachusetts.

Ms. Beck spent several years working as a freelance journalist and also writing advertising copy. Later she had a variety of jobs, which included working in an advertising agency, being a real estate broker, and lecturing on books and traveling. These different experiences have given her a rich background from which to work.

# Theme Connections

## Think About It

This selection gives a glimpse of what it was like to be in early Pilgrim homes. Form small groups to talk about what you have learned about Pilgrim homes. Here are some things to think about.

- What are all the things that early house builders had to make by hand that today you could buy?
- Why would Pilgrims cover their windows with oilpaper? What good was it?
- How were Pilgrim homes the same as our homes? How were they different?

Look at the Concept/Question Board to see if there are any questions that you can answer now. If the selection or your discussion raised new questions about colonial life, post them on the Concept/Question Board. Maybe the next selection will help answer the questions.

## Record Ideas

Did you find any new information or important details you would like to remember from this selection? Record them in your Writing Journal.

## Research Ideas

- Find out more about Pilgrim homes. How did the colonists make window glass, door hinges, and wooden planks? Build a model of one of the first homes or of a later Pilgrim home.
- Think about both Native American and non-Native American housing in North America. How was housing adapted to the many different climates? How was housing adapted to available resources?

# Pocahontas

### ▰▰▰▰ from *The Virginia Colony*

by Dennis B. Fradin
*illustrated by Robert Roth*

This painting of Pocahontas, done while she was touring England shortly before her death, shows her in English clothing.

Exactly when and where the Native American girl named Matoaka was born is not known, but it probably was in eastern Virginia around 1595. When the Jamestown colonists arrived in 1607, Matoaka was about twelve years old. Little is known about Matoaka's life away from the colonists, but when she was with them, she lived up to her nickname, Pocahontas, which means "The Playful One."

After Pocahontas saved John Smith's life in early 1608, there was a short time of peace between the colonists and the Native Americans. During this time Pocahontas often came to Jamestown, where she would challenge the young men to compete with her at performing handsprings and running races. The English youths taught her a phrase: "Love you not me?" which Pocahontas would repeat to them. In return, Pocahontas taught Captain Smith and the other colonists some Native American words.

In the spring of 1608, John Smith got into an argument with Pocahontas's people during a bargaining session and took seven of them captive. Powhatan tried to get the prisoners released, but nothing worked until he sent Pocahontas to Jamestown as his agent. Captain Smith and the other leaders of Jamestown let the prisoners go for the sake of Pocahontas.

About a year after this incident, Smith left Virginia, and relations between the Native Americans and the colonists worsened. Those few times when the Native Americans and the colonists met peacefully, Pocahontas and her people asked what had become of Captain Smith. The colonists always said that he was dead.

In 1613 Pocahontas was staying in a Native American village along the Potomac River when she was kidnapped and taken first to Jamestown and then to Henrico. In Henrico she was given fancy English petticoats and dresses to replace her deerskin clothes, taught the English language, and renamed Rebecca. How Pocahontas felt about this we do not know. We do know, however, that Pocahontas met the tobacco planter John Rolfe in the summer of 1613 and that the next spring the two were married in a ceremony that was Jamestown's big social event of the year.

In 1616 Pocahontas and her husband went with their year-old son, Thomas, and several other Native Americans to England. She was introduced to royalty and invited to balls and banquets. In England, Pocahontas also learned a startling piece of news: John Smith was still alive! One day in the fall of 1616 Captain Smith called at the house where she was staying near London.

Pocahontas, who by this time was ill because of England's damp and chilly weather, was both pleased and upset at the sight of Smith. "They did tell us always you were dead," she said. Pocahontas then teased Smith for having forgotten her, reminded him that she had adopted him long ago, and called him "Father." When Smith said that she should not call him "Father," Pocahontas answered, "I tell you then I will, and I will be forever and ever your countryman."

A few minutes later Captain Smith left, and the two never met again. In March of 1617, just as the Rolfes were about to sail home to Virginia, Pocahontas died of smallpox. The woman who had saved John Smith's life and who had once performed handsprings in Jamestown was only twenty-two years old when she died. Thomas Rolfe, her son, was educated in England. At age twenty he returned to Virginia, where he became a popular citizen and even helped defend the colony against the Native Americans.

# Pocahontas
### ▰▰▰ from *The Virginia Colony*

## Meet the Author

**Dennis Fradin** taught elementary school students before he became an author. Now he has written almost 150 books. He is a man who loves his work. He says, *"I have the time of my life as a children's book author. Each day I take about five steps from my bedroom into my office, where I spend my time reading, writing, rewriting, and phoning people for information. Often I travel to do in-person research."*

Mr. Fradin researches his books very carefully and sometimes rewrites them five or six times. He says, *"I also check over all my facts line by line to make sure everything is accurate. So all that keeps me pretty busy. I try not to let a day of the year go by without working."*

## Meet the Illustrator

**Robert Roth** grew up on Long Island, New York, and studied art at the Rhode Island School of Design.

Mr. Roth has been drawing since he could pick up and hold a pencil. Almost everywhere he goes he carries a sketchbook. He likes to draw from real life outside the studio to keep his eye alert and his work fresh.

# Theme Connections

## Think About It

Pocahontas was an important historical figure from colonial times. She existed in two very different worlds. Here are some things for you to think about.

- How did a young girl manage to be a more successful ambassador than the leaders of her tribe?
- Would you call Pocahontas's son a traitor to his people? Why or why not?

Look at the Concept/Question Board to see if there are questions that you can answer now. If the selection or your discussion raised new questions about colonial life, post them on the Concept/Question Board.

## Record Ideas

What did you think of this story? What did you like about it? What did you learn from it? Record your thoughts in your Writing Journal.

## Research Ideas

- Pocahontas has been the subject of legend, poems, and stories. Read several selections about Pocahontas and compare them. Try to decide what is fact and what is fiction. Make an information web for Pocahontas.

# FINE Art

***Sampler.*** c.1792. **Patty Coggeshall.** Linen embroidered with silk thread.
$19\frac{1}{2} \times 16\frac{5}{8}$ in. The Metropolitan Museum of Art, Rogers Fund, 1913.
Photograph © 1995 The Metropolitan Museum of Art.

*The Mason Children: David, Joanna, and Abigail.* 1670. **Attributed to the Freake-Gibbs Painter.** Fine Arts Museum of San Francisco, Gift of Mr. and Mrs. John D. Rockefeller 3rd, 1979.7.3.

*Quilled Buckskin Robe.* National Museum of the American Indian, Smithsonian Institution.

531

# Judith:
## The Life of a Slave

Cathleene Hellier and
Brandon Marie Miller
*illustrated by Alexander Farquharson*

She was known simply as Judith, and what she felt or thought about her life as a slave in eighteenth-century Williamsburg, we will never know. Slaves made up half of Williamsburg's population, but none left a written record of their feelings about slavery.

Many families in Williamsburg owned slaves, but most owned only one or two. Wealthier families might have owned ten to fifteen slaves but seldom more than twenty. Slaves were an important part of the daily life and business of the Virginia capital, although they were often overlooked by historians because they left no written record.

Most slaves in Williamsburg worked as domestic servants or were trained as craftsmen. Many domestic slaves performed several tasks, including nursing, ironing, spinning, gardening, and sewing. Slaves who worked as craftsmen included carpenters, blacksmiths, shoemakers, and cabinetmakers, among others.

From what we can gather, Judith was William Prentis's family cook. As cook, her workdays were long and demanding. The kitchen where she worked was separate from the house, and the open fire made it very hot during the long Virginia summers. Judith rose early to prepare the fire and to cook the Prentis family's breakfast. As soon as breakfast was cleared away, she began the preparations for dinner, the largest meal of the day, served early in the afternoon. Dinner in a household like the Prentis's might have included two courses, including several kinds of meat, vegetables, relishes, beverages, and desserts. Judith also cleaned the many pots, spits, and kettles required to make such a meal. Happily for her, the leftovers from dinner were served for supper in the early evening.

Judith had little spare time to spend with her family. Because she was the cook, however, her children often received special treats that their mother saved from the Prentis's table. Her older daughters probably helped her in the kitchen on occasion.

Judith and her children lived above the kitchen, under the eaves. They slept and kept their few possessions there. The slave owners supplied their domestic slaves with simple clothing and bedding. Sometimes the slaves even wore hand-me-downs from the master's family. Domestic slaves often received tips from guests, and some slaves earned money by raising chickens for sale. They could spend this money in the local stores, buying better clothing for special occasions or items to make their living quarters more comfortable.

Some slave children, including Judith's daughter Molly, went to special schools for blacks, an unusual opportunity for slaves in Colonial Virginia. One school, the Bray School, was founded by an English philanthropic (charitable) organization that listed Benjamin Franklin as a member. The school in Williamsburg opened in 1760.

Students were taught to read the Bible, keep themselves clean and behave well, and speak distinctly. The founders hoped that pupils would attend the school for three years, but this rarely happened. When children were old enough to work, they were usually taken out of school.

Like slaves everywhere, Judith lived under a strict legal code designed to prevent slave uprisings. Blacks could not possess weapons or assemble except for public worship. (Church teaching enforced the idea that it was their duty to be obedient and patient.) Punishments for stealing or for resisting a white man included whipping, mutilation, and hanging. Yet slaves who committed a crime in which a person was not killed usually received a light sentence if it was their first offense. Even though laws were strict, they were not always strictly enforced. For example, some masters allowed their slaves to have guns for hunting.

Runaway slaves were returned to their masters. Runaways were often trying to visit family members who lived in other parts of the colony. Some ran away because they were trying to escape a particular master. The busy capital was a favorite hide-out for runaways, and it seems that Williamsburg slaves did a fairly good job of hiding fugitives.

The family life of a slave was uncertain. If a master died or got into debt, some or all of his slaves might be sold. Sometimes the members of slave families were sold to different masters who lived far apart. Slaves must have feared these separations. When William Prentis died in 1765, he willed Judith and her three children to his teenage daughter Elizabeth. When Elizabeth died unmarried in 1770, Judith and her children passed to Elizabeth's older brother John. By then, Judith had at least five children. John also inherited the family home in Williamsburg, and Judith and her children continued to live on the property.

During each of these upheavals in the Prentis family, Judith probably worried about the fate of her own family.

Yet she had more cause to worry when John Prentis became very sick in 1775. John's wife was mentally ill and would not be able to manage the household if her husband died. When he did die, Judith was alarmed to learn that he had bequeathed only three of her children to his brother Joseph. Another daughter, Molly, was to be kept by John's family but hired out to work for others. Her work would provide money to help support John's widow. Finally, Judith learned that because the widow could not run a household, Judith would no longer be needed. She and her youngest son, Tom, were to be sold at auction. Her worst fears had come true; she and her children would be separated.

The slaves of Colonial Williamsburg had a big impact on the city's life. These men and women worked in almost every household, in the taverns, at the college, and in the craft shops. Overall, Williamsburg slaves were a trained and skilled group. Some even had a little education. But what a Williamsburg slave actually felt, feared, or hoped for, we can only imagine.

# Judith:
## The Life of a Slave

## Meet the Authors

**Brandon Marie Miller** grew up loving to read and loving history. *"I find history fascinating. You have to be a nosy person to want to read all about people's lives. I like finding the details that make people of the past seem human. That is why I often times have wanted to tell about women."*

**Cathleene Hellier** is a historian and character interpreter at Colonial Williamsburg. To help her identify with people in the past, Ms. Hellier reads diaries and letters to *"find out what people were really doing then."*

Besides reading, Hellier advises young writers to go to museums, listen to stories, and *"ask yourself if that is a story you think someone else would be interested in hearing."*

## Meet the Illustrator

**Alexander Farquharson** started out studying astronomy before deciding on a career in art. He attended the School of the Museum of Fine Arts in Boston, then continued his education at the Art Students League of New York and the Academy of Fine Arts in Rome. Mr. Farquharson has been an illustrator for 25 years and presently lives in Massachusetts with his wife, daughter, and cat. He also enjoys outdoor painting and playing the piano.

# Theme Connections

## Think About It

Because enslaved people in colonial America left no written records, their importance to the life of the colonies has often been overlooked. Here are some things for you to think about.

- How do you think the authors learned the facts about Judith? What parts did they have to guess at?
- Suppose you were a slave in a comfortable household in Williamsburg. What would be the worst thing for you about being in that situation?

Look at the Concept/Question Board to see if there are questions that you can answer now. If the selection or your discussion raised new questions about colonial life, post them on the Concept/Question Board. Maybe the next selection will help answer the questions.

## Record Ideas

Did this selection make you change any of your ideas about colonial America in general? Record your thoughts in your Writing Journal.

## Research Ideas

- You have read about laws concerning slavery. Find out more about those laws. What were these laws? How did they get passed?
- Many, many slaves were brought to America. How were the slaves captured? How were they transported to America? Who captured and transported them?

# Freedom

Langston Hughes
*illustrated by Tyrone Geter*

Freedom will not come
Today, this year
    Nor ever
Through compromise and fear.

I have as much right
As the other fellow has
    To stand
On my two feet
And own the land.

I tire so of hearing people say,
*Let things take their course.*
*Tomorrow is another day.*
I do not need my freedom when I'm dead.
I cannot live on tomorrow's bread.
    Freedom
    Is a strong seed
    Planted
    In a great need.
    I live here, too.
    I want freedom
    Just as you.

# Phillis Wheatley
## Poet

Susan Altman
*illustrated by George Crespo*

*Should you, my lord, while you peruse my song,*
*Wonder from whence my love of Freedom sprung,*
*Whence flow these wishes for the common good,*
*By feeling hearts alone best understood,*
*I, young in life, by seeming cruel fate*
*Was snatch'd from Afric's fancy'd happy seat.*

Those are the words of Phillis Wheatley, a young, African-born woman who was kidnapped by slave traders when she was about eight years old and brought to Boston, Massachusetts, in 1761. There she was bought by John Wheatley, a wealthy merchant tailor, as a lady's maid for his wife Susannah.

A small, frail child, Phillis was well cared for. She was assigned chores that she was able to do. Very intelligent, she learned English quickly and was taught to read. When she was fourteen, she began writing poetry. Her first work to receive widespread attention was "An Elegiac Poem, on the Death of that Celebrated Divine . . . George Whitefield." It was printed in Boston in 1770.

Phillis Wheatley was never very strong. When her health began to fail in 1772, the Wheatleys freed her and sent her to England. While she was there, she impressed several members of the nobility. They arranged for her book, *Poems on Various Subjects, Religious and Moral,* to be published. Many prominent Massachusetts men (including John Hancock) signed the foreword of her book.

Arrangements were made for Ms. Wheatley to be introduced to the king and queen of England. But before the meeting could take place, she received

word that Mrs. Wheatley was ill, so she quickly returned to America.

When Mrs. Wheatley died in 1774, Ms. Wheatley remained with the family and kept house for John Wheatley. She continued to write, and, in 1775, dedicated a poem to George Washington, which appeared in Thomas Paine's *Pennsylvania Magazine.* Washington was so impressed that he invited her to visit him at his headquarters in Cambridge, Massachusetts.

After the death of John Wheatley in 1778, Ms. Wheatley was forced to move from the house where she had grown up. Shortly thereafter, she married a man named John Peters. He was frequently away, and the marriage was unhappy. Although in ill health, Phillis Wheatley had to work as a servant to support herself.

Two of her three children died shortly after they were born. Then on December 5, 1784, she passed away at age thirty-one. Her third child died the same day.

Phillis Wheatley is remembered today because of her role in the development of black American literature. Her sensitive poetry proved at the time that blacks, when given the opportunity, were equal to whites, both intellectually and emotionally. At a time when the fight against slavery often seemed endless, Phillis Wheatley's poems provided both hope and ammunition.

# Phillis Wheatley
## Poet

## Meet the Author

**Susan Altman** is the producer of the Emmy Award-winning television programs *It's Academic, It's Elementary,* and *Pick Up the Beat.*

"I became an author by accident," she says. "I was tutoring a ten-year-old boy, and he asked me to get him a book on black history. I said, 'Sure. No problem.' But when I went to the store, there were very few books for children about African-Americans. So, I decided to write one."

## Meet the Illustrator

**George Crespo** studied art at the Parsons School of Design in New York City. After graduating, he decided to try writing children's stories. He illustrated and published two of these and illustrated three books for other authors. In addition to being an author and an illustrator, Mr. Crespo teaches art and sculpting. His sculptures have been exhibited at musuems and galleries throughout the United States.

# Theme Connections

## Think About It

Wheatley lived only twenty-three years after she was taken from Africa. However, she played an important role in the development of African-American literature. Here are some things for you to think about.

- What difficulties did Phillis Wheatley face during her short lifetime? How do you think these experiences affected her poetry? How did her poetry affect society?
- Phillis Wheatley was given her freedom but came back to the Wheatley home. What role did she fill when she came back? Why did she come back? Should she have returned? Why or why not?

Look at the Concept/Question Board to see if there are any questions that you can answer now. If the selection or your discussion raised new questions about colonial life, post them on the Concept/Question Board. Maybe the next selection will help answer the questions.

## Record Ideas

 Record your reaction to this selection in your Writing Journal.

## Research Ideas

- Not everyone believed in slavery during colonial times. Find out more about who was opposed to slavery. What arguments were presented on both sides of the slavery issue?
- Some freed African-Americans lived in the North during colonial times. What were their lives like? How did they make their living?

# Martha Helps the Rebel

A Play by Carole Charles

*illustrated by Charles Shaw and Dennis Hockerman*

**Cast of Characters**

1. Martha
2. Mother
3. 1st American Soldier
4. 2nd American Soldier
5. 3rd American Soldier
6. 1st British Soldier
7. 2nd British Soldier
8. 3–5 British Soldiers—
   non-speaking parts

*(Setting: South Carolina, 1780. From the back of their farmhouse, a mother and her ten-year-old daughter, Martha, watch three American soldiers walk through the nearby woods.)*

**Martha:** Look at the soldiers, ma!

**Mother:** I see them, Martha. They must be coming from Charleston.

**Martha:** Are they American soldiers?

**Mother:** Yes.

**Martha:** I wish I were big enough to be a soldier like pa. I'd chase all the British soldiers right back to England! Would you like to be a soldier, ma?

**Mother:** *(musing)* Sometimes I would. But you and I need to take care of the farm until your pa comes home.

*(Three American soldiers walking through the woods. British soldiers in hiding nearby.)*

**1st Am. Soldier:** *(sings)* "Come all you brave soldiers, Both valiant and free, It's for independence, We all now agree."

**2nd Am. Soldier:** Hey, quiet down! Everyone in South Carolina can hear you.

**1st Am. Soldier:** Good! Then all the British soldiers in the colony will run at the sound of my voice. *(Sings the song again, just as loudly.)*

**3rd Am. Soldier:** Come on, quiet down. If any British soldiers have landed this far south, I'd like to hear them before they hear us.

**1st Am. Soldier:** Ah, there aren't any British around here.

**3rd Am. Soldier:** Maybe not. That's what we're supposed to find out.

*(Woods. 1st Am. soldier whistling the tune from previous scene.)*

**2nd Am. Soldier:** When we get back to Charleston, I'd like to . . .

*(Interrupted by a musket shot, Whistling stops abruptly. 2nd Am. soldier yells and falls dead.)*

**3rd. Am. Soldier:** British! Stay down!

*(Shots fired from both sides.)*

**1st Am. Soldier:** *(whispering)* Let's run for it. We'll never be able to hold them off here.

**3rd Am. Soldier:** All right . . . now!

*(Musket shot strikes 3rd Am. soldier, who yells and falls.)*

**1st Am. Soldier:** Oh, no! *(Fiercely, to himself)* I have to get out of here!

*(Soldier exits, running, crouched. Sound of feet running, crashing through low brush. Muskets fire several more times.)*

*(Woods. American soldier enters, running through low brush. About eight British soldiers pursue. American soldier exits on other side.)*

**1st Br. Soldier:** Let's get him!

**2nd Br. Soldier:** *(panting heavily)* I can hardly run with this heavy pack.

**3rd Br. Soldier:** *(also panting)* Hey, just a minute. Slow down. Listen, he can outrun us easily. We're wearing winter uniforms and carrying packs. All the American has to carry is a musket.

**1st Br. Soldier:** But we have to stop him before he reaches Charleston. The American army must not know our position or strength.

**3rd Br. Soldier:** *(still breathing heavily)* I know. So let's outsmart that American soldier. Hide the packs somewhere in the bushes. Then spread out and we'll search the ways to Charleston. He'll have to stop for food and water, perhaps for rest. If we move quickly, we'll find him.

*(Martha grooms a riding horse. Mother enters. Mother and Martha see the American soldier running through the woods as if pursued.)*

**Martha:** Ma, look!

**Mother:** I see. Martha, ride old Jonathan as fast as you can to that soldier. Bring him back by the stream bed so no one will see him. I'll wait in the kitchen.

**Martha:** What if there are British soldiers right behind him?

**Mother:** You said you wanted to fight. This is your chance. Hurry, before it's too late.

*(Martha and horse exit. Sound of hoofbeats.)*

*(Kitchen. Mother is lowering a quilting frame from the ceiling. Frame has a nearly completed quilt attached. Soldier and Martha enter from side. Soldier appears haggard, exhausted.)*

**Mother:** Martha, go back outside and ride old Jonathan hard around the pasture, as though you were exercising him. If anyone comes, I don't want a panting horse tied to my front porch.

**Martha:** Yes, ma. *(Exits.)*

**Soldier:** Ma'am, I . . .

**Mother:** *(interrupting)* We can talk later. Right now I want you up on those rafters, right over the spot where the quilting frame will be.

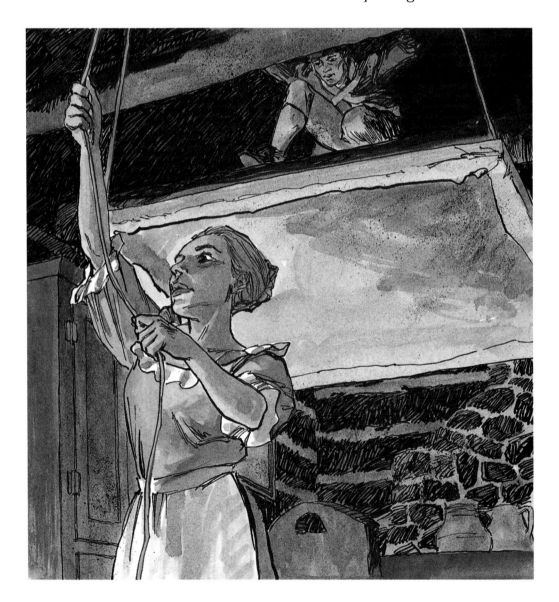

**Soldier:** Up there? But . . .

**Mother:** *(interrupting)* Soldier, if you want to live, you'd better get up on those rafters, and fast!

*(American soldier balanced on the rafters. Mother raising the quilting frame. British soldiers can be seen through a window, approaching the house from the woods.)*

**Am. Soldier:** Ma'am, you don't know how much I appreciate your help.

**Mother:** *(speaking as she raises the frame)* It's all right. My husband is a soldier with the Continental Army too. Maybe someone will help him one day.

**Am. Soldier:** I'm very grateful for . . .

**Mother:** *(interrupting)* Hush! *(whispering)* Soldiers coming! Don't make a sound!

*(Loud knocks on the door.)*

**Br. Soldier:** *(from outside)* Open up! *(More loud knocks.)* Open up, I say!

*(Kitchen. American soldier completely hidden from view by quilt and frame. Mother has lifted hot skillet off fireplace in pretense of busyness. Loud knocks continue.)*

**Mother:** Just a minute!

*(More loud knocks. British soldiers push open the door and enter the kitchen.)*

**Br. Soldier:** Sorry, ma'am. We're looking for someone.

**Mother:** *(indignant)* You might have waited until I opened the door!

*(Soldiers begin searching the house.)*

**Mother:** What are you doing!

**Br. Soldier:** Looking for someone, like I said. Arnold, you keep watch outside. Two of you search the barn and grounds. The rest of you search every inch of this house.

**Mother:** You have no right to search my house!

**Br. Soldier:** You have nothing to be afraid of, ma'am, *(threateningly)* unless we find an American soldier here.

*(Kitchen. Mother seated. British soldiers still searching. Martha comes running in.)*

**Martha:** Ma! What are they doing?

**Mother:** They're just looking for someone, Martha.

**Br. Soldier:** Where have you been, little girl?

**Martha:** *(defiant)* My name is Martha, not "little girl"! I've been out riding my horse.

**Br. Soldier:** *(quiet but threatening)* You wouldn't have been hiding an American soldier somewhere, would you?

**Martha:** *(still defiant)* I told you, I was riding my horse.

**Mother:** Martha, come sit down with me. They'll be leaving soon.

**Martha:** *(through clenched teeth)* I hope so!

*(Kitchen. American soldier climbing down from rafters. Twilight.)*

**Mother:** It's safe now. The British have gone.

**Soldier:** Thank you. I'm very grateful. *(Thoughtful)* Do you know if there are many British around?

**Mother:** We haven't seen British soldiers for several months, until today.

**Martha:** *(excited)* I'll bet there are thousands of British just over the hill, ready to attack Charleston!

**Soldier:** *(laughing gently)* Well, perhaps. But we rather expect an attack from the sea. That's how they attacked at the beginning of the war.

**Martha:** Maybe they're trying to trick you! You should go look for yourself. I'll bet there are thousands of British over there, just polishing their muskets and laughing.

**Soldier:** *(slowly)* That is possible. Perhaps I should take a look as soon as it's dark.

*(Early morning, outside the farmhouse. Mother milking a cow. Martha enters, carrying a basket of eggs. Soldier rushes on stage.)*

**Soldier:** You were right, Martha! The British are landing along the coast. It looks as though they are preparing to march on Charleston.

**Mother:** *(very nervous)* Keep your voice down! The British came back again last night. They're still looking for you, and for any other American soldiers. All the roads are guarded.

**Soldier:** And I know why! Most of our troops in Charleston are guarding the coast. If the British attack from the south, they will meet almost no resistance.

**Martha:** You'll have to tell them! You'll have to get through!

**Mother:** But how? It would be easier for . . . for this cow to pass the British. An American soldier couldn't make it!

**Martha:** I have an idea!

*(Martha, mother, and soldier taking clothes out of a chest. Soldier half dressed as an old farmer.)*

**Mother:** Pa won't mind our giving these clothes to you. They just might help you get past the British.

**Martha:** You really look like a farmer! *(Laughs with delight.)*

**Soldier:** Martha, you had a good idea. And making me look so old is the best part of the disguise.

*(Dirt road. British soldiers standing guard, blocking road. American soldier disguised as old farmer enters, accompanied by Martha, who leads a milk cow.)*

**"Farmer":** Afternoon, gentlemen.

**1st Br. Soldier:** Hold on, old man. Where are you taking the cow?

**"Farmer":** Yonder, to the next town. The little girl has a cousin who wants to buy her milk cow.

**1st Br. Soldier:** She looks old enough to take an old gentle cow to the next town by herself. Why are you going, mister?

**Martha:** I'll tell you why. Because I'm afraid to go by myself, that's why. I've never seen so many soldiers around here. I . . . I'm just afraid.

**2nd Br. Soldier:** Ah, let them go. You're scaring the little girl. The old man is harmless.

**"Farmer":** *(moving on)* Afternoon, gentlemen.

*(American soldier disguised as farmer and Martha walk off with cow. British soldiers still stand guard. British troops approach in formation from south.)*

**1st Br. Soldier:** I wish we knew what happened to that American soldier. If he makes it to Charleston, he'll tell them all about us.

**"Farmer", offstage:** *(sung in cracked old man's voice)* "Come all you brave soldiers, Both valiant and free, It's for independence, We all now agree."

# Martha Helps the Rebel

## Meet the Illustrator

**Charles Shaw** once served in the Army National Guard. He loves to illustrate the Texas frontier, children, and jazz musicians. His work can be found in a number of Texas museums and historical societies. Mr. Shaw is so well-known for his illustrations of Texas frontier life that the University of Texas asked him to create illustrations for a book called *Texas*, written by the famous novelist James Michener. Mr. Shaw has also contributed his illustrations to many other books and magazines.

## Meet the Illustrator

**Dennis Hockerman** has been a designer and illustrator for 23 years. Besides illustrating children's books, he has worked for the greeting card, gift wrap, and toy industries. In his spare time, Mr. Hockerman enjoys working at his printing press creating hand-colored etchings. He works out of his home in Wisconsin, where he lives with his wife, three children, and pets.

# Theme Connections

## Think About It

The Revolutionary War was an extremely important historical event in America. Because the colonists defeated the British, the colonial period ended. Here are some things for you to think about.

- How did Martha make a difference? What would have happened if Martha had not been there to help?
- In what ways might civilians have helped the Continental Army during the Revolutionary War?
- Is the story in this play realistic? Do you think things would have happened that way? Explain.

Look at the Concept/Question Board to see if there are questions that you can answer now. If the selection or your discussion raised new questions about colonial life, post them on the Concept/Question Board.

## Record Ideas

What did you think of Martha? How would you have reacted if you had been Martha? Record your ideas in your Writing Journal.

## Research Ideas

- The Revolutionary War was a long time coming. What events led up to the Revolutionary War? What major events took place during the war? What was the outcome?
- Some colonists remained loyal to England. Why do you think that was so? What did these colonists do about their loyalty? What happened to them?

# Bibliography

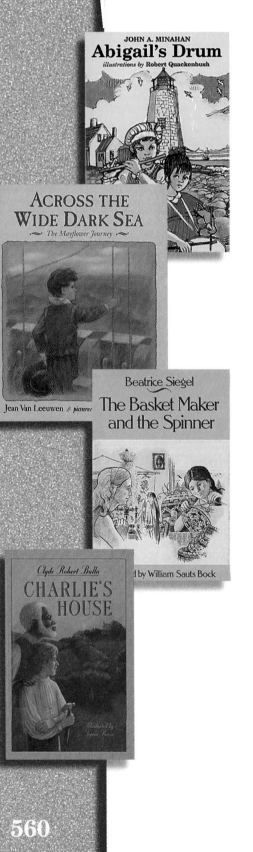

## Abigail's Drum

by **John A. Minahan.** Could two girls, one drum, and one fife hold off the British army? Abigail and Rebecca bravely give it a try.

## Across the Wide Dark Sea: The Mayflower Journey

by **Jean Van Leeuwen.** Set sail for the New World with a boy in search of a better life. Will he find it on the other side of the sea?

## The Basket Maker and the Spinner

by **Beatrice Siegel.** Spend a few days with a Native American basket weaver and a colonial spinner and see how their lives compare.

## Charlie's House

by **Clyde Robert Bulla.** Twelve-year-old Charlie comes to America and must survive cruel servitude before he runs away and fulfills his dream.

## Colonial Kids: An Activity Guide to Life in the New World

**by Laurie Carlson.** Tie knots, make soap, churn butter, stitch a sampler, or try one of the many other skills that colonial people practiced.

## The New Americans: Colonial Times 1620–1689

**by Betsy Maestro.** How did the North American settlers get along with the Native Americans? What brought them together and what tore them apart?

## Sarah Morton's Day: A Day in the Life of a Pilgrim Girl

**by Kate Waters.** Step back in time to the year 1627 and see how different life can be. We follow photographs of Sarah in her re-created Pilgrim village.

## What's the Big Idea, Ben Franklin?

**by Jean Fritz.** Discover the fascinating career of Benjamin Franklin, who started as a young Boston printer and became an internationally known inventor, writer, and politician.

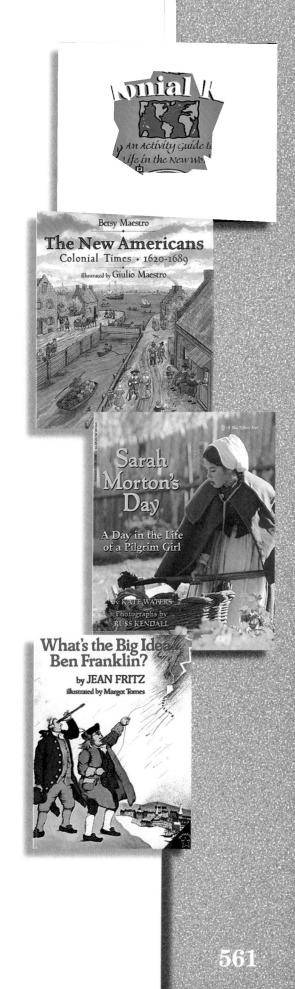

# **T**able *of* **C**ontents

## Grammar, Mechanics, and Usage

Complete and Incomplete Sentences .........564

Compound Subject and Predicate .............565

Compound Sentences .........................566

Phrases and Clauses .......................567

End Punctuation ...........................569

Using Commas in a Series, in Dates,

   and in Place Names ........................570

Using Parentheses and Dashes ...............572

Using Colons and Semicolons ................573

Capitalization ...................................574

Parts of Speech ...........................576

Using Possessive Nouns ......................577

Using the Right Pronoun for the Right Noun ...578

Using Present-Tense Verbs ...................580

Using Past-Tense Verbs .......................582

Making Subject and Verb Agree ..............584

Using Adjectives and Adverbs ................586

Using and Punctuating Dialogue ..............587

# Study Skills

**Parts of a Book** . . . . . . . . . . . . . . . . . . . . . . . . . . . . . . 588

**Using a Library** . . . . . . . . . . . . . . . . . . . . . . . . . . . . . 590

**Using a Dictionary or Glossary** . . . . . . . . . . . . . . . 592

**Using a Thesaurus** . . . . . . . . . . . . . . . . . . . . . . . . . . . 593

**Using an Encyclopedia** . . . . . . . . . . . . . . . . . . . . . . . 594

**Using Maps** . . . . . . . . . . . . . . . . . . . . . . . . . . . . . . . . . 596

**Making and Using a Time Line** . . . . . . . . . . . . . . . . 598

**Making and Using Charts** . . . . . . . . . . . . . . . . . . . . 600

**Using Diagrams** . . . . . . . . . . . . . . . . . . . . . . . . . . . . . 602

**Outlining** . . . . . . . . . . . . . . . . . . . . . . . . . . . . . . . . . . 604

**Making a Bibliography** . . . . . . . . . . . . . . . . . . . . . . . 606

# Writing and Technology

**Doing On-Line Research** . . . . . . . . . . . . . . . . . . . . . . 608

**Sending and Receiving Electronic Mail** . . . . . . . . 610

**On-Line Safety Tips** . . . . . . . . . . . . . . . . . . . . . . . . . . 612

# Complete and Incomplete Sentences

**Rule:** A **sentence** is a group of words that expresses a complete thought.

---

Every complete sentence has two parts: a subject and a predicate. The **subject** of a sentence tells *who* or *what* the sentence is about.

> **Subjects:** Dabney forgot her music book.
> (Who? Dabney)
> The recital begins at noon. (What? The recital)

The **predicate** of a sentence tells what happens or happened.

> **Predicates:** The funny song made us laugh.
> (What happened? made us laugh.)
> Lettie played the piano.
> (What happened? played the piano)

A sentence is incomplete if it is missing a subject.

> **Incomplete:** Left this morning at eight. (Who or what left this morning at eight?)
> Sounds like a good plan. (What sounds like a good plan?)

A sentence is incomplete if it is missing a predicate.

> **Incomplete:** The twins and their two dogs. (What happened to the twins and their two dogs?)
> A new student from Canton, Ohio. (What happened to a new student from Canton, Ohio?)

## Grammar, Mechanics, and Usage
# Compound Subject and Predicate

**Rule:** A subject of a sentence that has two or more parts is called a **compound subject**. A predicate of a sentence that has two or more parts is called a **compound predicate**. **Conjunctions** are words used to join sentence parts.

---

A compound subject has two or more parts. The parts are usually connected with the conjunction *and* or *or*.

**Subjects with one part:**
Marcus has curly hair. Terry has curly hair.

**Compound subject:**
Marcus and Terry have curly hair.

A compound predicate has two or more parts. The parts are usually connected with the conjunction *and* or *or*.

**Predicates with one part:**
The hawk swooped down.
The hawk scooped up the mouse.

**Compound predicate:**
The hawk swooped down and scooped up the mouse.

If a compound subject or predicate has three or more parts, use commas to separate the parts. Put the conjunction just before the last part.

**Compound subject:**
Ted, Luke, and Luke's brother watched the hawk.

# Grammar, Mechanics, and Usage
## Compound Sentences

**Rule:** Two sentences sometimes express ideas that are closely connected. The related sentences can be combined to form a **compound sentence**.

There are two different ways to form a compound sentence. One way is to join two related sentences by using a conjunction such as *and*, *or*, and *but*. Sentences can also be joined by using a semicolon (;).

Follow these rules to form compound sentences.

Use a conjunction to combine two sentences that express closely related ideas. Place a comma before each conjunction.

> **Two sentences:** The school play is about to start. The auditorium is filled with people.

> **Compound sentence:** The school play is about to start, and the auditorium is filled with people.

Use a semicolon to combine two sentences expressing closely related ideas. The semicolon takes the place of both a comma and a conjunction.

> **Two sentences:** The school play is about to start. The gym is filled with people.

> **Compound sentence:** The school play is about to start; the gym is filled with people.

Only combine two sentences that express ideas that are closely related. If the sentences do not express related ideas, keep them separate. For example, do not combine these sentences:

> **Two sentences:** Jenny was glad to be in the play. Jenny's mother gave her flowers after the show.

## Grammar, Mechanics, and Usage
# Phrases and Clauses

**Rule:** A **phrase** is a group of words that does not contain a subject and a verb. A **clause** is a group of words containing a subject and predicate.

A **preposition** shows how one word is related to another word in the sentence. A **prepositional phrase** begins with a preposition and is followed by a noun, a pronoun, and its modifiers.

You can use prepositional phrases to add details:

| Preposition | Noun or Pronoun |
|---|---|
| by | the window |
| after | school |
| up | a tree |

Here are some prepositions:

| | | | | |
|---|---|---|---|---|
| about | around | by | from | out |
| above | at | down | in | to |
| across | before | during | of | under |
| after | beside | for | on | with |

In the following sentences, the prepositional phrases are underlined:

A boy from India greeted us at the door.
During the concert, we sat with our parents.

In your writing, place a prepositional phrase as close as possible to the word it relates to. Study these two examples:

**Misleading:** The baby called her mother in the crib. (Who is in the crib?)

**Clearer:** The baby in the crib called her mother.

# Grammar, Mechanics, and Usage
## Phrases and Clauses (continued)

An **independent clause** can stand by itself as a sentence. A **dependent clause** has a subject and a predicate, but it cannot stand by itself. It usually begins with a connecting word. Often a dependent clause tells *when, where, how,* or *why* the action in the independent, or main, clause takes place.

| dependent clause | independent clause |
| --- | --- |
| When the rains came, | the village was ready. |

Here are some connecting words that are used to introduce a dependent clause:

| | | | | |
| --- | --- | --- | --- | --- |
| **after** | **because** | **since** | **until** | **which** |
| **although** | **before** | **that** | **when** | **while** |
| **as** | **if** | **though** | **where** | **who** |

Sometimes a dependent clause is not necessary to the meaning of the sentence. In that case, put a comma between the clauses.

**Examples:** Al likes my camera, which is new.
I got it from Ben, who works in a photo lab.

Sometimes a dependent clause is necessary to the meaning of the sentence. In that case, do not put a comma between the clauses.

**Examples:** Al took the photo that was on the front page.
It showed people who were caught in the flood.

Use a comma after a dependent clause that begins a sentence.

**Examples:** Although the rain stopped, the school closed.
If it rains again, we will all be prepared.

## Grammar, Mechanics, and Usage
# End Punctuation

**Rule:** Every sentence ends with a **punctuation mark**. Writers use different end marks for different kinds of sentences.

Follow these rules when you punctuate sentences.

If a sentence makes a statement, end it with a **period.**

**Statement:** Jackie has a blue striped kite.

If a sentence asks a question, end it with a **question mark.**

**Question:** Did you ever fly a kite?

If a sentence shows strong feeling, end it with an **exclamation point.**

**Exclamation:** The kite is going to hit the tree!

## Grammar, Mechanics, and Usage

# Using Commas in a Series, in Dates, and in Place Names

**Rule:** Use a **comma** when you write a series of three or more nouns, adjectives, verbs, or phrases. Use a comma when you write dates and certain place names.

In a series of three or more **nouns**, use a comma after each noun that comes before *and* or *or*.

> **Nouns:** The castle was protected by a <u>moat</u>, a <u>drawbridge</u>, and a wall.

In a series of three or more **adjectives**, use a comma after each adjective that comes before *and* or *or*.

> **Adjectives:** The castle was <u>cold</u>, <u>damp</u>, and drafty.

In a series of three or more **verbs**, use a comma after each verb that comes before *and* or *or*.

> **Verbs:** The lord and his family <u>lived</u>, <u>ate</u>, and slept in the tower.

In a series of three or more **phrases**, use a comma after each phrase that comes before *and* or *or*.

> **Phrases:** The people who lived in the castle defended themselves <u>by pulling up the drawbridge</u>, <u>by throwing spears and rocks</u>, and by shooting arrows.

# Grammar, Mechanics, and Usage

## Using Commas in a Series, in Dates, and in Place Names (continued)

When writing dates, use a comma between the day and the year. When writing addresses, use a comma between the parts of a place name.

**Date:** Our school year began on <u>August 29,</u> 1998.
**Place Name:** My new school is in <u>Miami,</u> Florida.

When writing a date or a place name in a sentence, use a comma after it (except at the end of a sentence) to separate it from the rest of the sentence.

**Date:** The play on <u>May 4, 1998,</u> was a great success.
**Place Name:** I went to school in <u>Boise, Idaho,</u> last year.

## Grammar, Mechanics, and Usage
# Using Parentheses and Dashes

**Rule:** Parentheses and dashes are special kinds of punctuation marks. Use **parentheses** to show extra information within a sentence. Use **dashes** to show an interruption.

---

Put parentheses around extra information in a sentence. The information may tell what one of the words in the sentence means.

> Navajos lived in hogans (mud-covered log structures).

Information inside parentheses may also tell the reader more about some part of the sentence.

> During the Ice Age, sheets of ice up to 3.2 kilometers (2 miles) thick covered North America.

You may use dashes to set off a phrase that breaks the even flow of a sentence.

> Corn—along with beans and squash—was the main food of some early Native Americans.

In dialogue, you can use a dash to show that a sentence was interrupted before it could be finished.

> "Don't forget to —" Mr. Lee said as the bell rang.

# Grammar, Mechanics, and Usage
# Using Colons and Semicolons

**Rule:** Colons and semicolons are punctuation marks. A **semicolon** (;) is used to separate two connected and complete thoughts in one sentence. A **colon** (:) shows that something more is to follow. It is also used in expressions of time, after salutations, and to show dialogue in plays.

Colons and semicolons look similar, but they have different uses.

---

Use a semicolon to separate two connected and complete thoughts in one sentence. You may use a semicolon instead of a comma and a connecting word such as *and, but, or,* or *so.*

> **Sentences joined with commas and connecting words:** The boys came home from school, and they were hungry.
> Peter ate an apple, and Paul ate carrot sticks.

> **Sentences joined with semicolons:** The boys came home from school; they were hungry.
> Peter ate an apple; Paul ate carrot sticks.

Use a colon between hours and minutes when you write a time.

> **Examples:** 6:45 A.M. 6:50 P.M.

Use a colon after the greeting in a business letter.

> **Examples:** Dear Mr. Melon: Dear Ms. Peach:

Use a colon after a character's name if that character is speaking.

> **Examples:** David: When will you visit your aunt?
>
> Susan: I leave tomorrow.

## Grammar, Mechanics, and Usage
# Capitalization

**Rule:** Always **capitalize** the first word in a sentence. Some words are always capitalized. Other words are capitalized only if they are used in a special way.

---

Capitalize the first word in a sentence.

**First word:** <u>How</u> do you program a VCR? <u>Many</u> people do not know how.

Always capitalize the word *I*.

**The word *I*:** There are several programs <u>I</u> would like to tape.
My mom and <u>I</u> tried to figure out what to do.

Capitalize the names of people and places.

**People and places:**
Patrick Henry     Cairo, Egypt     Balboa Park
John L. Fong      Africa           Red Sea

Capitalize the days of the week and months of the year.

**Days of the week and months of the year:**
<u>Monday</u>, <u>June</u> 2            <u>Wednesday</u> through <u>Friday</u>
<u>March</u>, <u>April</u>, <u>May</u>      the week of <u>July</u> 10

Capitalize titles used with people's names.

**Titles:**   <u>Dr.</u> Bea Carter        <u>Mr.</u> David Hope
              <u>Ms.</u> Leah Burke       <u>Mrs.</u> Diane Carson

## Grammar, Mechanics, and Usage
### Capitalization (continued)

Capitalize the first and the most important words in a title.

**Book title:** *Ben and Me*
**Poem title:** "In Time of Silver Rain"
**Movie title:** *Gone with the Wind*

Capitalize words used to show directions only when they are part of the name of a place or the name of a street.

**Directions capitalized:**
East Ninth Street      South Carolina

**Directions not capitalized:**
north      south      east      west

Do *not* begin the seasons of the year with capital letters unless they are the first words of sentences.

**Seasons of the year capitalized:**
Winter is the coldest season of the year.

**Seasons of the year not capitalized:**
Last summer, my family visited Washington, D.C.

## Grammar, Mechanics, and Usage
# Parts of Speech

**Rule:** All words can be classified into parts of speech. These are nouns, pronouns, verbs, adjectives, adverbs, prepositions, conjunctions, and interjections.

A **noun** names a person, place, or thing.

> <u>Louise</u> makes <u>furniture</u>.

A **pronoun** takes the place of a noun.

> Louise makes furniture. <u>She</u> is a carpenter.

A **verb** shows action or tells what someone or something is, was, or will be.

> Louise <u>makes</u> furniture.
> She <u>is</u> a carpenter.

An **adjective** describes a noun or a pronoun.
> Louise makes <u>beautiful</u> furniture.

An **adverb** describes verbs, adjectives, and other adverbs. It tells how, how often, when, or where.

> Louise <u>usually</u> hammers <u>noisily</u> in the barn.
> She rises <u>early</u> and works there <u>until</u> noon.

A **preposition** shows the relationship between a noun or pronoun and a verb, an adjective, or another noun.

> Louise makes furniture <u>in</u> the barn.
> She works there <u>until</u> noon.

A **conjunction** connects words, phrases, or sentences.

> She rises early <u>and</u> works there until noon.
> Louise is a carpenter, <u>but</u> she was once a nurse.

An **interjection** expresses strong emotion.

> <u>Wow!</u> This apple pie is delicious!
> <u>Ouch!</u> I stubbed my toe!

# Grammar, Mechanics, and Usage

# Using Possessive Nouns

**Rule:**  A **possessive noun** is used to show ownership. Possessive nouns can be singular or plural.

Follow these rules to form possessive nouns.

To form the possessive of a **singular noun**, add an apostrophe and *s* (*'s*). Remember that a singular noun names only one person, place, or thing.

> **Singular noun:**  <u>Sara</u> has special jobs to do around the house.

> **Possessive noun:**  <u>Sara's</u> jobs include taking out the trash and giving the dogs a bath.

To form the possessive of a **plural noun** that ends in *s*, add an apostrophe after the *s* (*s'*). Remember that a plural noun names more than one person, place, or thing.

> **Plural noun ending with *s*:**  The <u>dogs</u> do not like to take a bath.

> **Possessive noun:**  The <u>dogs'</u> bathtub is an old plastic wading pool.

To form the possessive of a **plural noun** that does not end in *s*, add an apostrophe and *s* (*'s*).

> **Plural noun not ending with *s*:**  All the <u>children</u> in the play have chores to do.

> **Possessive noun:** The <u>children's</u> chores keep them busy.

# Grammar, Mechanics, and Usage

# Using the Right Pronoun for the Right Noun

**Rule:** **Pronouns** are words that take the place of nouns. Use pronouns that agree in number, gender, and person with the nouns that they replace.

---

Use **singular pronouns** to take the place of singular nouns. Singular pronouns, such as *I, you, he, she,* or *it,* stand for one person or thing.

> **Singular nouns and pronouns:**
> Terry wrote a poem.
> She read it to the other students.

Use **plural pronouns** to take the place of plural nouns. Plural pronouns, such as *we, you,* or *they,* stand for more than one person or thing.

> **Plural nouns and pronouns:**
> Terry's classmates said, "We like the poem."

Use **subject pronouns** to take the place of subject nouns. The subject noun tells who or what the sentence is about. Subject pronouns include *I, you, he, she, it, we,* and *they.*

> **Subject pronouns:**
> Terry wrote a poem.
> She read the poem to the other students.

# Grammar, Mechanics, and Usage

## Using the Right Pronoun
## for the Right Noun (continued)

Use **object pronouns** to take the place of object nouns. The object noun follows the verb and shows what the subject does or did. Object pronouns include *me, you, him, her, it, us,* and *them.*

> **Object pronouns:**
> Terry wrote a poem for her classmates.
> Terry read it to them.

Use **possessive pronouns** to take the place of possessive nouns. Possessive pronouns show who or what owns or has something. Some possessive pronouns, such as *my, your, his, her, its, our,* or *their,* appear before a noun. Others, including *mine, yours, his, hers, its, ours,* or *theirs,* stand alone.

> **Possessive pronouns:**
> Terry's poem is well written. Her poem won first prize. The poem is better than ours.

Always be sure your readers know exactly to *whom* or *what* each pronoun refers. If it is not clear to which noun your pronoun refers, use the noun again.

> **Not clear:** Anna took Jill to see a movie. She thought the movie was very funny.

> **Clear:** Anna took Jill to see a movie. Jill thought the movie was very funny.

## Grammar, Mechanics, and Usage
# Using Present-Tense Verbs

**Rule:** A **verb** is a word that tells what the subject does. It tells about an action or a state of being. A **verb tense** is a form of a verb that tells the time an action takes place—in the present, in the past, or in the future. A verb in the **present-tense** form shows action that happens now or action that happens again and again.

---

Follow these rules when you use present-tense verbs.

If the subject of a sentence is singular (except for the words *I* or *you*), add *-s* or *-es* to the verb to form the present tense. For most verbs, add *-s* to the end of the verb. For verbs ending in *-ch, -sh, -s, -x,* or *-z,* add *-es.*

Also, if the verb ends with a consonant plus *y*, change the *y* to *i* and add *-es.*

> **Add -s:** Kevin <u>knows</u> that it is time for a nap. Joey <u>likes</u> his sandbox.

> **Add -es:** Kevin <u>watches</u> his little brother Joey.

> **Change *y* to *i* and add -es:** Joey <u>cries</u>.

If the subject of a sentence is plural, do not add an ending to the verb. Also, do not add an ending to the verb if the subject of the sentence is *I* or *you*.

> **No Ending:** Little children <u>like</u> me. They usually <u>listen</u> to me. I <u>enjoy</u> baby-sitting.

# Grammar, Mechanics, and Usage

## Using Present-Tense Verbs (continued)

Irregular verbs have special present-tense forms that you must remember.

| Irregular Verbs | Present-Tense Forms |
|---|---|
| be | I am. You are. We are. They are. He is. She is. It is. |
| do | I do. You do. We do. They do. He does. She does. It does. |
| have | I have. You have. We have. They have. He has. She has. It has. |

# Grammar, Mechanics, and Usage
## Using Past-Tense Verbs

**Rule:** A **verb** is a word that tells what the subject does. It tells about an action or a state of being. A **verb tense** is a form of a verb that tells the time an action takes place—in the present, in the past, or in the future. A verb in the **past-tense** form shows action that has already happened.

---

Follow these rules when you use verbs in the past tense:

- Add -*ed* to form the past tense of most verbs.

  **Add -*ed*:**   jump   jumped

For some verbs you must change the spelling before you add -*ed*.

- If the verb ends with *e*, drop *e* when you add -*ed*.

  **Drop *e*:**   hike   hiked

- If the verb ends with a consonant plus *y*, change the *y* to *i* and add -*ed*.

  **Change *y* to *i* and add -*ed*:**   worry   worried

- For most verbs that have one syllable, one short vowel, and one final consonant, double that final consonant before adding -*ed*.

  **Double final consonant:**   map   mapped

# Grammar, Mechanics, and Usage

## Using Past-Tense Verbs (continued)

Irregular verbs have special forms in the past tense. Here are some common examples.

| Irregular Verbs | Past-Tense Forms |
|---|---|
| be | I was. He was. She was. It was. You were. We were. They were. |
| do | did |
| have | had |
| go | went |
| come | came |
| say | said |
| give | gave |

# Grammar, Mechanics, and Usage
# Making Subject and Verb Agree

**Rule:** In a sentence, the verb must **agree** with, or match, the subject. A singular subject takes a singular verb. A plural subject takes a plural verb.

The **subject** of a sentence is the word or words that refer to the person(s) or thing(s) that performs or receives the action of the verb. The **verb** is the word that refers to the action.

---

Most verbs follow this pattern in the present tense:

| Present Tense ||
|---|---|
| **Singular** | **Plural** |
| I work. | We work. |
| You work. | You work. |
| He, she, it works. | They work. |

For all subjects except *he*, *she*, or *it*, the verb is the same. For *he*, *she*, or *it*, and for all subjects that can be referred to as *he*, *she*, or *it*, the verb usually takes the ending -*s*.

> **Takes -*s* ending:** Pepe plays soccer.
> He plays soccer.

However, verbs that end in -*s*, -*x*, -*z*, -*ch*, or -*sh* take the ending -*es*. In verbs that end in a consonant plus *y*, the *y* changes to *i* before adding the -*es* ending.

> **Takes -*es* ending:** The goalie touches the ball with his hands.

> **Final *y* changes to *i* before -*es*:** The sun dries the playing field.

# Grammar, Mechanics, and Usage

## Making Subject and Verb Agree (continued)

Some common verbs, such as *be* and *have*, are irregular. They have special patterns that you must memorize:

| *Be:* Present Tense | |
|---|---|
| I am. | We are. |
| You are. | You are. |
| He, she, it is. | They are. |

| *Have:* Present Tense | |
|---|---|
| I have. | We have. |
| You have. | You have. |
| He, she, it has. | They have. |

# Grammar, Mechanics, and Usage
# Using Adjectives and Adverbs

**Rule:** An **adjective** describes a noun (person, place, or thing). An **adverb** describes a verb. Adverbs answer the question *Where? When? How?* or *How often?*

Remember these guidelines when you use adjectives and adverbs.

An **adjective** describes a noun.

**Adjectives:**
The team has <u>new</u> shirts. They are <u>purple</u>.

An **adverb** describes a verb. Adverbs tell *where, when, how,* or *how often.*

**Adverbs:**
The players will wear the shirts <u>tomorrow</u>.
The first game will be played <u>here</u>.

You can form many adverbs by adding *-ly* to certain adjectives. Notice that the spelling of a word that already ends in *-y* will change when *-ly* is added to it.

**Adverbs:**
The fans clapped <u>eagerly</u>.  (eager + *-ly*)
The team played <u>steadily</u>.  (steady + *-ly*)

# Grammar, Mechanics, and Usage
## Using and Punctuating Dialogue

**Rule:** In a story, what characters say to each other is called **dialogue**. A speaker's exact words are called a **quotation**. These words are put inside **quotation marks** (" ").

Place quotation marks (" ") around a speaker's exact words.

> **Quotation marks:** Pat said, "My pen pal's name is Maria."

Begin the first word of a quotation with a capital letter, even if it is not at the beginning of a sentence.

> **Capital letters:** Ray asked, "Where does Maria live?"

Use a comma to separate a quotation from the speaker tag.

> **Comma:** Pat replied, "She lives in Venice, Italy."

Put the end punctuation mark for the quotation inside the closing quotation marks.

> **End marks:** "That's quite a place!" Ray said.
> "Why do you say that?" asked Pat.
> "Venice has canals for streets," answered Ray.

Use two sets of quotation marks when a speaker tag interrupts a quotation. Separate the speaker tag from the quotation with commas. Do not capitalize the first word after the speaker tag.

> **Example:** "Maria," said Pat, "likes boats."

Always start a new paragraph when the speaker changes.

> **Example:** "She lives in a house that's hundreds of years old," added Pat.
> "It sure would be fun to visit her," said Ray.

## Study Skills

# Parts of a Book

A book has other parts besides the main part, the part containing a story or information. All books have a **title page** and a **copyright page**. Some books also have a **table of contents, glossary, bibliography,** or **index**.

---

When you look for information about a story, question, or problem, you will use several books. You don't need to read every page of every book to find information. Use the parts of a book to find only the information you need.

The title page, copyright page, and table of contents are at the front of the book.

- The **title page** gives the title of the book, the name of the author or editor, and the name of the publisher.

- The **copyright page** comes after the title page. It gives the publisher's name and the place and year in which the book was published.

- The **table of contents** is a list, in order of appearance, of the units, chapters, or stories in the book, with the page number on which each item begins.

## Study Skills

### Parts of a Book (continued)

The glossary, bibliography, and index are at the back of the book. Sometimes a bibliography is found, instead, at the end of each chapter or unit.

- The glossary is an alphabetical listing of unfamiliar or special words that are used in the book along with their definitions.

- The bibliography is an alphabetical listing of books that the author used. It may also include other writings that the author thinks would interest the reader.

- The index is an alphabetical listing of names, places, and topics covered in the book, with the numbers of the pages on which they are mentioned or discussed. Indexes are usually found in nonfiction books.

## Study Skills
# Using a Library

Each library has a **card catalog**—a list of all the books in a library. Some libraries list the books on cards found in small cabinet drawers. Other libraries have the card catalog on computers. In both systems, you can find books listed in three ways: by the author's name, by the title of the book, and by the subject of the book.

---

The card catalog is a good place to start your research. By using it, you can quickly find out what books your library has on your question or problem. The following information can help you find books in your library:

- The catalog has three types of cards or ways to look for a book. An **author** card lists the author's name at the top of the card. A **title** card lists the book's title at the top. A **subject** card lists the subject of the book at the top. On a computer, you can look up an author's name, a book title, or a subject.

- A book entry may contain a **call number**. This number matches the numbers and letters on the spine of the book. The call number also matches numbers and letters on the shelf on which you can find the book. A *J* or *JUV* in front of the number means that the book is in the juvenile section. An *R* means that it is in the reference section.

- Every card shows the year in which the book was **published**. Make sure you check the publication date if you need to obtain recent information.

## Study Skills
### Using a Library (continued)

- Each card lists the **number of pages** in the book. The number of pages can give you some idea of how much information is in a book.

- If the book has **illustrations**, the abbreviation *ill.* is shown. Depending on your research problem, pictures might help you in your research.

- Each card includes a **summary** of the book. The summary briefly tells what the book is about. It will help you decide whether the book has the information you need.

- At the bottom of each card is a list of **headings**. This list gives all the headings under which the book is listed in the card catalog. If you look under the other headings in the subjects cards, you may find more books on your research problem.

## Study Skills
# Using a Dictionary or Glossary

A **dictionary** is a book that tells the meanings of most of the words that people use when they speak, read, and write. A **glossary** is the section in the back of a book that gives the meaning of words that appear in that book.

- Each word listed in a dictionary or glossary is called an **entry word**. All entry words are listed in alphabetical order and are printed in dark type.

- At the top of each dictionary or glossary page are two words called **guide words**. These words are usually printed in dark type. The word on the left is the first entry word listed on the page. The word on the right is the last entry word listed on the page. All other words on the page fall in alphabetical order between the two guide words. Guide words can help you find the page on which the word you are looking for is listed.

- The **entry** for a word gives the word's spelling, pronunciation, part of speech, and meaning or meanings. The part of speech is abbreviated; for example, *v.* stands for verb. Entries may also give spellings of the word with endings added, synonyms for the word, and information about the word's history. Here is how an entry might look.

     **de•fend** (di fend´) *v.* Protect from danger; guard. [from Latin *dēfendere*, to ward off.] —defendable **syn** *protect, shield, guard.*

- A **pronunciation key** is found at the beginning of a dictionary or glossary. The symbols in the pronunciation key stand for vowel and consonant sounds. The symbols are shown with example words. Pronounce these words to help you hear the sounds. Then use the symbols to help you pronounce the entry words.

## Study Skills
# Using a Thesaurus

A **thesaurus** is a dictionary of synonyms and antonyms. The words may be organized in alphabetical order or by topic of subject.

A thesaurus can help you select the most exact word to tell what you mean. It can also help you vary your word choices so that you don't use the same word too often.

Follow these guidelines when you use a thesaurus:

- A thesaurus may be a book or part of your word-processing program. In thesauruses that are books, words are usually arranged alphabetically. Some organize words according to ideas. When that is the case, check the index to see how to find a certain word.

- When you look up a word, you'll find a list of synonyms for that word and perhaps an antonym or two. For example, if you look up the word "find," you might see this entry:

  > **find**, *v.* detect, discover, locate, uncover, retrieve, spot, sight. Antonyms—see LOSE, OVERLOOK

- From the entry list, choose the word that says exactly what you mean.

- Remember that synonyms are words with meanings that are similar but are not always identical. You may want to check the meaning of the word in a dictionary to be sure you have the one that best expresses your thoughts or ideas.

## Study Skills
# Using an Encyclopedia

**Encyclopedias** are reference books that contain information on many subjects. The articles in encyclopedias usually are arranged in alphabetical order.

An encyclopedia is a good place to begin searching when you are looking for information on a research question or problem. You can find general information about your topic in its articles. Also, articles can lead you to other materials about your topic.

Follow these guidelines when you use an encyclopedia:

- Write down your research question or problem. Underline the key word or words of your topic.

  How early farm machines were made

- Look up those words in the index of an encyclopedia. For a question about how early farm machines were made, you might look in the index under "Farm machinery". If you need information about a person, look in the index under the person's last name.

  **Deere, John**
  **McCormick, Cyrus**

- From the index, make a list of the titles, volume numbers or letters, and page numbers of articles that might have information about your topic.

  **Farm machinery 7:49; 1:164**
  **Manufacture of 9:138**
  **Plows 14:432**

## Study Skills

### Using an Encyclopedia (continued)

- Check your list and select the encyclopedia volumes with information on your topic. Turn to the given pages to locate the articles.

- Notice any headings in the articles. Headings help you preview the information in the articles. They might also give you ideas for arranging information in your report.

- At the end of each article, look for other places in the encyclopedia where you might find more information about your topic.

  *See also* **Reaper**.

A list of books with more information about your topic may be given at the end of an article.

**Hawke, David F.** *Nuts and Bolts of the Past.*
**Patton, Phil.** *Made in the USA.*

## Study Skills

# Using Maps

**Maps** are drawings that show where places or landmarks are located. Most maps have certain features in common. These include a **title**, a **key**, a **scale**, and a **compass rose**.

Some maps show important and interesting information about the past, such as where battles were fought. These maps are called **historical maps**.

Maps can show a great deal of information in a small amount of space. However, because maps use symbols to show information, you must know how to read the symbols.

## Study Skills

### Using Maps (continued)

These are the features found on most maps:

- The **title** tells what information the map shows or what its purpose is. The map shown on this page is a historical map that shows the United States as it was at the time of the American Revolution.

- The **key** tells what each special symbol or color on the map stands for. Look at the key with the map on the previous page. It shows that a dot stands for a city.

- The **scale** shows how many miles or kilometers are represented by a given measure, usually some fraction of an inch or centimeter, on the map. On this map, for instance, you can see that an inch stands for 300 miles.

- The **direction arrows** or **compass rose** shows north, south, east, and west on the map.

Use the map features to find more information about places you are researching. For example, this map shows that 14 modern states formed the original 13 colonies. It shows that what is now the state of Maine was once part of Massachusetts.

## Study Skills
# Making and Using a Time Line

A **time line** is a graphic device on which important events are shown in chronological order on a line. The space between entries indicates the relative length of time between events. A time line may cover any chosen length of time, from the lifetime of a person to a historical period of hundreds or thousands of years.

Reading a time line can help you understand and remember the order of important past events. Making a time line can help you present the most important facts gathered in your research.

---

Here are guidelines for making a time line:

- Decide what you want to show in your time line. Choose a title for it.

  **Example:**
  Highlights in Neil Armstrong's Aviation Career, 1946-1969

- Make a list of the main events and the time of each one. Use short phrases.

  **Examples:**
  Licensed pilot–1946
  Naval air cadet–1947
  Research pilot–1955
  Becomes an astronaut–1962
  First space docking maneuver–1966
  First person to set foot on the moon–1969

## Study Skills

## Making and Using a Time Line (continued)

- Draw a line across a sheet of paper. Leave space above and below the line for writing the events and the times—in order, from left to right.

- On the line, make a dot for the time of each event. Vary the amount of space between the dots, according to the length of time between events.

- Below each dot, write a time.

- Above each dot, write an event.

| Licensed pilot | Naval air cadet | Research pilot | Becomes an astronaut | First space docking maneuver | First person to set foot on the moon |
|---|---|---|---|---|---|
| 1946 | 1947 | 1955 | 1962 | 1966 | 1969 |

# Study Skills

# Making and Using Charts

A **chart** can present much information in a small amount of space. A chart helps organize information so that readers can understand it more easily and quickly.

Charts can help you organize information clearly when presenting your research. They are also used for time schedules, work schedules, and other information.

---

The following guidelines will help you make charts and also understand them:

- Some information is easier and faster to read in a chart than if written out in sentences and paragraphs. For example, you might use a chart to tell about major earthquakes: the locations, dates, and number of deaths as well as Richter scale measurements.

| Major Earthquakes in the United States | | | |
|---|---|---|---|
| Location | Date | Deaths | Magnitude* |
| **New Madrid, Missouri** | Dec. 16, 1811 Jan 23 and Feb. 7, 1812 | unknown | 7.7 7.6 7.9 |
| **San Francisco, California** | April 18, 1906 | 700 | 7.7 |
| **Prince William Sound, Alaska** | March 28, 1964 | 130 | 9.2 |
| **Landers, California** | June 28, 1992 | 1 | 7.6 |

\*Based on the moment magnitude scale or the surface-wave magnitude used by the United States Geological Survey.

## Study Skills
## Making and Using Charts (continued)

- Choose a **title** that tells what the chart is about.

- Down the left side of the chart, write the items you will give information about. These are called **row headings**.

- Across the top of the chart, write **column headings**. These headings tell the kinds of information you will give about the items in the row headings.

- Draw lines between the columns and rows to make the chart easy to read.

- In the blank spaces, write brief information about the items in the row headings.

- To read a chart, find the row or column heading that shows the item or kind of information you want to find out about. Read down or across until you get to the information you are looking for.

## Study Skills
# Using Diagrams

A **diagram** is an illustration that shows the parts of an object or how something works. Diagrams help readers visualize information in the text. Labels on a diagram help explain the parts of an object or the steps in a process.

---

Diagrams can show the following kinds of information:

- how something is put together, such as roller skates
- how something is arranged, such as furniture in a room
- how something works, such as the hip or elbow joints
- how to make something, such as a model airplane
- what steps make up a process, such as making steel
- what stages make up a cycle, such as the life cycle of a frog

When you read, diagrams can help you visualize objects and processes. When you write, you may wish to include diagrams to help your readers understand scientific or technical materials. Knowing the features of a diagram will help you understand it.

## Study Skills

## Using Diagrams (continued)

### Parts of an in-line skate

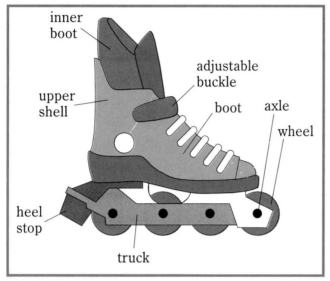

- The **title** of the diagram tells what the diagram shows.

- **Labels** of a diagram tell about the parts of an object or the steps in a process. On this diagram, for instance, a label tells you that an in-line skate has both a boot and an inner boot.

- **Lines** lead from each label to a part of an object or one step in a process.

- **Arrows** show the order in which the steps of a process or the stages in a cycle take place. They may also show movement or direction. This diagram contains no arrows. However, someone might add an arrow that shows which direction the wheels turn.

## Study Skills
# Outlining

An **outline** is a written plan that writers use to organize their notes and ideas before they begin to write a first draft. An outline arranges information into main topics and subtopics.

When you are doing research, put your ideas into outline form before you start writing. Then you can be sure that your report or project is organized logically.

Follow these guidelines:

- On a sheet of paper, write the **title** for your outline. This title will be the title of your paper or project.

- Check the headings on your note cards. Then separate the cards into piles by their headings. The large, obvious divisions will be **main topics**.

- Next, check your note cards to see how each main topic can be divided. These divisions will be **subtopics** and must relate to the main topic. In the outline here, the two main topics are "Antarctic lands" and "Natural resources."

- Number each main topic with a Roman numeral (I, II, III, and so on) followed by a period. Your completed outline should include at least two main topics.

- Under each main topic, indent and number each subtopic with a capital letter followed by a period, as shown in the sample outline. Include at least two subtopics under each main topic—or none at all.

## Study Skills
## Outlining (continued)

■ If subtopics need to be divided further, under each subtopic indent again as shown and number each subtopic with an Arabic numeral (1, 2, 3, and so on) followed by a period. If you use **sub-subtopics**, you should have at least two—or none.

### ANTARCTICA

I.  Antarctic lands

    A.  East Antarctica

        1.  Size

        2.  Landforms

    B.  West Antarctica

II.  Natural resources

    A.  Minerals

        1.  Coal

        2.  Ore deposits

    B.  Plants

        1.  Lichens

        2.  Moss

        3.  Flowering plants

## Study Skills

# Making a Bibliography

A **bibliography** is a list of writings about a particular subject. It may include books and other written material in which the author found information to use in a book, an article, or a report. A bibliography may also be a list of books in which the reader can find more information about the subject.

A bibliography tells readers where the writer got her or his information. It also tells readers where they can read more about the subject. Provide a bibliography when you write about your research.

Follow these guidelines:

- Make a separate note card for each book you use in your research. On the card, put the author's full name, with the last name first; the title of the book; the publisher's name; and the date of publication. The publisher's name is found at the bottom of the title page of a book. The date of publication is found on the back of the title page.

- When you create your bibliography, put the information in this form:

    Moreland, Jennifer. Industrial Revolution of the 19th Century 1760–1900. Tucson, Arizona: Zephyr Press AZ, 1992.

Note the form and punctuation: all lines after the first line are indented, the first and last names are inverted, a comma is placed after the last name, and a period after the first name. The title is underlined and followed by a period. A colon is placed after the city of publication. A comma is placed after the name of the publisher. A period is placed after the date of publication.

## Study Skills
## Making a Bibliography (continued)

Arrange your entries in alphabetical order by the last name of the author. If a book does not have an author's name, list the work alphabetically by title. Leave a space between entries.

### Bibliography

Industry. Broomall, Pennsylvania: Chelsea House, 1996.

Moreland, Jennifer. Industrial Revolution of the 19th Century 1760–1900. Tucson, Arizona: Zephyr Press AZ, 1992.

# Writing and Technology
## Doing On-Line Research

Doing on-line research can be both fun and rewarding. On-line you can find newspaper articles, encyclopedia articles, interviews, dictionaries, and many other kinds of information.

When you do research, you will probably use a **directory** or a **search engine**. A directory is a list of categories that you can look at and browse through. A search engine searches the Internet or Website for the keywords you input. Many Websites contain both, so they are listed together here. Some of the best known directories and search engines can be found at the following addresses:

http://www.aol.com/netfind
http://www.excite.com/Subject
http://www.search.com
http://www.yahoo.com

---

Be careful when you type a **URL**, or Internet address. Be sure you type every letter, colon, and slash correctly. Make sure you capitalize letters correctly and include all punctuation except for any at the end. Leave off an end punctuation mark, unless it is a slash (/).

Read the **search tips** or **help file** at each site. They will help you search successfully. For example, at some sites, you can use words such as AND to join terms or names. Other sites use symbols instead, such as a plus sign (+).

## Writing and Technology

### Doing On-Line Research (continued)

When you do research on-line, you should remember and follow a few simple guidelines:

- Try more than one search engine or directory, since each finds Websites in a special way. You may have no luck at one site and success at another.

- Think about where you found the information. Information from the Library of Congress or a major university is likely to be accurate. Information from a personal Website may not be accurate.

- Save information about your sources. If you used an on-line reference book, print out the page that gives its name, publisher, and date. If you used a Website, write down its URL, or Internet address.

## Writing and Technology
# Sending and Receiving Electronic Mail

Electronic mail, or **e-mail**, is fun to send and receive. It allows you to communicate quickly with people around the world. Before you can use e-mail, you must have an **identifying name**. This is also called a screen name, user name, or account name. This name will appear on all your e-mail.

## Sending E-mail

Make sure you know the correct **Internet address** of the person who will receive the mail. This address will contain three parts: the receiver's identifying name, the @ symbol, and a **domain name**. The domain name is the part of the address that comes after the @. A typical Internet address looks like this:

screenname@wordorname.com

Make sure that you type the identifying name correctly. Some programs may not deliver mail if the letters in the screen name are not capitalized correctly. Also, be sure not to type the letter *l* in place of the number *1*.

The domain name is actually made up of several parts. The part following the final dot often identifies the type of organization that is receiving the mail. For example, domain names ending with *edu* are schools. Ones that end in *com* are businesses. Domain names can also identify a country. For example, ones that end in *ca* or *fr* are Canadian or French.

## Writing and Technology
## Sending and Receiving
## Electronic Mail (continued)

Most e-mail contains a **subject line**. People see that in their list of incoming mail, before they read the message. A subject line should be short and useful or attention-getting. Typical subject lines might say:

help me!
homework question
directions to the ballpark

The **body** of your message should also be short. Break it into several paragraphs, since it is easier to read this way. For fun, you might want to try adding special symbols that show your mood. Many people enjoy using one of the following:

**<grin>** : - ) : - <

## Reading E-mail

Your mail program will show if you have e-mail to read. Select the command for reading mail. You will then see a list of your new messages. Just select and open the mail that you want to read.

## Writing and Technology
# On-Line Safety Tips

Computers can connect you to the entire world. You can look at Websites and post and read messages on bulletin boards. You can communicate by e-mail and "talk" in areas called chat rooms. You can make new friends all over the world.

Meeting people on-line can be fun and exciting. However, you need to follow certain safety rules, just as you do when you meet any stranger.

- Do not believe everything you read on-line. Many people make up on-line personalities different from their own. They might pretend to be older or younger than they really are. They may pretend to have another name or come from a different country.

- Never give out personal information on-line, unless you are sure that you are dealing with someone that you and your family knows well. Be careful what you post on bulletin boards. Never give out any of the following information:

    **your full name**
    **your address**
    **the name of your school**
    **your phone number**
    **your Social Security number**
    **your parent's or guardian's name**
    **where your parent or guardian works**

## Writing and Technology

## On-Line Safety Tips (continued)

- If someone asks for personal information, do not reply. If someone writes anything that makes you feel uncomfortable or scared, do not reply. Print out the letter or message that asked this information and give it to an adult.

- Never send a picture of yourself to someone you don't know. If someone asks for a picture, check with an adult.

- Never give out your password. Do not even tell it to your friends.

- Never agree to meet anyone in person unless you first tell a responsible adult and get that person's permission. Any meetings should be in a public place, not in a car or private home. Do not go alone.

# Glossary

## A

**abolitionist** (ab´ ə lish´ ən ist) *n*. A person who wants to end slavery.

**abreast** (ə brest´) *adv*. Alongside of; next to.

**accomplished** (ə kom´ plisht) *adj*. Good at something because of practice.

**accustomed** (ə kus´ təmd) *adj*. Used to or familiar with something.

**acute** (ə kyōōt´) *adj*. Very good; sharp.

**adapt** (ə dapt´) *v*. To adjust in order to make suitable for new conditions.

### Word Derivations

Below are some words derived from the word *adapt*.

| | | |
|---|---|---|
| adaptability | adapted | adapts |
| adaptable | adapter | nonadaptive |
| adaptation | adapting | unadapted |

**adjustable** (ə jus´ tə bəl) *adj*. Able to be changed in size or position.

**agate** (ag´ it) *n*. A playing marble with swirls or stripes of several colors in it.

**agent** (ā´ jənt) *n*. Someone who represents or stands in for another person.

**aggressive** (ə gre´ siv) *adj*. Working hard with a lot of energy and drive to get something.

**allotment** (ə lot´ mənt) *n*. A share or part of something.

**alloy** (a´ loi) *n*. A mixture of metals.

**amputation** (am´ pyōō tā´ shən) *n*. The act of cutting off a body part such as an arm or a leg.

615

**Pronunciation Key: a**t; l**ā**te; c**â**re; f**ä**ther;
s**e**t; m**ē**; **i**t; k**ī**te; **o**x; r**ō**se; **ô** in b**ou**ght;
c**oi**n; b**oo**k; t**oo**; f**o**rm; **ou**t; **u**p; **ū**se; t**û**rn;
**ə** sound in **a**bout, chick**e**n, penc**i**l, cann**o**n,
circ**u**s; **ch**air; **hw** in **wh**ich; ri**ng**; **sh**op;
**th**in; **th**ere; **zh** in trea**s**ure.

**anatomy** (ə nat′ ə mē) *n.* The
structure of the human body.

**ancestor** (an′ ses tər) *n.* A forefather;
a parent, grandparent, great-
grandparent, and so on.

**anesthesia** (an′ əs thē′ zhə) *n.* A loss
of feeling brought about by drugs so
that surgery can be performed.

**antibiotic** (an′ ti bī ot′ ik) *n.* A
chemical that kills disease germs.

**antiseptic** (an′ tə sep′ tik) *adj.* Free
from germs; germ-killing.

**applicant** (a′ pli kənt) *n.* A person
who tries for a certain job or position.

**appointment** (ə point′ mənt) *n.* A job
or office.

**arctic** (ärk′ tik) *adj.* Having to do with
the region of the North Pole.

**artifact** (är′ tə fakt′) *n.* A handmade
object from an earlier time or culture.

**artificial** (är′ tə fish′ əl) *adj.* Made
by humans rather than produced
by nature.

**asepsis** (ə sep′ sis) *n.* The methods
used to make sure there are no germs.

**assert** (ə sûrt′) *v.* To say firmly.

### Word History

**Assert** is a French word that comes from
the Latin word *asserere*. It can be traced
back to the terms *ad-*, which means
"toward," and *serere*, which means "to
join."

**astronomer** (ə stro′ nə mər) *n.* A
person who studies objects outside
Earth's atmosphere.

**authoritative** (ə thor′ i tā′ tiv) *adj.*
Bossy; masterful.

**awl** (ôl) *n.* A tool with a sharp point
used for making small holes in wood,
leather, or tin.

## B

**bacteria** (bak tēr′ ē ə) *n. pl., sing.*
**bacterium.** Disease germs; one-
celled organisms that can be seen
only with a microscope.

**bank** (bangk) *v.* To tilt an aircraft to
one side while flying it.

**bargaining** (bär′ gə ning) *n.* Discussing
terms; talking or arguing in order to
agree upon something.

**barge** (bärj) *v.* To rudely push oneself
into a place.

**befall** (bi fôl′) *v.* To happen to.

**beguile** (bi gīl′) *v.* To tempt; to charm;
to amuse.

**benefit** (be′ nə fit′) *n.* Something
given to workers in addition to pay,
such as insurance, paid vacations, or
sick days.

**bequeath** (bi kwēth′) *v.* To leave
something to another person when
one dies.

**blood pressure** (blud′ presh′ ər) *n.*
The amount of force with which
blood presses against the insides of
the body's blood vessels.

**blubber** (blub′ ər) *n.* Whale fat.

**bonito** (bə nē′ tō) *n.* A fish similar to
the tuna, found in the Atlantic Ocean.

**bow** (bou) *n.* The curved front part of a boat.

**brace** (brās) *n.* A pair; a couple.

**brainstorm** (brān´ storm) *v.* To come up with many ideas quickly.

**brandish** (bran´ dish) *v.* To shake; to wave.

**brazier** (brā´ zhər) *n.* A metal frame for holding fire.

**brush** (brush) *n.* A growth of shrubs, small trees, and bushes.

**brutality** (broo tal´ i tē) *n.* Cruelty; extremely harsh treatment.

# C

**calculate** (kal´ kyə lāt´) *v.* To measure; to figure out.

**capacity** (kə pas´ i tē) *n.* The ability.

**capsize** (kap´ sīz) *v.* To overturn in the water, as a boat.

**card** (kärd) *n.* An instrument used for combing cotton or wool fibers.

**caress** (kə res´) *v.* To stroke softly.

**caribou** (kar´ ə boo´) *n.* A large deer, related to the reindeer.

**cartilage** (kär´ tl ij) *n.* Firm yet flexible tissue that is inside the human body.

**casement** (kās´ mənt) *n.* A window that opens outward.

**catgut** (kat´ gut) *n.* A strong thread made of dried animals' intestines, used in surgery to make stitches.

**century** (sen´ chə rē) *n.* 100 years.

**chafing** (chā´ fing) *n.* A rubbing.

**chartreuse** (shär trooz´) *n.* A yellowish-green color.

**chattel** (chat´ l) *n.* Anything movable that is owned by someone.

**chemist** (kem´ ist) *n.* A scientist who studies what substances are made of.

**civilization** (siv´ ə lə zā´ shən) *n.* A culture, society, or group of human beings who have developed art, education, agriculture, trade, science, government, and so on.

**colleague** (kol´ ēg) *n.* A member of the same profession as another person.

**colonist** (kol´ ə nist) *n.* A person who is a member of a settlement formed by people who have come to a new land.

**colony** (kol´ ə nē) *n.* A settlement formed by people who have come to a new land.

| Word Derivations |
| --- |

Below are some words derived from the word *colony.*

| colonial | colonies | colonize |
| --- | --- | --- |
| colonially | colonist | colonized |
| colonialism | colonization | colonizing |

**compassionate** (kəm pa´ shə nət) *adj.* Being able to imagine another's feelings.

**complication** (kom´ pli kā´ shən) *n.* Another disease that makes a person's original disease get worse.

**compound** (kom´ pound) *n.* A closed-in area containing homes or other buildings.

**Pronunciation Key: at**; l**ā**te; c**â**re; f**ä**ther; s**e**t; m**ē**; **i**t; k**ī**te; **o**x; r**ō**se; **ô** in b**ou**ght; c**oi**n; b**oo**k; t**oo**; f**o**rm; **ou**t; **u**p; **ū**se; t**û**rn; **ə** sound in **a**bout, chick**e**n, penc**i**l, cann**o**n, circ**u**s; **ch**air; **hw** in **wh**ich; ri**ng**; **sh**op; **th**in; **th**ere; **zh** in trea**s**ure.

**compromise** (kom´ prə mīz´) *n.* A settlement made by both sides giving up a little.

### Word History

The French word **compromise** can be traced back to the Latin word *compromittere*. In Latin, *com-* means "with" or "together," while *promittere* means "to promise."

**concentrated** (kon´ sən trā´ tid) *adj.* Packed closely together.

**conclusive** (kən kloo´ siv) *adj.* Answering a question completely.

**concoction** (kon kok´ shən) *n.* Something made up or invented.

**condemnation** (kon´ dem nā´ shən) *n.* A judgment of guilty.

**confidence** (kon´ fi dəns) *n.* A belief in one's own ability.

**confirm** (kən fûrm´) *v.* To make sure.

**connect** (kə nekt´) *v.* To hook up with; to introduce someone to.

**conscious** (kon´ shəs) *adj.* Aware of; noticing the needs of.

**consent** (kən sent´) *n.* Agreement; permission. —*v.* To agree.

**console** (kən sōl´) *v.* To comfort.

**constellation** (kon´ stə lā´ shən) *n.* A group of fixed stars having a name.

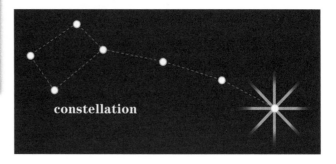

constellation

**consternation** (kon´ stər nā´ shən) *n.* Dismay; dread; anxiety.

### Word History

**Consternation** came into usage in the English language around 1611. It comes from the Latin terms *consternare*, which means "to throw into confusion," and *-ation*, which means "act" or "process."

**consult** (kən sult´) *v.* To ask advice.

**consumer** (kən soo´ mər) *n.* A person who buys and uses products.

**consumptive** (kən sump´ tiv) *adj.* Sick with the disease tuberculosis, a lung infection.

**contaminated** (kən tam´ ə nā´ təd) *adj.* Unclean; mixed with something dirty.

**contend** (kən tend´) *v.* To believe.

**continue** (kən tin´ yoo) *v.* To keep going; to last.

**contract** (kon´ trakt) *n.* A formal, written agreement.

**contradict** (kon´ trə dikt´) *v.* To go against; to disagree with.

**coronary artery** (kor´ ə ner ē  är´ tə rē) *n.* An artery in the heart that supplies blood to the parts of the heart.

**corps** (kor) *n.* A group formed for a specific purpose.

**county seat** (koun´ tē  sēt´) *n.* The town in which the government of a county is housed.

**cradle** (krā´ dl) *v.* To hold gently in one's arms.

**cranny** (kran´ ē) *n.* A slit; a small opening in a rock wall.

**crevasse** (krə vas´) *n.* A deep crack in a glacier or in Earth's surface.

**crimson** (krim´ zən) *adj.* Deep red in color.

**crouch** (krouch) *v.* To stoop or bend low, usually by bending the legs.

**crude** (kro͞od) *adj.* Rough; simple.

**culturally** (kul´ chər ə lē) *adv.* Having to do with the civilization of a given race or nation.

**curandera** (ko͞o´ rän de´ rä) *n.* A woman healer who uses folk medicine such as herbs and other plants to cure illness.

# D

**debt** (det) *n.* Anything one owes.

**Word Derivations**

Below are some words derived from the word *debt.*

| | | |
|---|---|---|
| debtless | debtors | indebted |
| debtor | debts | indebtedness |

**deed** (dēd) *n.* An action; a thing done.

**demanding** (di mand´ ing) *adj.* Requiring a lot of time or energy.

**desolately** (des´ ə lit lē) *adv.* In a hopeless or lonely way.

**desperately** (des´ pər it lē) *adv.* Hopelessly.

**destination** (des´ tə nā shən) *n.* The place where a journey ends.

**determined** (di tûr´ mənd) *adj.* Having a strong desire to complete something.

**devise** (di vīz´) *v.* To figure out; to make up.

**dietician** (dī´ i tish´ ən) *n.* A person who is an expert in food and nutrition.

**digestive system** (di jes´ tiv  sis´ təm) *n.* The stomach, intestines, and other organs that process food in the body.

**din** (din) *n.* A lot of noise; clamor; uproar; racket.

**discouraged** (dis kûr´ ijd) *adj.* Disappointed; let down.

**disinfect** (dis´ in fekt´) *v.* To cleanse of infection; to make free of germs.

**dismayed** (dis mād´) *adj.* Discouraged; alarmed.

**dispel** (di spel´) *v.* To drive away; to banish.

**Word History**

The word **dispel** comes from the Latin word *dispellare* and can be broken down into *dis-,* which means "apart," and *pellare,* which means "to drive." The prefix *dis-* can also mean "the opposite of," but not in this case.

**Pronunciation Key: at**; l**ā**te; c**â**re; f**ä**ther;
set; m**ē**; **it**; k**ī**te; **ox**; r**ō**se; **ô** in b**ou**ght;
c**oi**n; b**oo**k; t**oo**; f**or**m; **out**; **up**; **ū**se; t**û**rn;
**ə** sound in **a**bout, chick**e**n, penc**i**l, cann**o**n,
circ**u**s; **ch**air; **hw** in **wh**ich; ri**ng**; **sh**op;
**th**in; **th**ere; **zh** in trea**s**ure.

**diverse** (di vûrs´) *adj.* Different; varied.

**document** (do´ kyə ment´) *v.* To observe and record for future study.

**domain** (dō mān´) *n.* An area of knowledge.

**domestic** (də mes´ tik) *adj.* Belonging to or concerning the home.

**don** (don) *v.* To put on.

**douse** (dous) *v.* To splash.

**dressing** (dres´ ing) *n.* The cloth or other material used to cover a wound.

**dubiously** (doo´ bē əs lē) *adv.* Doubtfully; in an unsure way.

**durable** (dûr´ ə bəl) *adj.* Able to last a long time; able to hold up to rough handling.

## E

**ear mite** (ir mīt) *n.* A small bug that lives in the ears of animals.

**earshot** (ir´ shot) *n.* Within hearing range.

**eloquence** (el´ ə kwəns) *n.* The ability to present ideas in an expressive or effective way.

**eminent** (em´ ə nənt) *adj.* Celebrated; well-known; grand.

**enchain** (en chān´) *v.* To tie down or hold back.

**enforce** (en fors´) *v.* 1. To urge with force. 2. To make people obey a law.

**enviously** (en´ vē əs lē) *adv.* With jealousy.

**epidemic** (ep´ i dem´ ik) *n.* An outbreak of disease that spreads quickly to many people.

**escort** (e skort´) *v.* To go with and protect.

**etch** (ech) *v.* To make a pattern or design on a hard surface.

**ethnically** (eth´ nik lē) *adv.* Having to do with the national origins of a people.

**evolve** (i´ välv) *v.* To develop; to work out.

**exasperated** (ig zas´ pə rā´ təd) *adj.* Irritated; angry.

**executive** (ig zek´ yə tiv) *n.* A person who has the right or power to make decisions and run a company.

**expectancy** (ik spek´ tən sē) *n.* A state of waiting for something to happen. **life expectancy:** The number of years the average person will live.

**expedition** (ek´ spi dish´ ən) *n.* A journey made to accomplish something.

**external** (ik stûr´ nl) *adj.* Outside; outward.

## F

**facilities** (fə sil´ i tēz) *n. pl.* Things designed to make a task easier or more convenient.

**failure** (fāl´ yər) *n.* Something that does not turn out well; something that is not a success.

**faint** (fānt) *adj.* Dim; weak; not clear.

**falter** (fôl´ tər) *v.* To be tongue-tied; to talk awkwardly.

**farmer's market** (fär´ mərz mär´ kət) *n.* A place where people come to buy and sell fruits and vegetables for a short period of time.

**fascinate** (fa´ sən āt´) *v.* To completely and fully interest someone.

**fatal** (fāt´ l) *adj.* Deadly; causing death.

**feisty** (fī´ stē) *adj.* Full of energy.

**fell** (fel) *v.* To cut down.

**ferry** (fer´ ē) *v.* To carry across a river or a bay. —*n.* A boat that carries passengers, vehicles, or goods across a river or a bay; a ferryboat.

**fiber** (fī´ bər) *n.* Material or cloth.

---

### Word Derivations

Below are some words derived from the word *fiber*.

| | | |
|---|---|---|
| fiberboard | fiberglass | fiber optics |
| fiberfill | fiberize | fibers |
| fibered | fiber-optic | fiberscope |

---

**fibrous** (fī´ brəs) *adj.* Containing fibers, or long, narrow strips or cords.

**flank** (flangk) *n.* The side.

**floodgate** (flud´ gāt) *n.* Something that is holding something back.

**folly** (fol´ ē) *n.* Foolishness.

---

### Word History

**Folly** is from a French word, *fol*, which means "fool." Folly came into the English language in the 13th century.

---

**food-laden** (fo͞od´ lā´ dn) *adj.* Filled with food; having a load of food.

**forceps** (for´ səps) *n.* Small pliers used in surgery.

**fortunate** (for´ chə nət) *adj.* Lucky.

**fowl** (foul) *n.* A bird such as a chicken or a turkey.

**fowling piece** (fou´ ling pēs´) *n.* A shotgun used for shooting wild birds.

**fragrance** (frā´ grəns) *n.* A sweet smell that is pleasing.

**frustrate** (frəs´ trāt) *v.* To feel angry, upset, or powerless in a situation.

**fund** (fund) *v.* To pay for. — *n.* Money collected and saved for a special purpose.

---

## G

**galleon** (gal´ ē ən) *n.* A type of large sailing ship used from the 1400s through the 1600s.

galleon

**game** (gām) *n.* Wild animals that are hunted.

**game reserve** (gām´ ri zûrv´) *n.* An area of land set aside for wild animals to live in without being hunted.

**gaudy** (gô´ dē) *adj.* Showy or flashy in a crude way.

**generation** (jen´ ə rā´ shən) *n.* 1. A group of people who are all about the same age. 2. The process of bringing into existence.

**gesture** (jes′ chər) *n.* A body movement that shows meaning.

**gesundheit** (gə zōōnt′ hīt′) *interj.* An expression that wishes good health to someone who has sneezed.

**gibbon** (gi′ bən) *n.* A tailless ape from southeastern Asia.

**glacier** (glā′ shər) *n.* A large, slow-moving mass of ice.

**glassy** (glas′ ē) *n.* A glass marble with colored swirls.

**glib** (glib) *adj.* Smooth-talking; persuasive.

**gorge** (gorj) *n.* A steep, narrow opening between mountains; a small canyon.

**gossamer** (gos′ ə mər) *adj.* Light; thin; flimsy.

**grippe** (grip) *n.* Influenza; the flu.

**guild** (gild) *n.* During the Middle Ages, a group of merchants or crafters.

# H

**haggard** (hag′ ərd) *adj.* Having a worn look because of being very tired, afraid, or hungry.

**hail** (hāl) *n.* A greeting or a calling out to someone. *v.* To call out to; to greet.

**hammer out** (ham′ ər out) *v.* To discuss until an agreement is reached.

**hardship** (härd′ ship) *n.* Trouble; misfortune.

**haughty** (hô′ tē) *adj.* Full of pride.

## Word History

**Haughty** comes from the French word *haut*, which is derived from the Latin word *altus*. *Altus* means "high." **Haughty** came into the English language during the 15th century.

**haunting** (hôn′ ting) *adj.* Staying in the mind; not forgotten quickly.

**headland** (hed′ lənd) *n.* A high piece of land that sticks out into a large body of water.

**heap** (hēp) *n.* A pile; a mound.

**hearthstone** (härth′ stōn) *n.* The stone floor of a fireplace.

**heave** (hēv) *n.* An upward movement.

**hemorrhage** (hem′ ər ij) *n.* Heavy bleeding.

**heritage** (hâr′ ə tij) *n.* Something handed down to a person from his or her ancestors.

**hibernate** (hī′ bər nāt′) *v.* To pass the winter in a long sleep.

**highborn** (hī′ born) *adj.* Born to the noble class.

**hogback** (hôg′ bak) *n.* A steep ridge.

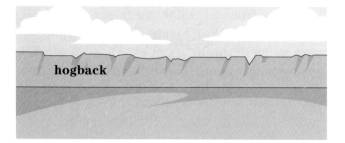

**horizon** (hə rī′ zən) *n.* The distant line where the ocean and the sky seem to meet.

**hose** (hōz) *n.* Stockings.

**house** (houz) *v.* To provide shelter for.

**hygiene** (hī´ jēn) *n.* Keeping oneself clean in order to stay healthy.

# I

**ice cap** (īs´ kap) *n.* A thick layer of ice covering an area.

**identity** (ī den´ ti tē) *n.* The condition that makes something special.

**idly** (īd´ lē) *adv.* Lazily.

**immaculate** (i mak´ yə lit) *adj.* Extremely clean; spotless.

**immune** (i myo͞on´) *adj.* Free from; not able to get a certain disease.

**impair** (im pâr´) *v.* To weaken; to injure.

**impracticable** (im prak´ ti kə bəl) *adj.* Not possible with the methods or equipment available.

**impression** (im presh´ ən) *n.* An idea; a picture in the mind.

**incision** (in sizh´ ən) *n.* A cut made into the body during surgery.

**income** (in´ kum) *n.* The total money received.

**incorporated** (in kor´ pə rā´ tid) *adj.* Legally made into a corporation, which is a type of business in which the company itself is separate from the people who own it.

**indentured servant** (in den´ chərd sûr vənt) *n.* A person who came to America under a contract to work for someone else for a period of time.

**indescribably** (in´ di skrī´ bə blē) *adv.* Unusually; extraordinarily.

**indignantly** (in dig´ nənt lē) *adv.* With anger; with an insulted feeling.

**induct** (in dukt´) *v.* To admit as a member.

**ineffectively** (in´ i fek´ tiv lē) *adv.* Uselessly; in vain.

**infirm** (in fûrm´) *adj.* Weak; sickly.

**infirmary** (in fûr´ mə rē) *n.* A place where sick people are treated.

**inherit** (in her´ it) *v.* To receive another's property after his or her death.

**insulation** (in´ sə lā´ shən) *n.* A material that keeps heat from being lost.

**intellect** (in´ tl ekt´) *n.* The ability to think and reason.

### Word History

**Intellect** comes from the Latin word *intellegere*, which means "to understand." This word came into the English language during the 14<sup>th</sup> century.

**interest** (in´ tər ist) *n.* Money received on an investment.

**intern** (in´ tûrn) *n.* A doctor who is being trained at a hospital.

**internal** (in tûr´ nl) *adj.* Inside; inner.

**interracial** (in´ tər rā´ shəl) *adj.* Including people of different races.

**intimidate** (in tim´ i dāt´) *v.* To threaten; to frighten.

**intrigue** (in trēg´) *v.* To fascinate; to interest.

**inundate** (in´ ən dāt´) *v.* To swamp; to flood; to overwhelm.

**invariably** (in´ ver´ ē ə blē) *adv.* Without changing; always.

**invest** (in vest´) *v.* To spend money on a company, hoping to receive profits.

> ### Word Derivations
>
> Below are some words derived from the word *invest*.
>
> | | | |
> |---|---|---|
> | invested | investment | investors |
> | investing | investment | invests |
> | investiture | investor | |

**investment** (in vest´ mənt) *n.* The use of money to gain profit.

**irrigate** (ir´ i gāt) *v.* To wash with water or other liquid.

**irritably** (ir´ i tə blē) *adv.* In a way that shows annoyance.

# K

**kidnap** (kid´ nap) *v.* To seize and carry off a person.

**kindling** (kind´ ling) *n.* Small pieces of wood or scraps used for starting a fire.

**knack** (nak) *n.* The ability to do something; a skill.

# L

**labor** (lā´ bər) *n.* The beginning of the process of birth.

**lapse** (laps) *v.* To fall; to sink.

> ### Word History
>
> The word **lapse** came into English language usage around 1526. It comes from the Latin word *labi*, which means "to slip."

**league** (lēg) *n.* A distance of roughly three miles.

**learned** (lûr´ nid) *adj.* Having knowledge; educated.

**limited** (li´ mə təd) *adj.* Having boundaries or limits.

**loft** (lôft) *n.* A room directly below a roof; an attic.

loft

**lofty** (lôf´ tē) *adj.* Noble; grand.

**lull** (lul) *v.* To put to sleep by soothing. —*n.* A short period of calm or quiet.

# M

**mandolin** (man´ də lin´) *n.* A stringed musical instrument.

mandolin

**maneuver** (mə nŌŌ´ vər) *v.* To change the position of something; to move in a planned way.

**manipulate** (mə nip´ yə lāt´) *v.* To handle or control.

**manuscript** (man´ yŌŌ skript) *n.* A handwritten document.

**market** (mär´ kit) *n.* The people who are likely to buy a certain product.

---

### Word Derivations

Below are some words derived from the word *market*.

| market order | market share | marketer |
| market price | marketability | marketing |
| market research | marketable | marketplace |
| market researcher | marketed | unmarketable |

---

**marketing** (mär´ ki ting) *n.* All the activities that lead to selling a product, including advertising, packaging, and selling.

**mast** (mast) *n.* A pole supporting a ship's sails.

**meander** (mē an´ dər) *v.* To wander aimlessly; to twist and turn at random.

**meditation** (me´ də tā´ shən) *n.* A practice of quiet thinking.

**menacing** (men´ is ing) *adj.* Dangerous; threatening.

**mesa** (mā´ sə) *n.* High, flat land, like a plateau but smaller.

**metalsmith** (met´ l smith´) *n.* A person who makes things out of metal.

**meticulously** (mə tik´ yə ləs lē) *adv.* In an extremely careful and precise way.

**microbe** (mī´ krōb) *n.* An organism that is too small to be seen without a microscope.

**milk wagon** (milk wa´ gən) *n.* A horse-drawn wagon used to deliver milk very early in the morning.

**millennia** (mə le´ nē ə) *n. plural* Thousands of years. One millennium equals 1,000 years.

**mite** (mīt) *adj.* A little bit.

**mock** (mok) *adj.* Pretended.

---

### Word Derivations

Below are some words derived from the word *mock*.

| mock turtle soup | mockery | mockingbird |
| mocked | mock-heroic | mockingly |
| mocker | mocking | mock-up |

---

**monastery** (mo´ nə stâr´ ē) *n.* A house for monks.

**monies** (mun´ ēz) *n. pl.* Funds; a plural of *money.*

**monk** (mungk) *n.* A man who belongs to a religious order.

**monotonous** (mə no´ tn əs) *adj.* Said with no change in tone or emphasis; having all the same sound.

**mural** (myŌŌr´ əl) *n.* A large painting, often on a wall.

**musket** (mus´ kit) *n.* An old-fashioned kind of gun, used before the modern rifle.

**muslin** (muz´ lin) *n.* A kind of cotton cloth.

**muster** (mus´ tər) *v.* To gather.

**mutilation** (myŌŌ´ tl ā´ shən) *n.* Injury; disfigurement by cutting, removing, or damaging a part.

**mystified** (mis´ tə fīd´) *adj.* Bewildered; confused.

# N

**native** (nā´ tiv) *adj.* Belonging to by birth.

**nauseate** (nô zē āt´) *v.* To make sick to the stomach.

**nomadic** (nō mad´ ik) *adj.* Wandering from place to place.

**notion** (nō´ shən) *n.* An idea.

**novel** (nov´ əl) *adj.* New.

# O

**obnoxious** (əb nok´ shəs) *adj.* Annoying or offensive.

## Word History

The word **obnoxious** comes from the Latin word *obnoxius* and can be broken down into the following parts: *ob-*, which means "in the way of" or "exposed to," and *noxa*, which means "harm." "Exposed to something harmful" is actually an archaic, or out-of-date, definition of **obnoxious.**

**odds** (odz) *n.* The chances that something will or will not happen.

**omen** (ō´ mən) *n.* A sign of a future event.

**ominous** (om´ ə nəs) *adj.* Unfavorable; threatening misfortune.

**ornery** (or´ nə rē) *adj.* Disagreeable.

**overawed** (ō´ vər ôd´) *adj.* Extremely respectful or fearful.

# P

**P.S.** Public School.

**pachyderm** (pak´ i dûrm´) *n.* Any large, thick-skinned, hoofed animal, such as the elephant.

**page** (pāj) *v.* To call for someone over a loudspeaker.

**parlor** (pär´ lər) *n.* A sitting room set aside for seeing guests.

**passage** (pas´ ij) *n.* A narrow corridor; a hallway.

**peculiar** (pi kyool´ yər) *adj.* Strange; unusual.

**peer** (pir) *v.* To look carefully.

**pemmican** (pem´ i kən) *n.* A mixture of powdered dried meat, dried berries, and fat.

**perception** (pər sep´ shən) *n.* The ability to experience things through one's senses.

**persuade** (pər swād´) *v.* To lead another person to agree with oneself; to sway.

**peruse** (pə rooz´) *v.* To read over; to study.

**physicist** (fi´ zə sist) *n.* A person who studies matter and energy and how the two work together.

**pilgrim** (pil´ grim) *n.* 1. A person who travels to a holy place. 2. **Pilgrim:** A member of a religious group that came to America to find freedom of religion.

**piñon** (pin´ yən) *n.* A kind of pine tree with edible seeds.

**pitch** (pich) *n.* A dark, sticky substance used to make things waterproof. —*v.* To lurch or fall suddenly.

**plague** (plāg) *n.* Any widespread disease; a disease that is spread in an epidemic.

**pneumonia** (no͞o mōn´ yə) *n.* A disease of the lungs.

**poacher** (pō´ chər) *n.* A person who catches animals in a place where hunting is against the law.

**ponder** (pon´ dər) *v.* To think about.

**poppet** (pop´ it) *n. British. dialect.* A nickname showing affection, meaning "child."

**popular** (pop´ yə lər) *adj.* Well-liked by many.

**porcelain** (por´ sə lin) *n.* A fine, delicate china.

**port** (port) *n.* A place or town where ships come to load or unload.

**portion** (por´ shən) *v.* To share among; to distribute.

**poultice** (pōl´ tis) *n.* A wad of something soft and moist, placed over a wound to heal it.

**precision** (pri sizh´ ən) *n.* Exactness; accuracy with details.

**pretense** (prē´ tens) *n.* A false show or appearance for the purpose of deceiving others.

**prevailing** (pri vā´ ling) *adj.* The most frequent; occurring most often.

**privileged** (priv´ lijd) *adj.* Enjoying luxuries and special treatment.

**procession** (prə se´ shən) *n.* A line of people moving forward in an orderly and ceremonial manner.

**profit** (prof´ it) *n.* The earnings gained from a business.

---

**Word History**

**Profit** came into the English language during the 14th century. The word derives from the Latin word *profectus*, which means "advance" or "profit."

---

**profitable** (prof´ i tə bəl) *adj.* Making gains; making money.

**profusely** (prə fyo͞os´ lē) *adv.* In abundance; in large amounts.

**prominent** (prom´ ə nənt) *adj.* Important; well-known.

**prospect** (pros´ pekt) *n.* A future possible event; something that could happen.

**prostration** (pros trā´ shən) *n.* Exhaustion; extreme tiredness.

**provisions** (prə vizh´ ənz) *n.* Things that are supplied for a special task, especially food and the necessary tools.

**pulse** (puls) *n.* The regular beating of the heart.

**puree** (pyo͞o rā´) *v.* To make a solid food into a thick liquid.

**pursue** (pər so͞o´) *v.* To chase.

# Q

**qualified** (kwä´ lə fīd´) *adj.* Having the skills or education needed for a certain job or position; capable.

**quarter** (kwor´ tər) *n.* Usually **quarters:** Living accommodations; a place to live.

**quiver** (kwiv´ ər) *v.* To tremble; to shake with a quick, slight motion.

**Pronunciation Key: at**; lāte; câre; fäther; set; mē; it; kīte; ox; rōse; ô in bought; coin; boŏk; toō; form; out; up; ūse; tûrn; ə sound in about, chicken, pencil, cannon, circus; chair; hw in which; ring; shop; thin; there; zh in treasure.

# R

**rafter** (raf´ tər) *n.* Any of the long, heavy pieces of wood or metal that support a roof.

**rambunctious** (ram bungk´ shəs) *adj.* Active and noisy in a violent way.

**rankle** (rang´ kəl) *v.* To cause bitterness.

**ransom** (ran´ səm) *n.* A large amount of money paid to free something or someone from captivity.

**rash** (rash) *adj.* Hasty; reckless.

**ration** (rash´ ən) *n.* A fixed allowance of something; a limited share.

**reception** (ri sep´ shən) *n.* A party held to welcome someone.

**recruit** (ri krooōt´) *v.* To gain fresh people for a task. — *n.* A new member of a group or organization.

**reflect** (ri flekt´) *v.* To represent; to show.

## Word Derivations

Below are some words derived from the word *reflect*.

| | | |
|---|---|---|
| reflected | reflection | reflector |
| reflecting | reflective | reflects |

**refugee camp** (re´ fyoō jē  kamp) *n.* A place where people who are forced to leave their homes live temporarily.

**relations** (ri lā´ shənz) *n.* The connections between people; people's associations with each other; the dealings people have with each other.

**relay** (rē´ lā´) *n.* The passing along of something (like a message). (rē´ lā´) *v.* To send along; to pass from one person to another.

**rendezvous** (ron´ di vooō´) *v.* To meet or get together at a certain place.

**renew** (ri noō´) *v.* To repair; to restore.

**repertoire** (re´ pə twor´) *n.* The number of different songs one can sing.

**resentment** (ri zent´ mənt) *n.* A feeling of being insulted.

**reservation** (rez´ ər vā´ shən) *n.* The land set aside for Native Americans to live on.

**resolve** (ri zolv´) *v.* To make a decision.

**resume** (ri zoōm´) *v.* To start up again; to continue.

## Word History

The word **resume** came into English usage in the 15th century. It comes from the Latin word *resumere*. *Resumere* can be broken down into the word parts *re-*, which means "again," and *sumere*, which means "to take up."

**retire** (ri tīr´) *v.* To go away to a private place.

**runnel** (run´ l) *n.* A small stream or channel. *Used as a verb in the story:* To make streams or channels.

**rush** (rush) *n.* A long-stemmed water plant.

# S

**S.S.** or **Schutzstaffel** (shoots′ stä′ fəl) *German.* A special Nazi police force.

**sac** (sak) *n.* An inner body structure that is like a bag.

**sandspit** (sand′ spit) *n.* A bar of raised sand that juts out from an island.

**satchel** (sach′ əl) *n.* A small bag; a school bag.

### Word History

Satchel comes from an older English word, *sachel. Sachel* is derived from the Latin word *saccus,* which means "bag." This word came into the English language during the 14th century.

**scalpel** (skal′ pəl) *n.* A small, straight, light knife used by surgeons.

scalpel

**scavenge** (skav′ inj) *v.* To gather discarded material; to look for things that people have thrown away.

**scholarship** (sko′ lər ship′) *n.* Money given to a student, often to help pay for college.

**scribe** (skrīb) *n.* A person who copies manuscripts by hand.

**scullery** (skul′ ə rē) *n.* A small room off the kitchen where dishes are washed, vegetables are prepared, and other chores are done.

**seep** (sēp) *v.* To flow a little at a time.

**serpent** (sûr′ pənt) *n.* A snake.

**serum** (sēr′ əm) *n.* The liquid part of blood.

**settlement** (set′ l mənt) *n.* A colony; a new community in a new land.

**shan't** (shant) Contraction of **shall not:** Will not.

**shock** (shok) *n.* 1. A thick, bushy mass. 2. A dangerous condition in which a person's blood circulation becomes extremely slow.

**shortage** (shor′ tij) *n.* Not enough of something.

**siege** (sēj) *n.* A group of illnesses, one after the other.

**signify** (sig′ nə fī′) *v.* To be a sign of; to stand for.

**silkworm gut** (silk′ wûrm gut′) *n.* Silk thread used in surgery.

**simulate** (sim′yə lāt) *v.* To make something seem like something else; to imitate.

**sinew** (sin′ yoo) *n.* A tough substance that joins muscle to bone; a tendon.

**site** (sīt) *n.* The ground occupied by a building.

**skirt** (skûrt) *v.* To move around the edge of.

**sledge** (slej) *n.* A sled or sleigh.

**snare** (snâr) *n.* A trap.

**sole** (sōl) *adj.* Single; one and only.

**solution** (sə loo′ shən) *n.* A liquid that has something dissolved in it.

**sough** (sou) *v.* To make a sound like rushing, rustling, or murmuring.

**spout** (spout) *v.* To come out through a narrow opening with great force.

spout

## Word Derivations

Below are some words derived from the word *strain*.

| | | |
|---|---|---|
| restrain | restrains | straining |
| restrained | strained | strains |
| restraining | strainer | unrestrained |

**startling** (stärt´ ling) *adj.* Surprising; astonishing.

**stave** (stāv) *n.* One of the thin, curved wood strips used to make a barrel.

**steadily** (sted´ ə lē) *adv.* In a regular or methodical way.

**sterilize** (ster´ ə līz´) *v.* To make free from germs.

**sternum** (stûr´ nəm) *n.* The breastbone; the flat, narrow, bony area to which the ribs are attached.

**stethoscope** (steth´ ə skōp´) *n.* An instrument for listening to sounds within the body.

### Word History

**Stethoscope** comes from the French word *stéthoscope. Stéthoscope* is derived from the Greek word *stethos*, which means "chest," and *-scope*, which means "instrument." The word came to mean an instrument for listening to the chest.

**stifled** (stī´ fəld) *adj.* Suffocated or smothered.

**stock** (stok) *v.* To keep a supply of a product ready for sale. — *n.* All of the animals on a farm; livestock.

**strain** (strān) *v.* 1. To make something pass through a filter or object with small holes in order to remove water or larger pieces. 2. To overwork; to work to the utmost.

**strike zone** (strīk zōn) *n.* A baseball term used as an analogy to mean the range or area where people will understand (what is said).

**studious** (stoo´ dē əs) *adj.* Dedicated to study and learning.

**stunt** (stunt) *v.* To stop the growth of.

**stylus** (stī´ ləs) *n.* A pointed writing instrument.

**submit** (səb mit´) *v.* To give something for consideration.

**suburb** (su´ bərb) *n.* A community at the edge of, but outside of, a large city.

**summon** (sum´ ən) *v.* To send for; to call someone to come.

**superstition** (soo´ pər stish´ ən) *n.* A belief in magic; a belief that is not based on reason.

**suture** (soo´ chər) *v.* To stitch together; to sew up.

**sympathy** (sim´ pə thē) *n.* A feeling of sadness shared by others.

**symptom** (simp´ təm) *n.* A sign that indicates what kind of illness someone has.

## T

**tally** (tal´ ē) *v.* To count or add up.

**taut** (tôt) *adj.* Stretched tight; tense.

**tedious** (tē´ dē əs) *adj.* Wearisome; tiring; boring.

**terrain** (tə rān´) *n.* The type of natural features in an area of land.

**thatched** (thacht) *adj.* Covered with straw.

theorize (thē´ ə rīz´) *v.* To make a guess based on some known facts.

**thrash** (thrash) *v.* To thresh; to beat the grain from stalks; to beat.

**threshold** (thresh´ ōld) *n.* The bottom part of a doorway; the sill.

**throes** (thrōz) *n.* Any violent spasm or struggle.

**tidal** (tīd´ l) *adj.* Having to do with the rise and fall of the sea.

**tide** (tīd) *n.* A current or flowing water.

### Word Derivations

Below are some words derived from the word *tide*.

| ebb tide  | tidal wave | tidemark   |
|-----------|------------|------------|
| high tide | tide table | tides      |
| low tide  | tideland   | tidewater  |
| tidal     | tideless   | tideway    |

**tinker** (ting´ kər) *v.* To experiment with something.

**toll** (tōl) *n.* Damage; destruction.

**toll-gate** (tōl´ gāt) *n.* A gate where people must pay in order to use a road.

**tottery** (tot´ ə rē) *adj.* Unsteady; shaky.

**tousle** (tou´ zəl) *v.* To make disordered or messy.

**trace** (trās) *n.* One of the two straps or chains that connect an animal to a load being pulled.

**tradition** (trə dish´ ən) *n.* A custom that has been handed down or preserved through many generations.

**transfusion** (trans fyoo´ zhən) *n.* A transfer of blood into a person.

### Word History

**Transfusion** came into English usage in the 16th century. It can be traced back to the Latin word *transfundere*. *Trans-* means "across" or "beyond," and *fundere* means "to pour." The suffix *-ion*, a Latin term, means "act" or "process." In this case, the word came to mean the act or process of pouring blood beyond one person to another.

**trek** (trek) *n.* A difficult journey or trip.

**trespassing** (tres´ pəs ing) *n.* Going onto another's property without permission.

**tribute** (trib´ yoot) *n.* Praise given in recognition of worth or value.

**trifling** (trī´ fling) *adj.* Not important.

**trot** (trot) *n.* A slow run. —*v.* To run slowly.

# U

**uncharted** (un chär´ tid) *adj.* Not shown on a map; not explored; not known.

**unclench** (un klench´) *v.* To open; to relax.

**unconscious** (un kon´ shəs) *adj.* Without physical or mental awareness; senseless.

**unsupervised** (ən soo´ pər vīzd) *adj.* Without being watched over by someone. (from **supervise** — *v.* To watch over, oversee.)

**upheaval** (up hē´ vəl) *n.* A violent change or disturbance.

**urge** (ûrj) *v.* To beg; to persuade.

**usher** (ush´ ər) *v.* To escort or take someone someplace.

## V

**vaccine** (vak sēn´) *n.* A preparation, usually liquid, given to prevent a disease.

**valiant** (val´ yənt) *adj.* Courageous or brave.

**veranda** (və ran´ də) *n.* A covered balcony; a porch.

**verge** (vûrj) *n.* The place where something begins; the brink.

**vertical** (vûr´ ti kəl) *adj.* Upright; from top to bottom.

**via** (vī´ ə) *adv.* By way of; passing through.

**vinyl** (vī´ nl) *n.* A plastic-like fabric made by humans.

**vital** (vīt´ l) *adj.* Necessary for life.

### Word History

The French word **vital** can be traced back to the Latin word *vita*, which means "life." The word came into the English language during the 14th century.

**vouch** (vouch) *v.* To bear witness; to confirm.

## W

**W.C.** Water closet: A bathroom.

**warden** (wor´ dn) *n.* An officer in charge; a supervisor.

**wash** (wosh) *n.* An area of land that has been shaped partly by the action of water moving over it.

**weed-infested** (wēd in fes´ td) *adj.* Filled with unwanted or undesirable plants.

**wick** (wik) *n.* A braided or twisted string of a soft substance that soaks up the fuel in a candle or lamp and holds the flame.

**wrath** (rath) *n.* Anger; rage.

**wreckage** (rek´ ij) *n.* The remains of something that has been wrecked or destroyed.

## Z

**zephyr** (zef´ ər) *n.* The west wind.